We Take Great Ideas...
& Make Them Even Better.™

W9-BHS-700

NEW! FREE! NOW HARDBOUND!

The 1990/91 OMEGA Complete Measurement and Control Handbooks & Encyclopedias®

OMEGA® Complete pH and Conductivity Measurement Handbook and Encyclopedia™

Who we are

OMEGA ENGINEERING is committed to offering its customers the quality service and support that they simply won't find anywhere else in the field of process measurement and control.

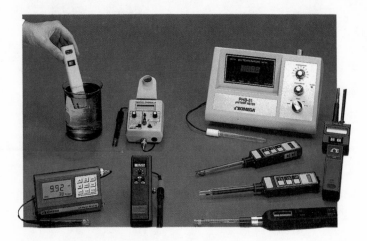

Quality Products and Complete Systems

At OMEGA our philosophy is to offer quality products as well as complete systems. Our selection of over 40,000 products is unparalleled, but what's more impressive is how they can be integrated into complete process measurement and control SYSTEMS. Our skilled engineering staff is pleased to discuss your custom application requirements.

Made in USA

MADE IN USA

We manufacture over 90% of what we sell, the rest is built to conform to our rigid specifications. The "Made in USA" logo can be seen throughout the handbook designating quality American made products.

Exclusive Warranty Programs

WARRANTY

Every electrode, pH controller, and accessory must meet our high quality standards. At OMEGA we also have a special warranty that adds an additional month to cover shipping and handling time . . . a guarantee that you receive the maximum benefit from your warranty. Many products also feature extended warranties, beyond the industry standard.
In addition, we are proud to offer the OMEGACARE™ Extended Warranty Plan available for 1, 2, or 3 years additional to the standard product warranty. Ask an OMEGA sales representative for complete details on prices and qualified products.

Customer Service that can't be Beat!

At OMEGA we understand that when any instrument malfunctions the results can be equipment downtime and lost productivity. If a repair is needed on any OMEGA instrumentation it will be initiated promptly. In the meantime you'll see how we can keep your process running smoothly. Call us for details!

Service from Trained Professionals

Our Sales and Engineering representatives are "product experts." A new technical training facility provides actual hands-on experience with our instrumentation, and allows simulation of many applications. One of them may be yours!

TABLE OF CONTENTS

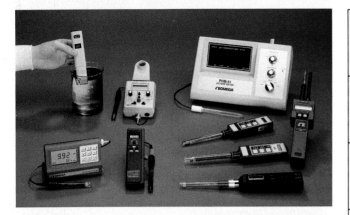

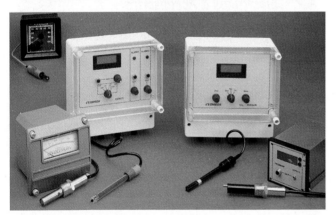

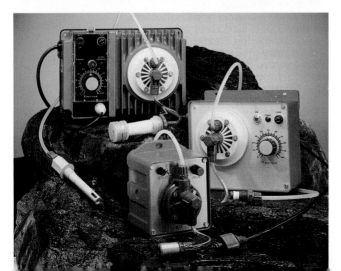

A New Product Showcase

Handheld pH Meters
Conductivity Meters
pH Controllers
Industrial Electrodes
Transmitters
Conductivity Controllers
Pumps

B Field Service Products

C Laboratory Instrumentation

D Electrodes & Accessories

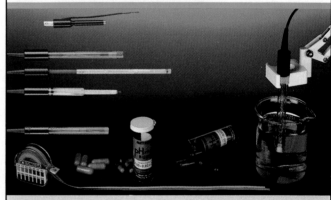

E — Industrial Equipment

F — Industrial pH Transmitters

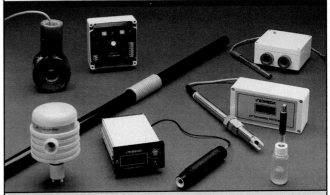

G — Industrial Conductivity Controllers

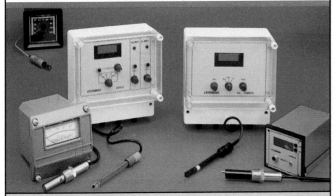

H — Pumps, Valves, Mixers

J Auxiliary Equipment

K Data Acquisiton

L Humidity

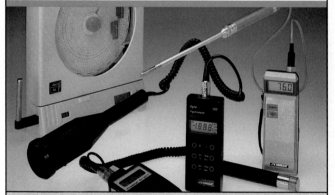

Y Scientific and Technical Books

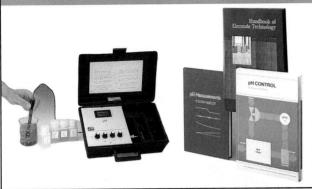

OMEGA Engineering Trademarks

Biomega®	Omegalok™
Book of Books®	Omegalux™
Chart-Temp™	Omegamarker™
DialTemp™	Omegameter™
Digicator™	Omegapellets™
iOmega™	Omegaphone™
Litmustik™	Omegaprobe®
New Horizons®	Omegarometer™
OMEGA®	Omegasays™
Omega-Flo®	Omegascope®
Omega-N™	Omegasez™
Omega-P™	Omegasnap™
Omegabasic™	Omegasoft®
Omegabench™	Omegastik®
Omegabond®	Omegatemp®
Omegabus™	Omegatherm®
Omegabyte™	Omegatite™
Omegacare™	Omni-Amp™
Omegaclad®	OmniCal™
Omegaette™	Temperature
Omegaflex™	Developments®
Omegalabel®	White Box®
Omegalaq®	Whyte Box®
Omegaline®	Wite Box®
Omegalloy™	Wyte Box®
Omegalog™	μMega®
	μMegaBasic™

Trademarks

Apple Computer Co.
Apple®

BriskHeat Corp.
Samox®

E.I. DuPont de Nemours
KEL-F®
Teflon®
Viton®

General Electric Co.
Noryl®
Triac®

Hoskins Mfg. Co.
Alumel®
Chromel®

Huntington Alloys
Hastelloy®

**International Business
Machines, Inc.**
IBM®
PC®
PC AT®
PC XT™

International Nickel Co.
Inconel®

**Laboratory Technologies
Corp.**
Labtech Notebook®

Lotus Development Corp.
1-2-3®
Symphony®

Pennwalt Corp.
Kynar®

NEW PRODUCT SHOWCASE

pH/Conductivity/Temperature Tester PHH-10   From $357

One compact unit measures pH, conductivity and temperature. The PHH-10 has full pH range with 0.01 accuracy at 77°F; selectable conductivity ranges of 0 to 20, 200, 2,000 and 20,000 μmhos; and a temperature measurement range of 0-160°F. An integral cup holds a liquid sample for testing, making it ideal for field work.
Page B-18

Conductivity Meter and Printer CDB-75, CDB-75-P   From $1295

This sophisticated microprocessor based conductivity meter allows the user to select and set operating parameters for improved accuracy and resolution. The CDB-75 features six selectable conductivity ranges from 0 to 19.99 μS thru 0 to 1000 mS and temperature compensation from 0 to 100°C. A factory fitted printer unit with a clock and RS232 output, model CDB-75-P, is also available.
Page C-9

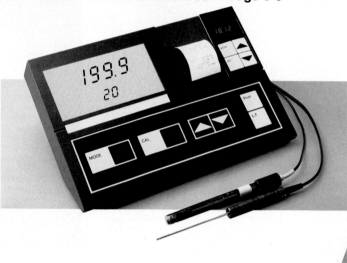

Non-Indicating Resistivity Transmitter RSTX-201-202 $470

The RSTX-201-202 resistivity transmitter requires only two wires for output and power transmission. The unit's electronics are fully encapsulated; terminal strips are provided for field connections. It is supplied with a resistivity sensor; an optional polycarbonate NEMA-4X enclosure is available for environmental protection. The transmitter can be surface mounted in any position.
Page F-7

Portable pH Meter PHH-20 $395

The PHH-20 portable pH indicator is pocket size for handy use in the field. It has ±0.01 pH accuracy, automatic or manual temperature compensation, single or dual point calibration. The microprocessor determines the correct temperature, characteristics of the electrode and buffer solutions. No recalibration is required; the unit retains calibration values after shutoff.
Page B-8

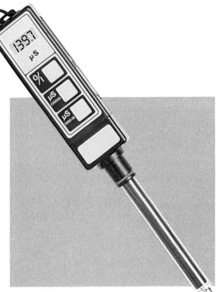

Conductivity Meter with Pre-calibrated Cells CDH-40 $323

Measure conductivity from 0 to 2000 μS with the CDH-40 dual range meter. Portable and precise, the unit has pre-calibrated conductivity cells with ATC from 0 to 50°C. It will measure 0 to 199.9 μS and 0 to 1999 μS with an accuracy of ±1%, ±2 digits, and a resolution of 0.1 μS and 1 μS, respectively. Additional features include 1 KHz excitation frequency and 25°C reference temperature.
Page B-19

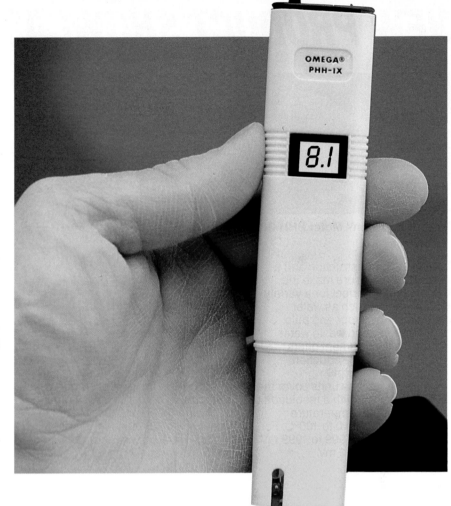

Litmustik™ pH Tester PHH-1X $44

Introducing Litmustik™ -- the newly designed, colorful pH tester, model PHH-1X, which features large display numerics for easy reading, single point calibration, and pocket size convenience. Built for fast evaluations, the Litmustik™ measures the entire pH range from 0 to 14 units, with 0.1 pH resolution, ±0.2 pH accuracy, and an operating temperature of 0-50°C.
Page B-4

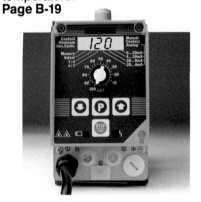

Chemical Metering Pumps PHP-200, PHP-210   From $512

Programmable, solenoid-driven diaphragm liquid metering pumps, PHP-200 series, can be operated automatically utilizing a pulse frequency signal from a pH controller or watermeter. They can also be operated manually with an adjustment from 10 to 100% and the stroking rate from 1 to 120 pulses per minute. These pumps have 3½ digit LCD readout for stroke rate, stroke control and fault indication. The PHP-210 series accepts a current input signal.
Page H-3

Microprocessor Based pH Controller PHCN-28   From $625

Auto buffering, solution temperature compensation, self diagnostics, and communications capabilities are features of the PHCN-28 microprocessor pH controller. Four tactile membrane keypads allow for the selection and input of set-up parameters, input of calibration data and alarm setpoint adjustments. Two 5 A, 230 Vac relays can be configured as hi/hi, hi/lo or lo/lo.
Page E-9

NEW PRODUCT SHOWCASE

Waterproof pH/mV Meter PHH-30
$194

Rugged ABS construction and a waterproof enclosure make the PHH-30 meter perfect for a variety of applications such as water quality testing, paper and pulp manufacturing and waste water control. This instrument offers pH/ORP (oxidation-reduction potential) units. For pH measurement these units cover the full 0-14 pH scale with a resolution of 0.01 and manual temperature compensation from 0 to 100°C. For ORP the range is -1999 to 1999 mV with a resolution of 1 mV.
Page B-3

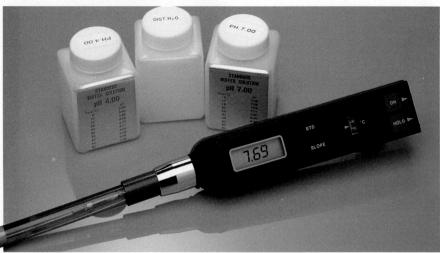

Portable pH Stick Meter PHH-12
$169

The PHH-12 portable handheld pH meter covers the 0-14 pH range with a resolution of 0.01 pH. An 8 mm LCD with hold function is readable under bright ambient conditions. Manual temperature compensation is 0-60°C. Features include low drift and high stability, fast input response and slope adjustment. Gel-filled electrode, buffer bottles, capsules and carrying case supplied.
Page B-5

Portable pH/mV Meter PHH-23
$175

For convenient field applications the PHH-23 offers laboratory instrument speed and precision -- in compact lightweight combination pH/ORP (oxidation-reduction potential) units. For pH measurement these units cover the full 0-14 pH scale with a resolution of 0.01 and manual temperature compensation from 0-100°C. For ORP measurement the range is -1999 to 1999 mV with a resolution of 1 mV.
Page B-3

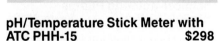

pH/Temperature Stick Meter with ATC PHH-15
$298

Featuring a combination pH electrode with an integral temperature sensor, the PHH-15 portable stick meter measures pH and temperature. It has a 3½ digit LCD display, ATC from 0-100°C and touch pad control which allows the user to switch easily between pH and temperature. Unit includes a sheath to protect the electrode when not in use and keep it moist, a carrying case, and 4 and 7 buffer powders.
Page B-6

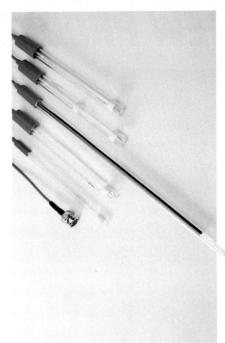

s_

Peristaltic Pumps PHP-1S, PHP-SX
From $123

OMEGAFLEX has peristaltic pumps for continuous operation (PHP-1S series) and for handling large capacitites (PHP-SX series). Both series have a sliding compression action and a silicone membrane tube. The continuous operation pumps have a modular ABS enclosure, and are offered with an optional regulating knob with a 0-100% adjustment. The large capacity pumps come without an enclosure and can handle from 15 to 65 L/hr.
Page H-10

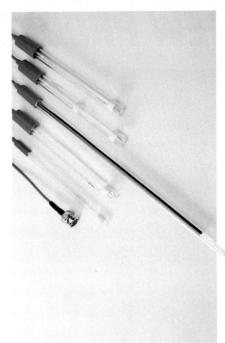

Clear Epoxy-Bodied, Gel-Filled Combination Electrodes PHE-4200 **From $49**

The unique clear-epoxy design enables the PHE-4200 electrodes to offer reliable quality at a reasonable cost. They measure from 0 to 14 pH units at 0 to 100°C and feature an Ag/AgCl reference and a polypropylene liquid junction. Each one comes in a soaker storage bottle to keep it moist and ready for use. There are five styles to choose from.
Page D-13

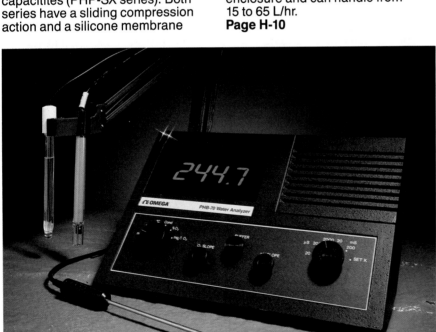

Laboratory Water Analyzer PHB-70X **$1430**

The PHB-70X offers complete and precise measurement of pH, conductivity, ORP, dissolved oxygen, ionic strength and temperature in most water and chemical samples. Included are conductivity probe (K=1) with ATC, glass combination pH electrode, temperature measurement probe, swing arm electrode holder and a pack of pH 4 and 7 buffers.
Page C-6

Microprocessor-Based Controllers PHCN-86, PHCN-86A **From $675**

For a variety of applications including waste-water treatment, plating and food processing the PHCN-86/86A controllers are ideal. The tactile feedback keypad is easy to use and allows access for readouts for pH, temperature and millivolts. Also, there is a current output of 0-20 mA or 4-20 mA for input to recorder, computer or other control device. The signal may be inverted and the 4-20 mA signal may be ordered isolated or non-isolated.
Page E-18

NEW PRODUCT SHOWCASE

**By-Pass Flow Electrodes
PHE/ORP-4580**   **From $95**

The PHE/ORP-4580 electrodes have a flat surface, modified CPVC tee and cable assembly. Each GPM flowing through the tee results in a 2 ft/sec velocity which performs self-cleaning action. No moving parts, liquid jets or power are required. These electrodes can be used with emulsions, slurries, oily waste-water and other difficult flowing samples. ATC is optional.
Page E-29

**In-Line Flow Electrodes
PHE/ORP-5460**   **From $95**

Turbulence causes the scrubbing action of the PHE/ORP-5460 in-line flow electrodes. These flat abrasion-free units can be used in applications with 0-100°C temperatures, pressures up to 100 PSIG and 0-14 pH measurement range. Having fresh material sweep past the electrode's surface improves response time as well as accuracy. The electrodes accept a cable assembly with a gland mounted in a ¾″ NPT tee.
Page E-30

**Submersible Flat Surface
Electrodes PHE/ORE-6510**
     From $95

The flat sensing surface of PHE/ORE-6510 electrodes is surrounded by a porous polyethylene reference junction which minimizes fouling. Installation is as easy as connecting a coupling and pipe to the electrode's cable assembly cap with a simple ¼ turn. The resulting assembly is lightweight for convenient handling in the event maintenance is needed. ATC is optional.
Page E-30

**Conductivity/Resistivity
Controllers CDCN-001, CDCN-002,
CDCN-003, RSCN-400**   **From $625**

The CDCN/RSCN family of ultrapure water analyzers has two cell inputs, two types of conductivity cell calibrations, ATC, self-diagnostics and communications capabilities.

Four tactile membrane keypads provide selection and input of all setup parameters. These units provide a system accuracy of better than ±1% (of reading) by employing an interactive dual matrix temperature compensation.
Page G-5

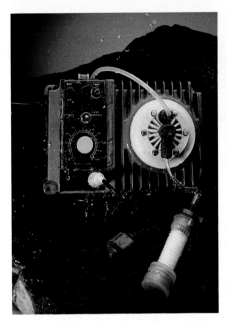

Open and Closed Loop Chemical Metering Pumps PHP-80
From $270

Open and closed loop dosing enables the PHP-80 to maintain a constant flowrate which can be set by manual control from 0-100% with ±5% accuracy. The setting varies the number of strokes. These pumps, offered in a wide range of flowrates, are chemically compatible with a variety of liquids. They come with an input for a level switch, injection and foot valves, liquid filter, and tubing for immediate operation.
Page H-5

Panel Mounted Conductivity Controller CDCN-36   **$249**

The CDCN-36 is a compact 1/8 DIN on/off conductivity controller with two outputs for high and low setpoints. A one millivolt per count recorder output is included as standard. An internal switch allows the selection of four conductivity ranges which make the controller useful in diverse applications. A flow-thru electrode and three types of in-line submersible electrodes are available for use with the CDCN-36.
Page G-8

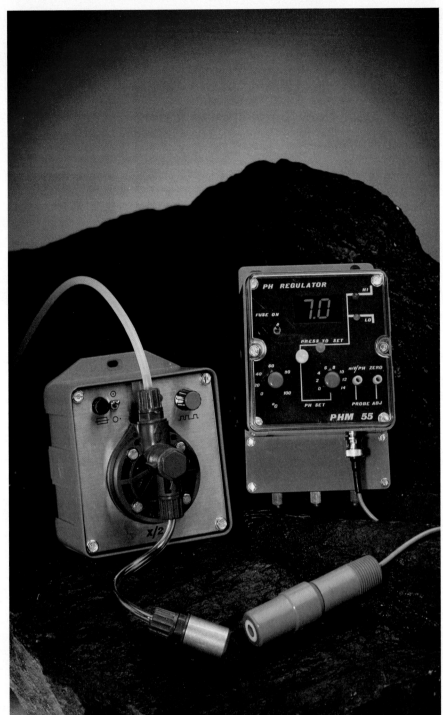

Wall Mounted Chemical Dosing Pumps PHP-165   **$174**

PHP-165 pumps are an economical choice for such applications as well-water chlorination, water treatment, swimming pools and chemical dosing. They are equipped with EDPM-PTFE diaphragm valves and seal gaskets, polypropylene suction and outlet valves, regulation from 0-100% via external knob and an anti-corrosion stainless steel front. Supplied with injection and foot valves, filter and tubing.
Page H-6

Compact, Modular pH Controller PHM-55   **$428**

For applications as wide-ranging as water purification and waste water control the PHM-55 is ideal. It has an adjustable setpoint, 5 Amp control relay and 3-digit pH display. Also featured are 0-14.0 pH range with ±0.1 resolution; automatic and manual temperature compensation; ±0.1 pH setpoint hysteresis; 4-20 mA recorder output and rugged plastic enclosure with IP512 protection. An extended bottom section allows for terminal board connections.
Page H-6

Pumps for On/Off or Proportional Control PHP-70
From $179

PHP-70 series chemical metering pumps are designed for applications requiring on/off or proportional control. The PHP-74 is supplied with lip valves and Viton seal gaskets; all other models are equipped with ball valves and silicone seal gaskets. Pumps will accept a milliamp input and can operate in manual or automatic mode by changing the position of the electrical switch; they also include an input for a level switch.
Page H-7

Pumps with 4-20 mA Input for Proportional Control
PHP-50
From $365

For applications such as nickel plating baths and water chlorination the PHP-50 series pumps are perfectly suited. These large capacity metering units accept a 4-20 mA input signal and have PTFE diaphragms. They are wall mounted, have an aluminum cast enclosure coated with a special polymer resin to prevent atmospheric and chemical corrosion while providing electrical insulation, and feature manual control with an external knob for 0-100% adjustment of pump capacity.
Page H-8

Large Capacity, Heavy Duty Pumps PHP-120
From $307

The PHP-120 pumps can accept pulse signals from pH controllers and water meters. They can take a maximum of 166 pulses per minute with a ratio of 1:1 (one stroke per pulse). This ratio can be modified by an external thumbwheel selector switch so that the pump can accept a faster frequency of up to 1200 pulses per minute. The enclosures are aluminum coated with Rilsan for protection from atmosphere and chemical corrosion.
Page H-8

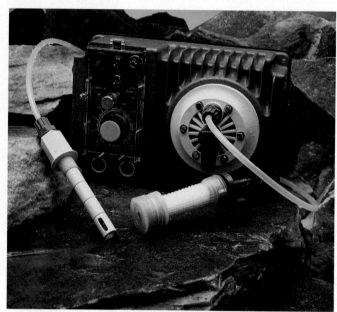

Pumps for Continuous or Automaic Operation
PHP-180
From $405

A pulse frequency signal enables PHP-180 pumps to operate continuously or automatically. These pumps are designed for applications involving chemical dosing of a solution in relation to the volume of liquid being treated, such as the chlorination of water. Features include Viton wetted parts, polyethylene ogival valves with hastelloy springs and Viton gaskets, and aluminum housing coated with a polymer resin for protection.
Page H-9

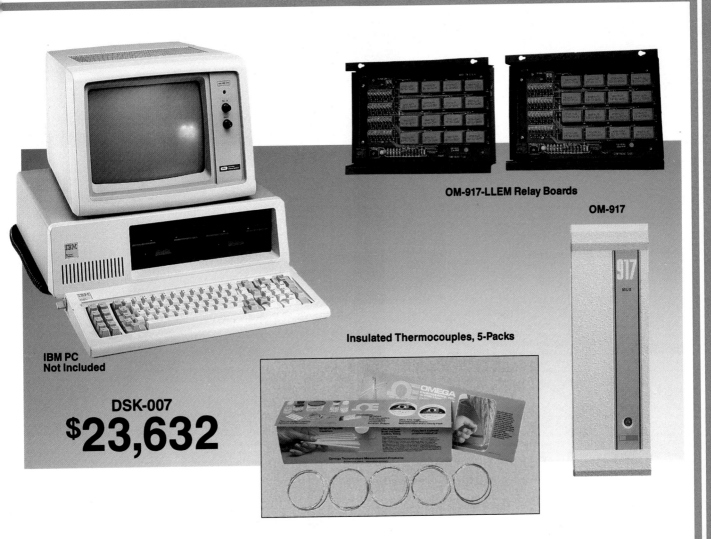

OM-917-LLEM Relay Boards

OM-917

Insulated Thermocouples, 5-Packs

**IBM PC
Not Included**

DSK-007
$23,632

For monitoring large numbers of temperature points, the DSK-007 is one of the most economical, reliable, and accurate systems available. The key to this system is the OMEGA OM-900 interface and OM-917 multiplexer modules. The system accepts up to 256 thermocouple inputs at an extremely low dollar-per-channel cost. Each OM-917-LLEM accepts up to 16 inputs and multiplexes the inputs to the one output channel.

The OM-917-LLEM resides externally to the main OM-900 system and is connected to the main system through an OM-917 module. The output channel of the OM-917-LLEM is connected to one of the eight inputs on the OM-931 thermocouple input module. Up to eight OM-917- LLEM's may be attached to one OM-917 module, providing 128 thermocouple or low level analog inputs.

The system works with an IBM PC (not included). Supplied with the system are enough thermocouples and wire for all the temperature measurements. For simple programming-free operation, LTControl software provides Complete monitoring, control, display, and datalogging capabilities.

System Includes:

Qty	Description	Price
1	**OM-992** Central Processing Unit Module	**$1350**
1	**OM-903** 115/236 Vac supply, 60 W capacity	**595**
2	**OM-917** Low Level Multiplexer Controller ($575 each)	**1150**
16	**OM-917-LLEM** Low Level Multiplexer Relay Board ($600 each)	**9600**
2	**OM-931** 8-Channel Thermocouple Input Module ($1350 each)	**2700**
10	**EXPP-K-20-1000,** 1000' Thermocouple Wire ($230 each less 20% for quantity)	**1840**
52	**5TC-GG-K-20-36** Thermocouples, 5-Packs ($39 each less 20% for quantity)	**1622**
260	**SMP-K-MF** Thermocouple Connector Pairs ($4 each less 25% for quantity)	**780**
1	**SWD-LCT-1** LTControl Software	**3995**

Order No. DSK-007	**$23,632**

Data Acquisition and Control with the Macintosh II

WB-FAI-M2-16 Analog Input/Output Card

Note: Macintosh II not included

WB-DIO-NB-40 Digital Input/Output Card

**KQSS-316U
Thermocouples**

DSK-006
$5132

The DSK-006 provides complete data acquisition and control using the Macintosh II computer. This versatile system provides analog inputs and outputs, digital inputs and outputs, and the ability to interface to IEEE-488 instruments. The system is centered around three plug-in cards: the WB-FAI-M2-16 provides 16 analog inputs and two analog outputs, the WB-DIO-NB-40 offers 40 channels of digital input/output plus six timer counters, and the OMB-MAC2-488 allows IEEE-488 interface.

The Omegabench software is a powerful, easy-to-use icon-based program. The software allows full access to all the functions provided by the plug-in cards.

OMB-MAC2-488 IEEE-488 Interface

System Includes:

1	Analog input/output card **Model WB-FAI-M2-16**	**$1145**
1	Digital input/output card **Model WB-DIO-NB-40**	**$345**
1	IEEE-488 Interface **Model OMB-MAC2-488**	**$595**
2	Screw terminal panel for WB-FAI-M2-16 **Model WB-T21 (2 required) $300 each**	**$600**
1	Screw terminal panel for WB-DIO **Model WB-DIOX-T400**	**$395**
10	**ACO5-B** Solid State Switch - Isolated AC output $15 each	**$150**
10	**DCO5-B** Solid State Switch - Isolated DC output $15 each	**$150**
10	**ACI5-B** Solid State Switch - Isolated AC input $15 each	**$150**
10	**DCI5-B** Solid State Switch - Isolated DC input $15 each	**$150**
1	**OMBX-CA-7-3** 6′ Shielded IEEE-488 cable	**$90**
10	**KQSS-316U** K type thermocouples $28 each less 10% quantity discount	**$252**
1	**EXTT-K-20-500** 500′ thermoucouple wire	**$115**
1	Omegabench software **Model SWD-WBMA**	**$995**
	Order No. DSK-006	**$5132**

Flexible RS-232 Data Acquisition System

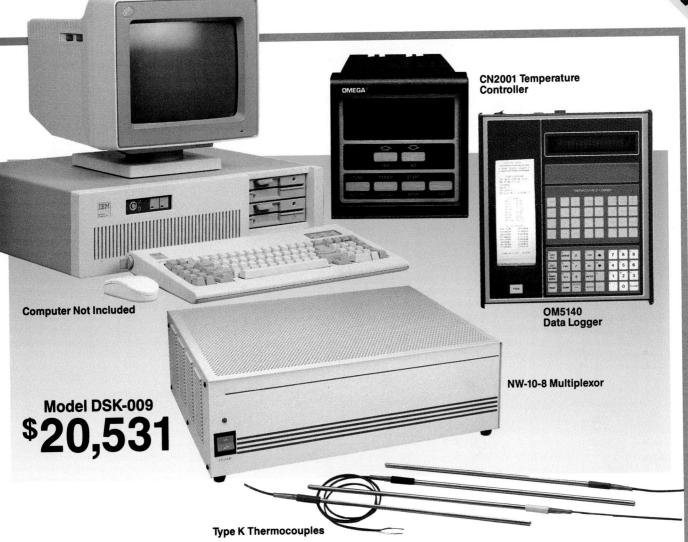

Computer Not Included

CN2001 Temperature Controller

OM5140 Data Logger

NW-10-8 Multiplexor

Model DSK-009
$20,531

Type K Thermocouples

The OMEGA DSK-009 system provides monitoring of controllers and a variety of sensors via datalogging equipment. The key to the system is the OMEGA NW-10-8 eight channel multiplexor. It allows eight RS-232 ports to be linked together, thus enabling a single RS-232 port on your host computer (not included) to access a mixture of data acquisition and control equipment.

The DSK-009 system includes two CN2001-D3 controllers, an OM-5140 40-channel datalogger, and an OM-272 32-channel trend/data recorder with display. This system also includes an assortment of sensor types for measuring temperature, air velocity, pressure, and pH.

System includes:

Qty	Item	Price
1	**NW-10-8** Eight channel multiplexor	$1895
1	**OM-272** Trend/data recorder (32 channels)	4400
1	**OM-5140** Data logger (40 channels)	2670
4	**OC4-NM-MM-5** RS-232 Cable, null-modem, 5' ($20 each)	80
2	**CN2001-D3** Temperature controller ($590 each)	1180
1	**EXPP-K-20-1000** Extension wire, type K, 1000'	230
40	**SMP-K-MF** Thermocouple connectors ($4.25 each, less 15% qty. discounts)	145
40	**KTIN-316U-12** Type K thermocouples, 3/16" ($22 each, less 20% qty. discount)	704

Qty	Item	Price
2	**SRFH-105/120** Flexible rubber heater (25 watt)($12 each)	24
2	**FMA604-V** Air Velocity Sensor (0-2000FPM) ($750 each)	1500
2	**PST-18** Power Supply for FMA ($190 each)	380
3	**FP-5800** Paddlewheel flow sensor (0.5-4" pipe)($415 each)	1245
3	**PSU-24** Power supply for paddlewheel sensor ($40 each)	120
2	**FLR6102-DG** Remote reading flowmeter ($815 each)	1630
3	**PX613-100G5V** Pressure transducer, 100 PSI gauge ($249 each)	747
3	**PX304-050A5V** Pressure transducer, 50PSI absolute ($349 each)	1047
1	**U24Y100** Power supply for pressure transducers	110
4	**LCJA-1K** Load cells, 1000 lbs (4000 lb system) ($370 each)	1480
1	**JBOX-4** Summing box for load cells	315
1	**DMD-465** Power supply & amplifier for load cells	285
1	**TX4-100** Wire, 100 feet, 24 AWG with shield	29
1	**PHTX-91** pH Transmitter	215
1	**PHE-7151-15** pH Electrode	100

Order No. DSK-009 **Total $20,531**

"The Night Watchman"

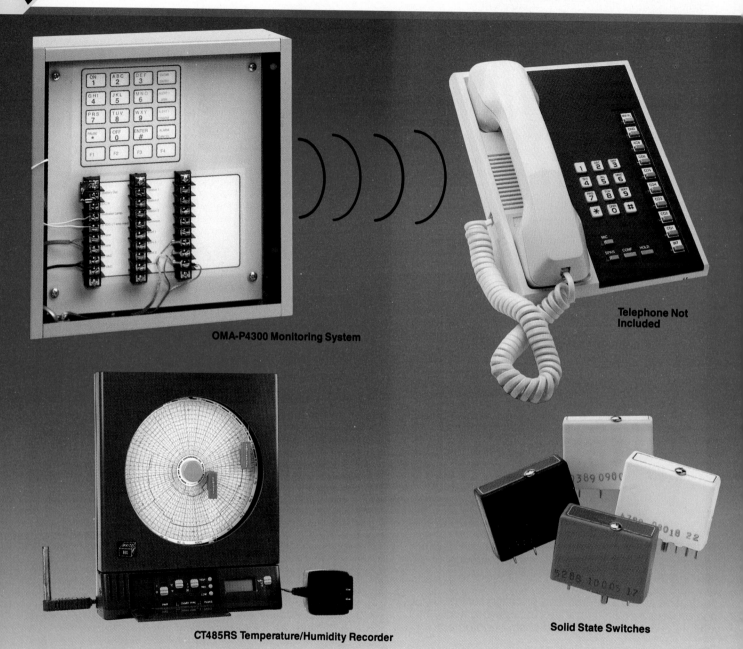

OMA-P4300 Monitoring System

Telephone Not Included

CT485RS Temperature/Humidity Recorder

Solid State Switches

The OMEGA DSK-008 "Night Watchman" system provides alarm monitoring and recording for industrial and laboratory environments. The heart of the system is the OMA-P4300, which can monitor environmental temperature, one 4-20 mA analog input, and three switch closure inputs. Upon alarm condition the OMA-P4300 will dial a pre-programmed telephone list and report the alarm in voice-synthesized English.

OMEGA solid state switches are used to interface high level, real world signals to the OMA-P4300 digital inputs. The OMEGA CT485RS circular chart recorder provides reliable hardcopy backup of ambient temperature and humidity.

System Includes:

Qty	Description	Price
1	**OMA-P4300** Monitoring System	$1127
1	**CT485RS** Circular Temperature/Humidity Recorder	497
1	4-Channel Solid State Switch Backplane **Model SSS-PC4**	35
4	Solid State Relay Module - AC input **Model ACO5-B** ($15 each)	60
1	Cable for Solid State Switch Backplane **Model SSS-CA6**	25
1	1 Amp Control Module for OMA-P4300 **Model OMA-PX101**	160
1	**CT485-CWF,** Extra Charts for CT485RS, 7 day	12
1	**CT485-PS,** Extra Pens for CT485RS	8

Order No. DSK-008	$1924

Now For Your Convenience, Technical and Scientific Selections From OMEGA... Your Source for Over 10,000 Titles!

- ✔ Electrical, Industrial, Civil and Mechanical Engineering
- ✔ Chemistry, Chemical Engineering
- ✔ Computing, Mathematics, Self Help, Safety

To Order Your Books, Call This Toll-Free Number in the USA

Books Hot Line (For Book Orders Only):

1-800-222-Book ™
1-800-222-2665

In CT Dial **(203) 359-1660**

See Section "Y" in this handbook for additional information on the texts shown below as well as an extended list of titles selected from over 10,000 offered by OMEGA. Choose the books which are vital not only to your work in pH/Conductivity, but also those which are related to other fields: temperature, heaters, pressure/force, flow/level and data acquisition.

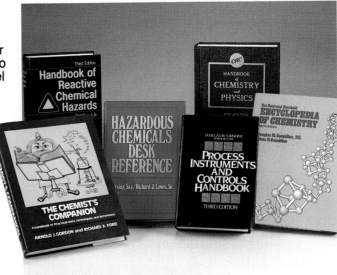

THE CHEMIST'S COMPANION
Gordon, Ford
WILEY
ISBN 0-471-31590-7
ORDER NO. CH-0169 **$55.00**

HANDBOOK OF CHEMISTRY AND PHYSICS, 69TH ED.
Weast
CRC PRESS
ISBN 469-8493-0469-5
ORDER NO. SD-0503 **$89.95**

VAN NOSTRAND REINHOLD ENCYCLOPEDIA OF CHEMISTRY 4TH ED.
Considine, Considine
ISBN 0-442-22572-5
ORDER NO. CM-0160 **$107.95**

HANDBOOK OF REACTIVE CHEMICAL HAZARDS, 3RD ED.
Bretherick
BUTTERWORTHS
ISBN 0-408-01388-5
ORDER NO. CM-0480 **$128.00**

HAZARDOUS CHEMICALS DESK REFERENCE
Sax, Lewis
VAN NOSTRAND REINHOLD
ISBN# 0-442-28208-7
ORDER NO. CM-0452 **$79.95**

PROCESS INSTRUMENTS AND CONTROLS HANDBOOK
Considine
MCGRAW-HILL
ISBN 0-07-012436-1
ORDER NO. MS-0333 **$102.00**

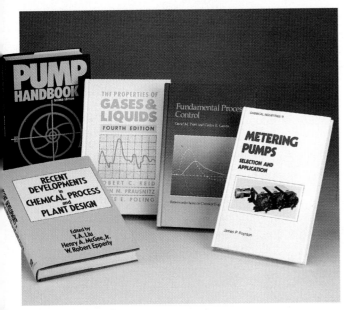

METERING PUMPS
Poynton
MARCEL DEKKER
ISBN 0-8247-1759-7
ORDER NO. MS-0919 **$59.75**

THE PROPERTIES OF GASES & LIQUIDS, 4TH ED.
Reid, Prausnitz, Poling
MCGRAW-HILL
ISBN 0-07-051799-1
ORDER NO. CM-0142 **$56.00**

PUMP HANDBOOK, 2ND ED.
Karassik, Krutzsch, Fraser, Messina
MCGRAW-HILL
ISBN 0-07-033302-5
ORDER NO. ME-0341 **$96.00**

RECENT DEVELOPMENTS IN CHEMICAL PROCESS AND PLANT DESIGN
Liu, McGee, Epperly
WILEY
ISBN 0-471-84780-1
ORDER NO. CM-0506 **$80.00**

FUNDAMENTAL PROCESS CONTROL
Prett, Garcia
BUTTERWORTHS
ISBN 0-409-90082-6
ORDER NO. CM-0492 **$39.95**

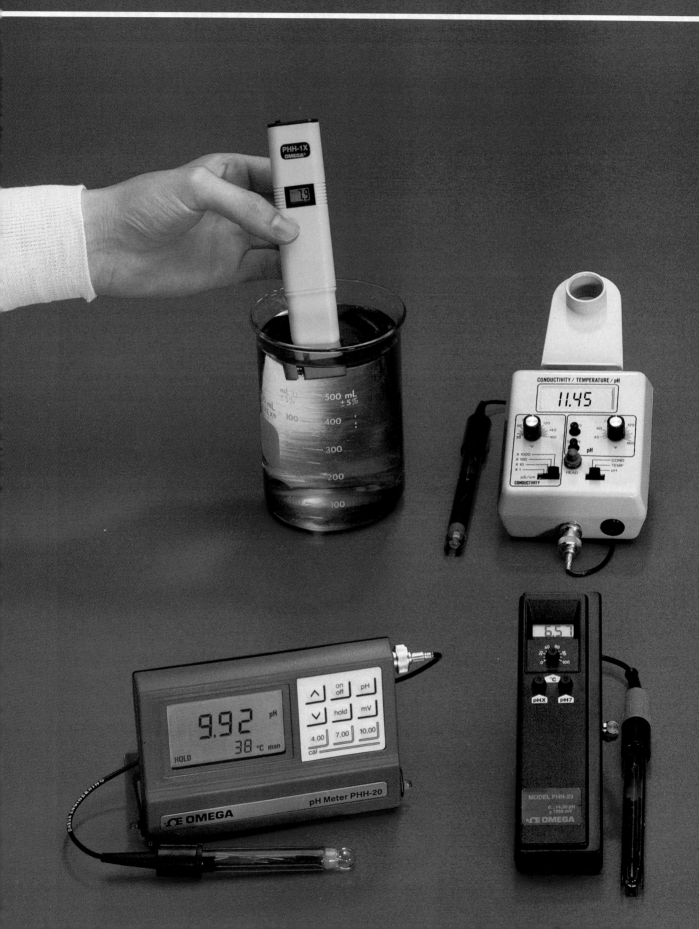

B-3 thru B-11, B-15, B-16, B-18, B-19	B-15, B-20	B-12 thru B-14	B-14 THRU B-17, B-19, B-20
HANDHELD pH METERS	**HAND HELD DISSOLVED OXYGEN METER**	**PORTABLE BENCHTOP METERS**	**HANDHELD CONDUCTIVITY METERS**

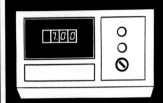
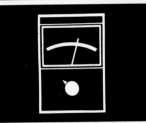

B

FIELD SERVICE PRODUCTS

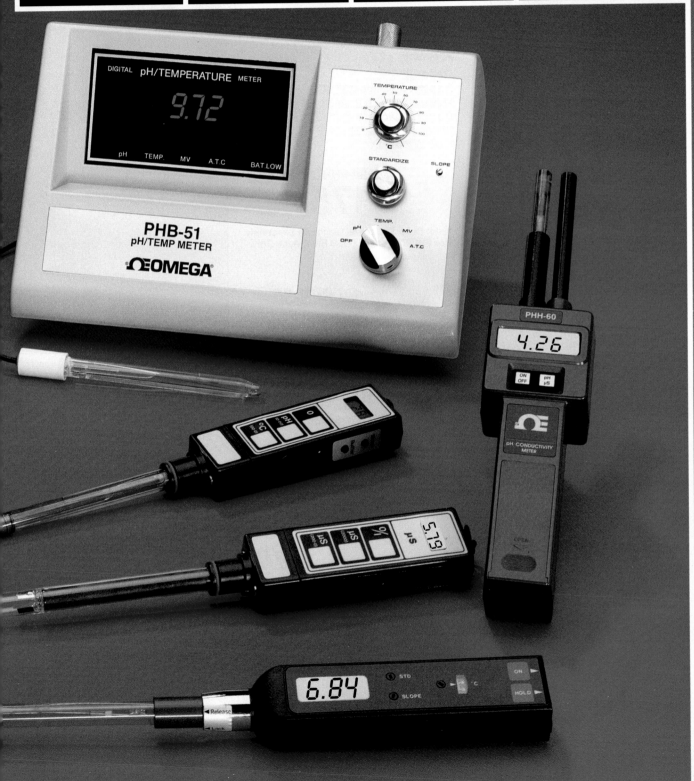

Portable pH/mV Meters

Models PHH-23/30

- ✔ **Economical**
- ✔ **Easy to Use**
- ✔ **Compact, Lightweight**
- ✔ **0.01 pH Resolution**

OMEGA digital PHH-23 and PHH-30 meters offer laboratory instrument speed and precision — in compact, lightweight combination pH/ORP (oxidation-reduction potential) units. For pH measurement these units cover the full 0 to 14 pH scale with a resolution of 0.01 and manual temperature compensation from 0 to 100°C. For ORP the measurement range is −1999 to 1999 mV with a resolution of 1 mV. They can be used for a variety of applications such as water quality testing, paper and pulp manufacturing, textiles, waste water control, electroplating and food processing.

Specifications:

pH Mode
Measuring Range: 0 to 14 pH units
Resolution: 0.01 pH units
Accuracy: ±0.02 pH units
Temperature Compensation:
Manual, 0 to 100°C

ORP Mode
Measuring Range: −1999 to 1999 mV
Resolution: 1 mV
Accuracy: ±2 mV

General
Display: 3½ digit, 0.3″ LCD
Power Source: 9 V long lasting lithium battery
Dimensions: 6.2″H x 1.8″W x 0.9″D

Model PHH-23
$175

Note: Order Meter and Electrode Separately. Use PHE-23D or ORE-23D Electrodes Only.

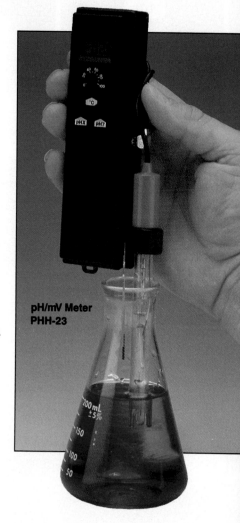

pH/mV Meter PHH-23

Waterproof pH/mV Meter PHH-30

Model PHH-30

- ✔ **All features of the PHH-23**
- ✔ **Waterproof Enclosure**
- ✔ **Rugged ABS Construction**

Model PHH-30
$194

To Order *(Specify Model Number)*

Model No.	Price	Description
PHH-23	$175	Meter w/3 ft cable
PHH-30	194	Waterproof meter w/3 ft cable
PHE-23D	58	detachable pH electrode, epoxy body, gel filled combination, 12 mm dia, 110 mm long
ORE-23D	82	detachable ORP electrode, epoxy body, gel filled, 12 mm dia, 110 mm long
PHCC-23	79	Accessory kit, includes carrying case, pH buffer solutions (2 vials, 50 ml each), electrode cleaning solution (250 ml), and plexiglass instrument stand with mounting hardware

Note: Order Meter and Electrode Separately. Use PHE-23D or ORE-23D Electrodes Only.

Litmustik™ High Performance pH Tester
Model PHH-1X

NEW!

- ✔ **For Any Application Where Litmus or pH Paper is Used but Better Accuracy is Required**
- ✔ **Measures 0 to 14 pH**
- ✔ **Where Portability is Required**
- ✔ **High Performance/Low Cost**
- ✔ **Large Digit Display**
- ✔ **0.1 pH Resolution**

OMEGA Engineering introduces the PHH-1X Litmustik. This newly designed, colorful tester features large display numerics for easy reading, single point calibration, and pocket-sized convenience. Designed for fast evaluations in the field, this high performance tester measures the entire pH range from 0 to 14 pH units and encompasses applications from water quality to soil testing. A handy pocket clip and removable cap make this unit ideal for field applications.

Model PHH-1X Comes Complete with Protective End Cap and Four 1.4 V Batteries.

Specifications:

Range: 0 to 14 pH
Resolution: 0.1 pH
Accuracy: ±0.2 pH
Battery: 4 × 1.4 V
Battery Life: 1000 h

Operating Temperature: 0 to 50°C
Dimensions: 5.91″ H × 1.26″ W × 0.75″ D
Weight: 0.13 lbs.

To Order *(Specify Model Number)*

Model No.	Price	Description
PHH-1X	$44	Portable pH Tester
PH-BATT	1	1.4 V replacement battery (four required)

Model PHH-1X
$44

Litmustik Finds Applications in Many Industries

Water Treatment/Wastewater
Textiles
Electroplating
Printing
Photo Finishing

Paper and Pulp
Nurseries and Garden Centers
Commercial Fisheries and Aquariums
Pools

Handheld pH Meters

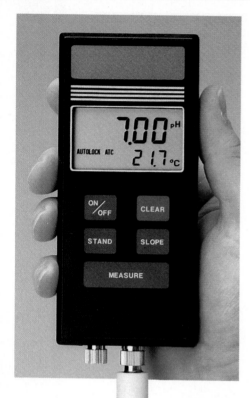

"3 in 1" Electrode Included

Microprocessor pH Meter PHH-50

Model PHH-50
$239

- **Measures pH and Temperature**

The PHH-50 is a hand held microprocessor based meter for pH and temperature measurements. To automatically sense the endpoint value and lock the display, an AUTOLOCK feature is provided for pH measurements.

For added versatility, a "3 in 1" pH/ref/temperature electrode is provided for single probe operation. The PHH-50 can be used in the "stick" format or used as a standard portable pH meter with the optional PHEC-1050 cable. Includes meter, buffer capsules, buffer bottles, carrying case, and "3 in 1" pH/Ref/Temp electrode.

Optional Accessories:

Replacement "3 in 1" pH/Ref/Temp electrode **PHE-1062 $59**
Extension Cable for **PHE-1062 PHEC-1050 $20**
Triaxial to BNC Adapter: **PHMA-TR $20**
ATC/Temp Probe **PHAT-1050 $39**
AC Adapter **PHAD-1050 $10**

Specifications:

Range: pH −2.00 to 16.00, Temp. 0 to 99.9°C

Resolution: pH 0.01, Temp. 0.1°C

Accuracy: pH ±0.1%, Temp. ±0.5°C

Input Impedance: > 10^{12} ohms

Temperature Compensation: Automatic 0 to 99.9°C

Connector: "3 in 1" electrode connector (may be used with BNC if adapter PHMA-TR is used)

Power: 9V battery, optional ac adapter PHAD-1050

Dimensions: 5.9" × 2.8" × 1.2"

Weight: 0.44 lb

Portable pH Stick Meter with Digital Readout

The PHH-12 portable handheld pH meter covers the 0 to 14 pH range with a resolution of 0.01 pH. An 8 mm LCD with display hold function is readable under bright ambient conditions. Manual temperature compensation is 0 to 60°C. Features low drift and high stability, fast input response, and slope adjustment. The PHH-12 is supplied with detachable gel-filled electrode, buffer bottles and capsules, and carrying case. For replacement electrode, order PHE-12D.

Optional Accessory:

Replacement electrode (must be used as replacement for PHH-12). **PHE-12D, $50**

Specifications:
Range: 0 to 14 pH
Resolution: 0.01 pH
Accuracy: ±0.05 pH ±1 digit

Temp. Compensation: Manual, 0 to 60°C
Power: 9V long-life lithium battery (supplied)
Dimensions: 6.78" H x 1.38" W x 1.10" D (172 x 35 x 28 mm)
Weight: 0.28 lbs (0.18 kg)

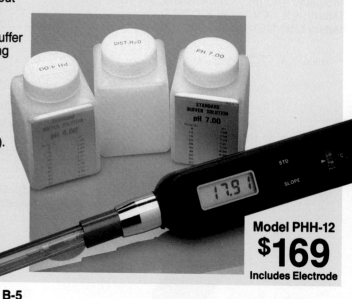

Model PHH-12
$169
Includes Electrode

pH/Temperature Stick Meter with ATC

✔ **Fast, Accurate Performance In the Field**
✔ **Splash-Proof Membrane Switching**
✔ **LCD Display**
✔ **Replaceable Electrode with ATC**

Measure pH and temperature with the OMEGA PHH-15 portable stick pH meter. The PHH-15 features a combination pH electrode with an integral temperature sensor, a 3½ digit LCD display, automatic temperature compensation from 0 to 100°C and touch

pad control which allows the user to easily switch between pH and temperature. pH can be measured from 0 to 14.00 pH units and temperature from 0 to 100°C with an accuracy of ±0.02 pH units and ±0.5°C and resolution of 0.01 pH units and 0.1°C. The unit comes complete with a combination pH electrode with ATC, a sheath to protect the electrode when not in use and keep the electrode moist, a carrying case, and 4 and 7 buffer powders.

Conductivity Stick Meter Also Available!
Model CDH-40, $323. See Page B-19.

Model PHH-15
$298

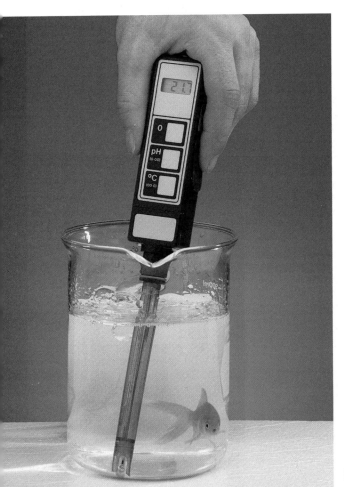

Specifications:
Range: 0 to 14.00 pH, 0 to 100°C
Accuracy: ±0.02 pH units, ±0.5°C
Resolution: 0.01 pH, 0.1°C
Automatic Temperature Compensation: 0 to 100°C
Isopotential Adjustment: 6 to 8 pH
Input Resistance: 10^{13} ohms
Display: 3½ digit LCD
Display Size: 6.8 mm (0.27 in)
Power Supply: 12 V battery (VR22, EL12, SP23A)
Size: 4.7″ H × 1.4″ W × 0.87″ D(excluding probe)
Weight: 0.29 lbs.

To Order *(Specify Model Number)*

Model No.	Price	Description
PHH-15	$298	pH/Temp stick meter and electrode with ATC
PHE-15	80	Combination gel-filled electrode with ATC, 12 mm dia, 110 mm length (only electrode for use with PHH-15)
PH-BATT-12	2	Replacement 12 V battery

pH, mV and Temperature Meter
pH Electrode Simulator

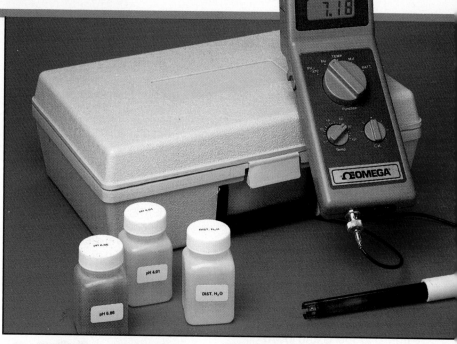

- **Complete Kit Including Meter, Gel Filled Combination Electrode, Buffer Solution, and Carrying Case**
- **Measures pH, mV, Temperature**
- **Rugged and Comfortable to Use**
- **Simple and Accurate Operation**

The PHH-88 is a unique meter that is comfortable to hold and rugged enough for field use in a variety of applications. It features pH with automatic temperature compensation, millivolt, and temperature measurement capabilities. Because it is designed with the user in mind, it is easy to operate and has a large high contrast LCD display which is highly visible even in direct sunlight. It is sold as a complete kit including meter, gel filled combination electrode, buffer solution and a foam lined carrying case.

Model PHH-88
$372

Optional Accessories:
General Purpose Automatic Temperature Compensation Probe (0-100°C)   **PHAT-8 $83**

Specifications:
Range: pH 0 to 14 pH, mV 0 to ±1999 mV
Temperature: −100 to 400°C
Automatic Temperature Compensation: 0 to 14 pH, 0 to 100°C
Resolution: pH 0.01, mV 1, Temp. 1°C
Accuracy: pH ±0.01 mV ±1, temp. ±1°C
Connector: BNC
Size: 12″ x 8″ x 4″
Weight: 2.5 lb

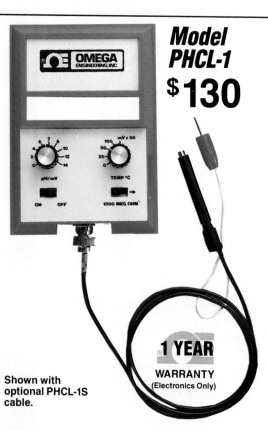

Shown with optional PHCL-1S cable.

1 YEAR WARRANTY (Electronics Only)

Model PHCL-1
$130

The PHCL-1 electrode simulator conveniently tests all types of pH meters, controllers, transmitters, recorders and alarms by simulating the characteristics of a pH electrode. With an accuracy of 1%, the simulator can also be used for routine calibration. Switch selectable 0 to 14 pH and millivolt ranges allow simulation of redox and specific ion probes as well as pH electrodes. Temperature values from 0 to 100°C can be selected to check pH meter temperature and slope compensators. A switch also provides 1000 megohm series resistance for checking meter input impedance.

Specifications:
Outputs: 0 to 14 pH switch-selected in 2 pH increments (1 pH increments between pH 6 and 8 for checking meters with expanded scales). 0 to 700 mV switch selected in 100 mV increments.
Temperature/Slope Compensation: Switch selects temperature values of 0, 25, 50, and 100°C. Simulates changes in

electrode output with temperature.
Impedance: Switchable 1000 megohm series resistance for checking pH meter input impedance.
Accuracy: Within 1%
Connector: BNC. Supplied with BNC to BNC cable
Size: 3½″ wide x 5″ high x 2″ deep
Weight: 0.5 lb
Power: 1.35 V "AA" mercury battery with expected life in excess of one year.

Optional Accessories:
PHCL-1C:
Industrial interface cable — terminated with alligator clips for use with industrial pH equipment, recorders, etc.   **$10**

PHCL-1K:
Field kit — leather carrying case with adjustable shoulder strap. Holds 2 oz. bottles of 4.00 and 7.00 buffers. Has space for test leads and spare electrode. Permits mini-test operation without removal from case. Only 7 oz.   **$19**

PHCL-1S:
BNC to U.S. Standard Connector **$10**

Portable Microprocessor-Based pH Meter Displays pH, mV, and °C

- ✓ Displays pH, mV, and °C
- ✓ Automatic Single or Dual Point Calibration
- ✓ Recorder Output
- ✓ Manual or Automatic Temperature Compensation
- ✓ Convertible for Benchtop or Portable Use
- ✓ Hold Function

1 YEAR WARRANTY **CARE**

Model PHH-20

$395

The PHH-20 microprocessor-based pH meter offers the carrying convenience of a pocket calculator and the precision of a laboratory meter. With two LCD's pH or mV and °C can be displayed simultaneously. The PHH-20 features automatic touch-key setup, buffer recognition, and hold function to retain the displayed reading. Designed with the end user in mind, the PHH-20 functions equally well on a benchtop or in the field, using a convenient neck strap for hands-free operation. The unit comes complete with carrying case, ampules of buffer 4 and 7 solution, and four 1.5 V alkaline batteries affording 6000 hours of operation. PHE-1311 general-purpose electrode and PHAT-20 automatic temperature compensating probe are sold separately.

Specifications:

Displays: pH, mV-13 mm LCD; Temperature-7mm LCD

Annunciators: WAIT, ΔpH, battery, HOLD, pH, °C, auto, CAL

Measurement Range: 0.00 to 14.00 pH; −199 to 199°C; −1000 to 1700 mV

Resolution: 0.01 pH, 1°C, 1 mV

Accuracy: 0.01 pH, 0.2°C, 1 mV

Temperature Compensation: Automatic or manual, 0 to 100°C

Slope Matching: 85 to 105%

Combination Electrode Zero-Point Matching: 5.5 to 8 pH

Calibration: Automatic, single- or dual-point; 4.00, 7.00, 10.00 pH

Electrode Connection: BNC for combination electrode

Temperature Sensor: 1000 ohm Pt RTD, 2 mm socket

Chart Recorder Output: 118 mV/pH; 1mV/mV 2 mm socket

Power Supply: four 1.5 V AA batteries

Automatic Switch-Off: after 60 minutes; also continuous operation

Battery Life: 6000 hrs.; automatic low battery indication

Dimensions: 1.5″H x 5.5″W x 3.5″D; 0.62 lb weight

Accessories Included: carrying strap, four AA batteries, carrying case, 25 mL 4.00 pH buffer, 25 mL 7.00 pH buffer, 50 mL KCl solution (3 molar), 4 plastic beakers, 1 electrode container

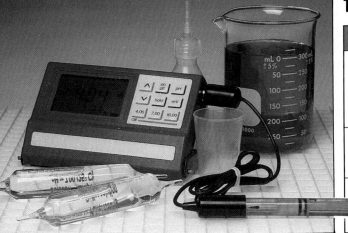

To Order *(Specify Model Number)*

Model No.	Price	Description
PHH-20	$395	Portable pH meter with carrying case, buffer 4 and 7 solutions, carrying strap, and 4 1.5 V alkaline batteries
PHE-1311	54	General-purpose, gel-filled, epoxy bodied combination electrode
PHAT-20	90	Automatic (Pt 1000) temperature compensating probe

Waterproof Hand Held Microprocessor pH Meter

- **Watertight Under 3 Feet of Water**
- **Measures pH, Temperature and Millivolts**
- **Rechargeable Batteries**
- **Touch Keyboard with Audio Feedback**

Model PHH-63

$329

When you need a truly weatherproof meter that can read pH, millivolts and temperature, the PHH-63 will fill the bill. The PHH-63 is completely watertight. It can operate under three feet of water, making it an "environment-proof" instrument for all weather applications. The built-in microprocessor stores, calculates and compensates for various measurement parameters. An LCD displays the pH (mV) and temperature values simultaneously as well as prompting the user and indicating mode. An AUTOLOCK feature is provided for pH and millivolt measurements; it enables the meter to automatically sense the end point and lock the display. If desired, the "triaxial" to BNC connector supplied with the meter enables the PHH-63 to use standard pH electrodes with a BNC connector.

Replacement "3 in 1" pH/Ref/Temp electrode **PHE-1062 $59**

Optional Accessories:
ATC/Temp Probe **PHAT-1050 $39**
Triaxial to BNC adaptor **PHMA-TR $20**

Specifications
Range: pH −2.00 to 16.00, mV ±999, temp 0 to 99.9°C

Resolution: pH 0.01, mV 1, temp 0.1°C
Accuracy: pH ±0.1%, mV ±0.1%, temp ±0.5%
Input Impedance: > 10^{12} ohms
Temperature Compensation: manual or automatic 0 to 99.9°C

Power: 9 V long lasting lithium battey

The PHH-63 is Supplied with ac Adaptor/Charger, 'Triaxial' to BNC Adaptor, Buffer Capsules, Buffer Bottles, Carrying Case, '3 in 1' pH/Ref/Temp Electrode, and Triaxial Probe Extension Cable.

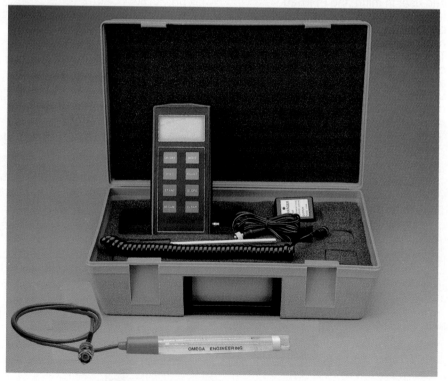

pH Meter and Calibration Kits

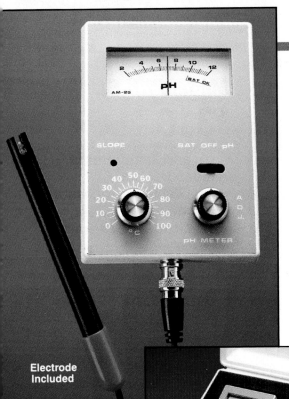

Electrode Included

Analog Hand Held pH Meter
Model PHH-45

- **Rugged, Solvent and Acid Resistant Case**
- **Extremely Cost-effective**
- **Easy to Use**

The PHH-45 pH meter is a cost-effective unit with a taut band meter movement in a sturdy solvent and acid resistant housing. It is a full function solid state instrument capable of measuring pH from 0 to 14 with the aid of offset ranging. Attractive and durable, the meter comes packaged in a kit with a gel-filled combination pH electrode, three buffers (pH 4, 7, 10), plastic screwdriver for calibration, battery, and a foam lined carrying case. This inexpensive but reliable pH meter is simple to use and is perfect for use in the field, laboratory, or plant.

Optional:
Replacement Electrode **PHE-1304 $33**

Specifications:
Range: pH 2 to 12 (0 to 14 with offset ranging)
Readability: 0.1 pH
Accuracy: ±0.1 pH
Precision: ±0.1 pH
Temperature Compensation: Manual, 0 to 100°C
Scale Divisions: 0.2 pH
Connector: BNC
Battery: 9V, included
Size: 4″ x 5¾″ x 2¼″
Weight: 9 oz

Model PHH-45

$165

Complete Kit Includes Rugged Carrying Case

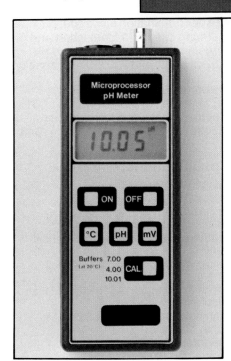

Microprocessor pH Meter

The PHH-70 is a compact microprocessor-based pH meter that measures pH, millivolts and temperature. This instrument features built-in buffer comparison memories, touch pad calibration and non-volatile back up memory to retain all information when the unit is off. To ensure correct data entry, there is an audible data accept signal plus a visual error display. The PHH-70 is supplied with an automatic temperature compensator probe, a pack of pH 4 and 7 buffers and a 9 V battery.

Specifications:
Ranges: 0 to 14.00 pH, −30 to 150°C, 0 to ±1999 mV
Accuracy: 0.02 pH, ±0.5°C, ±1 mV
Resolution: 0.01 pH, 0.1°C, 1 mV
Input Impedance: 10^{13} ohms
Temperature compensation: Automatic 0 to 100°C
Power: One 9 V battery
Dimensions: 5.9″ × 2.4″ × 1″
Weight: 0.31 lb

Optional Accessories:
General purpose rugged combination electrode **PHE-1304 $33**
Foam lined carrying case **PHCC-70 $35**
Battery charger and rechargeable cell **PHAC-70 $45**
Replacement ATC/temperature probe **PHAT-70 $60**

Model PHH-70

$457

Electrodes Sold Separately, See Section D.

Portable pH Meters
For Handheld or Bench Top Use

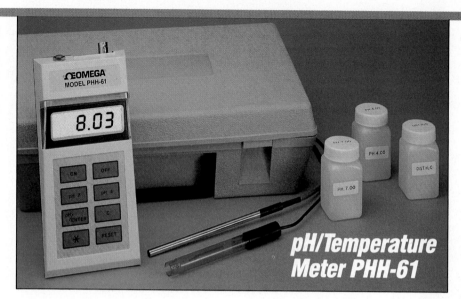

pH/Temperature Meter PHH-61

Model PHH-61
$310 Complete Kit

- **pH and Temperature Measurements**
- **CMOS Microprocessor Recognizes Buffers, Electrode Slope and Offset**
- **LCD Readout With Error Indicators**
- **Rugged Carrying Case**

The PHH-61 is a hand held CMOS microprocessor based digital pH/temperature meter. It provides the user with a rugged portable unit able to recognize and compensate for electrode offset and slope. The meter may also be powered by the optional AC line adaptor.

Includes:
Epoxy combination electrode
Carrying case with foam insert and three containers labeled pH 4.01, pH 7.00, and H_2O (50 mL capacity) Automatic temperature compensation probe

Optional Accessories:
AC adaptor **PHAD-61**   **$8.50**
Replacement automatic temperature compensation probe **PHAT-61**   **$78**
Electrode, combination general purpose gel-filled **PHE-1317**   **$48**

Specifications:
Range: pH 0 to 14, temp −10 to +125°C
Resolution: pH 0.01, temp. 0.1°C
Accuracy: pH ±0.01, temp. ±0.5°C
Input Impedance: > 10^{12} ohms
Buffer Recognition: pH 4.00, pH 7.00
Electrode Offset Recognition: ±60 mV at pH 7
Electrode Slope Recognition: ±20% at pH 4
Connector: BNC
Power: One 9V battery or ac adaptor
Size: 7″ x 3½″ x 1¾″
Weight: 0.8 lb

Model PHH-47
$199 Complete Kit

Shown with Optional AC Adaptor

The PHH-47 is a battery or line powered hand held pH meter. Low drift, high stability, and fast response are assured by incorporating the latest CMOS and LSI circuitry. The batteries in the PHH-47 typically will last for a year of intermediate use or 100 hours continuous use, or the unit may be powered by the AC line adaptor. If desired, the PHH-47 may be hooked up to a recorder through the standard recorder output.

- **LCD Display**
- **Recorder Output**
- **0 to 14 pH Range**
- **High Stability, Low Drift, Fast Response**
- **Extra Long Battery Life**

Includes:
Epxoy combination electrode
Carrying case with foam insert and three empty containers labeled pH 4.01, pH 7.00, and H_2O (50 mL capacity)

Optional Accessories:
AC line adaptor **PHAD-47**   **$11**
Replacement epoxy combination electrode **PHE-1301**   **$43**

Specifications:
Range: 0 to 14.00 pH
Resolution: 0.01 pH
Accuracy: 0.01 ±1 digit when standardized within 2 pH units
Temperature Compensation: Manual 0-100°C
Recorder Output: 0 to 1400 mV (full range)
Power Source: Six "AA" batteries; or ac adaptor
Dimensions: Meter: 5.4″ x 3.6″ x 1.9″ Case: 12.4″ x 8.3″ x 3.9″
Weight: Meter 0.8 lb, Complete kit 4.1 lb
Connector: BNC

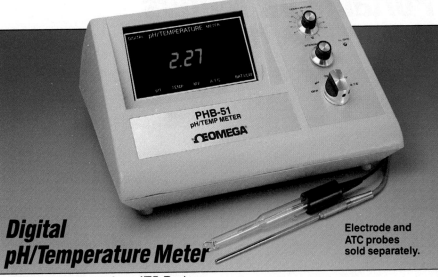

Model PHB-51
$300

2 YEAR
WARRANTY
(Electronics Only)

- **Auto-Polarity mV, Temperature Measurement**
- **Manual and Automatic Temperature Compensation**
- **Karl Fischer Current Output, Recorder Output**

The PHB-51 combination meter features a solid state design that ensures low drift and high reliability. This sophisticated unit offers measurement of pH with manual or automatic temperature compensation, auto-polarity mV, and temperature. The PHB-51 includes a recorder output and a Karl Fischer current output for water determinations.

Digital pH/Temperature Meter

Electrode and ATC probes sold separately.

Optional Accessories: ATC Probes: Stainless steel with phone plug
OL-703-PP $70
Glass with phone plug **OL-704-PP $91**

Recommended electrode
PHE-1317 $48

Adaptor for ac: **PHAD-47 $11**

Specifications:

Range: 0 to 14.00, Temp. 0 to 100°C, mV ±1999 mV; Automatic Temperature Compensation 0-14.00 pH
Accuracy: pH 0.01, ±1 digit; temp. 0.5°C ±1 digit, mV 0.1% ±1 digit, Automatic Temperature Compensation ±1.0°C

Resolution: pH 0.01, temp. 0.1°C, mV 1 mV, Automatic Temperature Compensation 0.01 pH
Recorder Output: pH 0 to 140 mV, temp. 0-100 mV, mV ±200 mV, Automatic Temperature Compensation 0 to 140 mV
Input Impedance: 10^{12} ohms
Temperature Compensation: Manual or auto 0 to 100°C
Karl Fischer Output: 10 μA
Readout: 0.56″ bright red LED
Connector: BNC; recorder: banana plugs
Power Source: 115-230 Vac ±20% or 6 ea. "AA" batteries
Dimensions: 11″ x 7.9″ x 4.7″
Weight: 3.2 lb

Model PHB-52
$305 Complete Kit

1 YEAR
WARRANTY
(Electronics Only)

- **Manual and Automatic Temperature Compensation**
- **Auto Polarity mV and Temperature Measurements**
- **Recorder Output**

The PHB-52 is a versatile combination pH, mV, and temperature meter that is equally at home in the lab or in the field. It features an all solid state design for low drift and high stability, low power consumption, and an LCD readout. CMOS and LSI circuitry permit auto-polarity mV measurement, and either manual or automatic temperature compensation may be performed. Includes carrying case with two containers, ac Adaptor, batteries and electrode stand.

Optional Accessories:
General purpose combination electrode
PHE-1304 **$33**
Temperature probe:
Tubular stainless steel probe with phone plug
OL-703-PP **$70**
Tubular glass probe with phone plug
OL-704-PP **$91**

pH/mV/ Temperature Meter

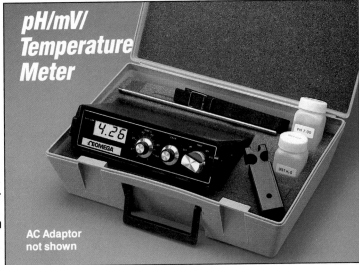

AC Adaptor not shown

Specifications:

Range: pH to 14.00; Temp. 0 to 100°C; mV ±1999
Resolution: pH 0.01 pH; Temp. 0.1°C; 1 mV
Accuracy: pH ±0.01 ±1 digit; Temp. 0.5°C ±1 digit; mV ±0.1% ±1 digit
Recorder Output: pH 0 to 1400 mV; Temp. 0 to 1000 mV; ±1999 mV
Input Impedance: > 10^{12} ohms
Temperature Compensation: Manual 0 to 100°C; Auto. 0 to 100°C
Power: 115/230 Vac or six ea. "AA" batteries
Dimensions: 7.9″ x 4.7″ x 2.5″; Weight: 1.7 lb
Connector: BNC; recorder: banana plugs

Portable pH Meters
Models PHH-65A, PHH-65D

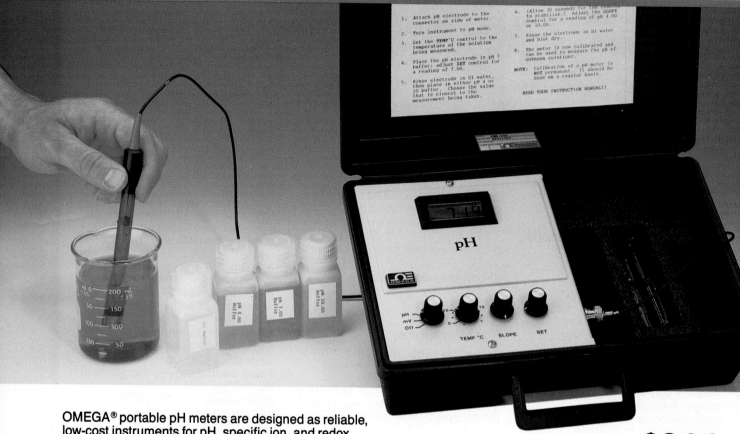

OMEGA® portable pH meters are designed as reliable, low-cost instruments for pH, specific ion, and redox potential measurements directly at the sampling site. The PHH-65A and PHH-65D are equipped with 8 AA batteries and are housed in rugged high-impact cases that contain the meter and associated accessories. For ease of use, brief operating instructions are contained in the inside cover for handy reference. These units come complete with a gel filled combination pH electrode, buffer solutions (pH 4, 7, 10) and rack, and operator's manual.

PHH-65D Digital pH Meter
Model PHH-65D **$299** Complete Kit

The PHH-65D meter features a 3½ digit, ½″ high LCD display that is easy to read even in the brightest sunlight. This instrument is capable of measuring pH 0 to 14 with an accuracy of 0.05 pH and 0 to 1,999 mV with an accuracy of ±1 mV.

PHH-65A Analog pH meter
Model PHH-65A **$250** Complete Kit

The PHH-65A meter features a large 6 inch analog scale for reading both normal (pH 0 to 14, ±700 mV) and 10x expanded scale reading (±70 mV and any 1.4 pH full scale). Using the expanded scale, accuracies as great as 0.01 pH can be achieved for critical applications.

Specifications:
Range: 0 to 14 pH, ±700 mV (±1999 mV with PHH-65D)
Accuracy: ±0.05 pH, PHH-65A; ±0.01 pH, PHH-65D and PHH-65A expanded scale; ±1 mV, both models
Input Impedance: $>10^{10}$ ohms
Temperature Compensation: 0 to 100°C, manual
Connector: BNC
Power: 8 AA batteries
Dimensions: 4½″ H x 12¼″ W x 8″ D
Weight: 4 lb
Optional Accessories: Recommended replacement electrode PHE-1304 $33
220 V models available, please consult Sales.

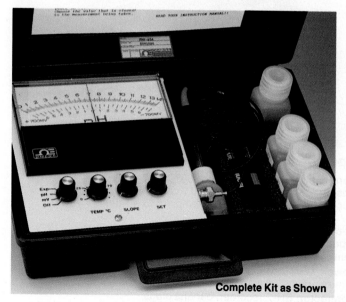

Complete Kit as Shown

Portable pH and Conductivity Instruments

Model PHB-58

$199

The PHB-58 is an economical, high accuracy portable unit for both pH and millivolt measurements. User friendly controls, redox capability and temperature compensation makes this unit an exceptional value. The PHB-58 features a large, easy to read 6″ mirror backed analog display and ±0.05 pH accuracy over the 0 to 14 pH range. For higher accuracy and resolution, the pH may be expanded by a factor of ten (10X). In the expanded mode, any 1.4 pH span can be read full scale on the meter with an increase in accuracy to 0.01 pH. The PHB-58 is powered by 8 AA batteries. Electrodes sold separately.

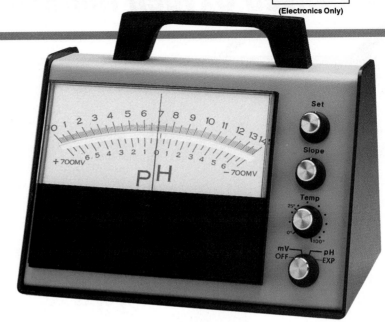

Specifications:

Normal Ranges
Range: 0 to 14 pH, ±700 mV
Accuracy: 0.05 pH, 5 mV

Expanded Ranges
Range: any 1.4 pH span
Accuracy: 0.01 pH
Readout: 6 inch analog
Temperature Compensation: manual, 0 to 100°C
Connector: BNC, pin
Input Impedance: 10^{12} ohms
Power: 8 AA batteries
Dimensions: 8″ × 5½″ × 5½″
Weight: 2.75 lb

Optional Accessories:
115 V ac Adapter **PHAD-58** $15
220 V ac Adapter **PHAD-58-220** $39

Recommended Electrode:
PHE-1301 $43

Model CDH-37

The CDH-37 conductivity meter provides excellent cost-effective performance in a field unit that measures ionized materials in solution. Housed in a protective case made of high density polyethylene, the CDH-37 includes a break resistant probe with an internal thermistor for automatic temperature compensation. To ensure versatility, the CDH-37 operates on 8AA batteries and comes complete with probe and standard solution.

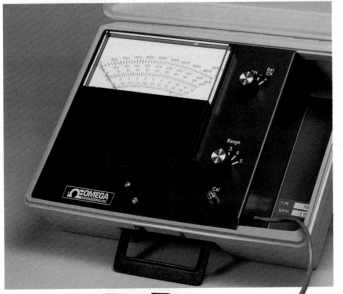

Model CDH-37

$289
Complete Kit

Specifications:

Readout: 6″ Analog meter
Ranges: (μmhos/cm) 0 to 2, 0 to 20, 0 to 200, 0 to 2000, 0 to 20,000
Accuracy: ±2% Full scale
Temperature Compensation: Auto, 5 to 45°C
Sensor: DIP type
Power: 8 AA batteries
Size: 12¼ x 4¼″ x 8″
Weight: 3.9 lb

Optional Accessory:
Replacement Conductivity Cell
CDE-37 $69

Handheld pH, ORP, Conductivity and Dissolved Oxygen Meters

PHH-81 **$169**

CDH-80 **$249**

PHH-82 **$349**

PHDG-80 **$399**

Dissolved Oxygen Meter PHDG-80

The PHDG-80 combines a polarographic dissolved oxygen sensor with an integral RTD for dissolved oxygen and temperature measurements in the lab, plant or field. By using a small cathode which consumes minimal oxygen, the need for sample stirring is minimized to provide a more stable response. Included are the sensor, screwdriver and vinyl case.

Specifications:
Range: 0.00 to 19.99 ppm O_2, 0 to 199.9°C
Accuracy: ±1.5% F.S. O_2, ±2°C
Resolution: 0.01 ppm O_2, 0.1°C
Automatic Temperature Compensation: 0 to 40°C
Power: 9 V battery
Dimensions: 6¼″ x 1¼″ x 2¼″
Weight: 8.5 oz

Optional Accessories:
Extension Cable, Two Meter:
PHEC-8200 $50
Replacement Membrane Kit for Probe:
PHDG-8200 $20

Digital Conductivity Meter CDH-80

The CDH-80 is a handheld four range conductivity meter that may be used to test samples ranging

from pure water to seawater. For accuracy of measurement, automatic temperature compensation is provided from 0 to 70°C. The meter is supplied complete with probe, battery, screwdriver and handy carrying pouch.

Specifications:
Range: 0 to 200, 0 to 2000, 0 to 20,000, 0 to 200,000 μS
Accuracy: ±1% F.S.
Temperature Compensation: Automatic 0 to 70°C
Power: 9 V lithium battery
Dimensions: 6¼″ x 1¼″ x 2¼″
Weight: 8.5 oz

Optional Accessories:
Two Meter Extension Cable:
PHEC-8200 $40
Replacement Conductivity Probe:
CDE-8002 $70

pH/ORP Meter PHH-82

The PHH-82 is a dual function instrument that measures pH and ORP (oxidation-reduction potential). It is ideal for measurements of ORP that are pH dependent. Applications include swimming pool maintenance, drinking water disinfection, chrome reduction and cyanide destruction of electroplating waste water. The PHH-82 is supplied with electrodes, pH 7 buffer, carrying case and screwdriver.

Specifications:
Range: 0 to 14 pH, ±1000 mV
Resolution: 0.02 pH, 1 mV
Accuracy: ±0.015 pH, ±1 mV
Automatic Temperature Compensation: 0 to 100°C (pH only)
Power: 9 V battery
Dimensions: 6¼″ x 1¼″ x 2¼″
Weight: 8.5 oz

Optional Accessories:
Replacement ORP Probe:
ORE-8200 $89
Replacement pH Probe:
PHE-8200 $50

pH Meter PHH-81

The PHH-81 is an ideal pH meter for general purpose measurements in the plant, field, production line or lab. The PHH-81 is supplied with electrode, screwdriver, pH 7 buffer and vinyl case.

Specifications:
Range: 0 to 14 pH
Resolution: 0.01 pH
Accuracy: ±0.2 pH
Temperature Compensation: Manual 0 to 100°C
Power: 9 V lithium battery

Optional Accessories:
Replacement pH Electrode:
PHE-8100 $50

Hand Held Conductivity/ pH Meter

- **Measures pH and Conductivity**
- **Two Buttons Control All Operations**
- **Electrodes May Be Used in Either 90° or 180° Position**
- **Electrodes Fold Into Handle When Not In Use**
- **Automatic Temperature Compensation**

For versatility in the field, the PHH-60 and 80 feature both pH and conductivity measurements in one hand held instrument. The PHH-60 measures pH from 0 to 14 and conductivity from 0 to 19,999 μmhos, and the PHH-80 extends the conductivity capability to 199,999 μmhos. While in use, the electrodes fold out and lock into a 90° or 180° position. When testing is completed, the electrodes are folded back into the instrument case. Recessed switches control all functions and an easy access panel reveals adjustments for pH calibration and slope and zero and span for conductivity.

Specifications:

pH

Range: 0 to 14
Accuracy: ±0.01 pH
Temperature Compensation: Automatic 0 to 70°C

Conductivity

Range: PHH-60: 0 to 19,999 μmhos; PHH-80: 0 to 1,999, 0 to 19,999, 0 to 199,999 μmhos
Resolution: 10 μmhos
Accuracy: ±2% of span
Temperature Compensation: Automatic 0 to 50°C
Power: 9 V battery
Dimensions: 6¼″ × 1¼″ × 2¼″
Weight: 8.5 oz

Optional Accessories:

Replacement pH electrode
PHE-8200 $50
Replacement conductivity probe
CDE-8200 $70

Model PHH-60
$295

Model PHH-80
$349
(not shown)

Conductivity Meters

Model CDH-27

Model CDH-27
$269
Model CDH-26
$249

2 YEAR
WARRANTY
(Electronics Only)

- **Large 3 Inch Scale for Easy Readability**
- **Scales in Both Micromhos and Parts Per Million**
- **Automatic Temperature Compensation**

The CDH-26 and CDH-27 are lightweight, easy to operate conductivity meters that read out in both parts per million and micromhos. The conductivity measurement is used to indicate the amount of dissolved solids in a water sample by calibrating the meter to read in PPM using characteristics closely approximating municipal water supplies. For industrial applications, the CDH-27 is housed in a rugged ABS case which provides greater protection. The case features a tongue-in-groove seal, booted switches and a sealed meter window. Both meters are supplied complete with 9 V long-life lithium battery.

MADE IN
USA

Model CDH-27   Model CDH-26

Optional
Carrying
Case Shown,
Model
CDCC-2 $22

Model No.	PPM	µmhos	Price
CDH-26	0-50, 0-500, 0-5000	0-75, 0-750, 0-7500	**$249**
CDH-27	0-50, 0-500, 0-5000	0-75, 0-750, 0-7500	269

Optional Accessories:

Carrying case: **CDCC-2 $24**
Replacement conductivity probe **CDE-26 $85 (for CDH-26)**
Replacement conductivity probe **CDE-27 $45 (for CDH-27)**
Conductivity standard solution:
45 µmhos/cm **CDS-45 $10/qt**
Conductivity standard solution:
450 µmhos/cm **CDS-450 $10/qt**
Conductivity standard solution:
1500 µmhos/cm **CDS-1500 $10/qt**
Conductivity standard solution:
4500 µmhos/cm **CDS-4500 $10/qt**

Specifications:

Resolution: 2% full scale
Dimensions: 8″ × 3″ × 2½″
Weight: 1½ lb
Accuracy: ±2% of full scale
Temperature Compensation:
Automatic 0 to 55°C

Conductivity Stick Model CDH-53

The CDH-53 is a low-cost conductivity tester that directly reads total dissolved solids. Advanced microcircuitry and a solid state LED bargraph produce accuracies to within 10% of scale. The conductivity tester is provided with a pocket clip and easily accessible test and scale selector switches. A six volt battery is included.

Specifications:

Range: 0 to 100, 100 to 1000 ppm
Accuracy: ±10% of scale
Power: 6 V battery, included
Size: 6½″ x 0.5″
Weight: 0.5 lb
Optional Accessories: Replacement battery **CDH-53-BATT $3**

$89

Digital Conductivity/Temperature/pH Tester Model PHH-10

1 YEAR WARRANTY

B

FIELD SERVICE PRODUCTS

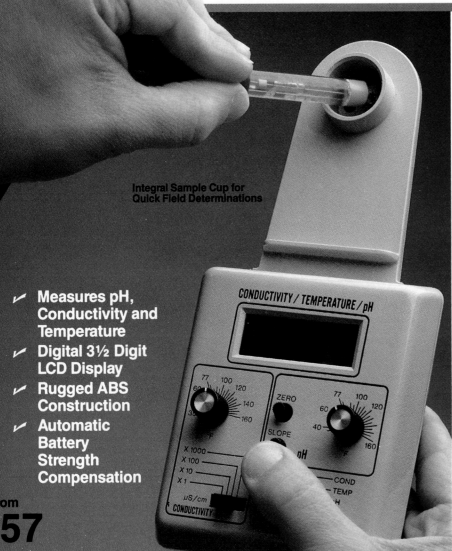

Integral Sample Cup for Quick Field Determinations

CONDUCTIVITY / TEMPERATURE / pH

ZERO

SLOPE

pH

X 1000
X 100
X 10
X 1
µS/cm
CONDUCTIVITY

COND
TEMP

✔ **Measures pH, Conductivity and Temperature**

✔ **Digital 3½ Digit LCD Display**

✔ **Rugged ABS Construction**

✔ **Automatic Battery Strength Compensation**

from

57

The OMEGA PHH-10 measures pH, temperature, and conductivity in a single unit and covers the full range of pH and conductance.

An integral sample cup makes it ideal for field work and quick determinations. The conductivity probe and temperature sensor are incorporated in the sample cup. The pH electrode is the only external connection.

It covers the pH range with 0.01 pH accuracy at 77°F, comes with buffer solutions, and has slope and zero adjustments on the unit face.

The PHH-10 has selectable conductivity ranges of 0 to 20, 200, 2,000, and 20,000 µmhos and an accessible calibration adjustment. Multiple range selection provides improved resolution.

The PHH-10 has a 3½ digit LCD display, a low-battery warning, and automatic battery strength compensation.

Specifications:

Range: Conductance, 0-20, 0-200, 0-2000, 0-20,000 µmhos; Temperature, 0 to 160°F; pH, 0 to 14

Accuracy: Conductivity, ±2% full scale; Temperature, ±2°F; pH, ±0.01 pH at 77°F

Power: 9V lithium battery (supplied), visual "LO BAT" warning

Dimensions: Controller, 11″ L x 8½″ W x 4″ H

Weight: 3 lb

Connection: BNC for pH electrode

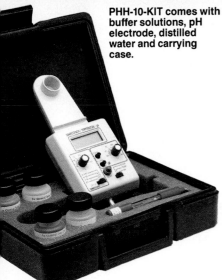

PHH-10-KIT comes with buffer solutions, pH electrode, distilled water and carrying case.

To Order *(Specify Model No.)*

Model No.	Description	Price
PHH-10-KIT	Conductivity/Temp./pH Tester with case, buffer solutions, pH electrode, and distilled water	**$420.00**
PHH-10	Conductivity/Temp./pH Tester with case	**$357.00**
PHE-1010	Replacement pH electrode, combination, gel-filled, epoxy bodied	52.50
PHA-101	Buffer solution kit	10.50

Conductivity Standardizing Solutions

Model No.	Description	Price
CDS-45	45 µmhos/cm solution	**$10/qt**
CDS-450	450 µmhos/cm solution	10/qt
CDS-1500	1500 µmhos/cm solution	10/qt
CDS-4500	4500 µmhos/cm solution	10/qt

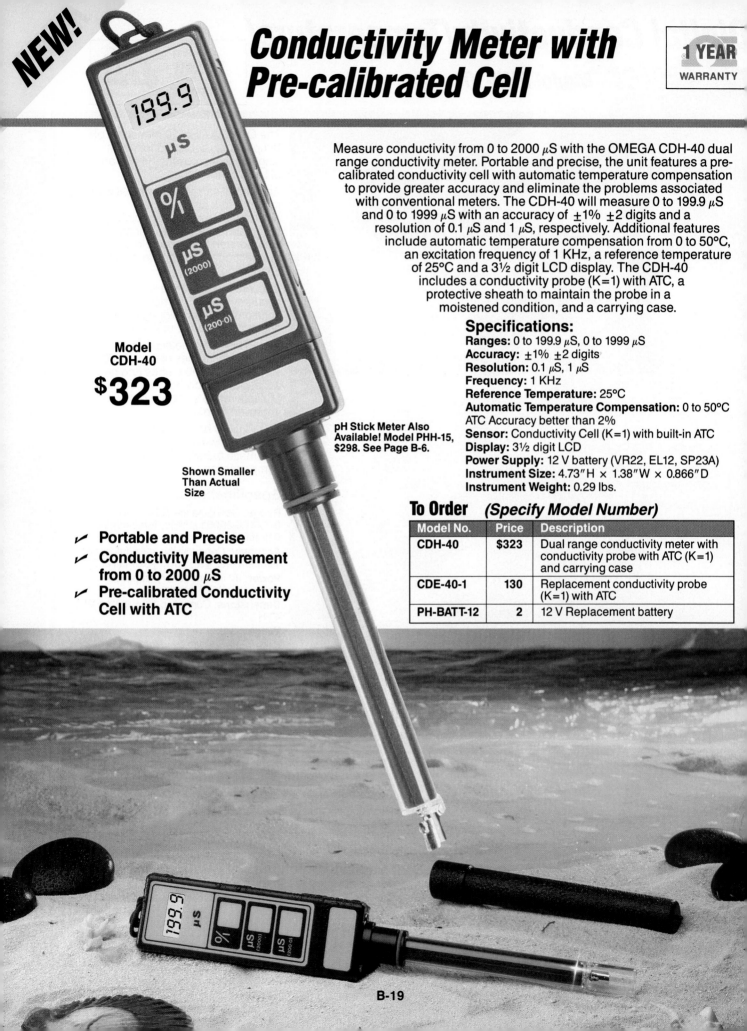

NEW!

Conductivity Meter with Pre-calibrated Cell

199.9 µS

%

µS (2000)

µS (200·0)

Model CDH-40

$323

Measure conductivity from 0 to 2000 µS with the OMEGA CDH-40 dual range conductivity meter. Portable and precise, the unit features a pre-calibrated conductivity cell with automatic temperature compensation to provide greater accuracy and eliminate the problems associated with conventional meters. The CDH-40 will measure 0 to 199.9 µS and 0 to 1999 µS with an accuracy of ±1% ±2 digits and a resolution of 0.1 µS and 1 µS, respectively. Additional features include automatic temperature compensation from 0 to 50°C, an excitation frequency of 1 KHz, a reference temperature of 25°C and a 3½ digit LCD display. The CDH-40 includes a conductivity probe (K=1) with ATC, a protective sheath to maintain the probe in a moistened condition, and a carrying case.

pH Stick Meter Also Available! Model PHH-15, $298. See Page B-6.

Shown Smaller Than Actual Size

✔ **Portable and Precise**
✔ **Conductivity Measurement from 0 to 2000 µS**
✔ **Pre-calibrated Conductivity Cell with ATC**

Specifications:
Ranges: 0 to 199.9 µS, 0 to 1999 µS
Accuracy: ±1% ±2 digits
Resolution: 0.1 µS, 1 µS
Frequency: 1 KHz
Reference Temperature: 25°C
Automatic Temperature Compensation: 0 to 50°C
ATC Accuracy better than 2%
Sensor: Conductivity Cell (K=1) with built-in ATC
Display: 3½ digit LCD
Power Supply: 12 V battery (VR22, EL12, SP23A)
Instrument Size: 4.73"H × 1.38"W × 0.866"D
Instrument Weight: 0.29 lbs.

To Order *(Specify Model Number)*

Model No.	Price	Description
CDH-40	$323	Dual range conductivity meter with conductivity probe with ATC (K=1) and carrying case
CDE-40-1	130	Replacement conductivity probe (K=1) with ATC
PH-BATT-12	2	12 V Replacement battery

Hand Held Dissolved Oxygen and Conductivity Meters

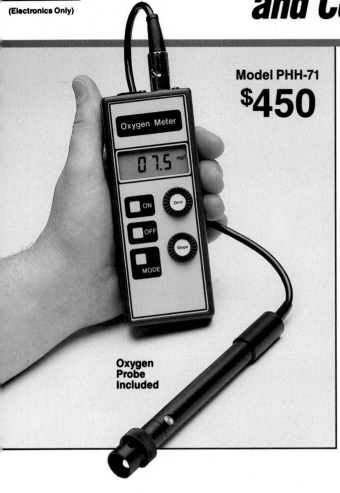

Model PHH-71

$**450**

Oxygen Probe Included

Portable Dissolved Oxygen Meter

The PHH-71 is a hand held instrument that will measure both oxygen and temperature quickly and accurately. Housed in a tough plastic case, the PHH-71 has a membrane keyboard and a high contrast LCD which also displays mode and range. The meter is supplied with an ultra stable DO sensor that incorporates dual temperature compensators and a pretensioned screw on membrane to ensure instant replacement and repeatability of readings. The PHH-71 comes with a dissolved oxygen electrode, a temperature measuring probe, a pack of replacement membranes and a bottle of electrolyte. An optional BOD attachment ring is available for the DO2 probe so the unit may be used for BOD determinations.

Optional Accessories:

Foam lined carrying case **PHCC-71** $37
BOD attachment ring **PHAC-71** $37
Replacement membranes and electrolyte
PHAC-71A $70

Specifications:

Ranges: 0 to 200%, 0 to 19.9 mg/L, −30 to 150°C
Accuracy: ±2% F.S. within ±10°C of cal. temp., ±0.5°C
Resolution: 1%, 0.1 mg/L, 0.1°C
Automatic temperature compensation: 0 to 40°C
Power: 9V battery
Dimensions: 5.9″ × 2.4″ × 1″
Weight: 0.31 lb

Portable Conductivity Meter

Perfect for field measurements of conductivity and temperature, the CDH-70 is housed in a chemically resistant case with a membrane keyboard for range and function selection. The meter features direct readout of temperature, conductivity and cell constant. The CDH-70 is supplied with a conductivity cell with a 1.0 constant with built in temperature compensation.

Optional Accessories:

Conductivity Cell Constant 10 **CDE-70-10** $180
Conductivity Cell Constant 0.1 **CDE-70-01** $139
Foam lined carrying case **CDCC-70** $47
Replacement temp. compensation probe **PHAT-70** $60
Replacement conductivity cell **CDE-70-1** $139

Specifications:

Ranges: 0 to 200 μS, 0 to 2000 μS, 0 to 20 mS, −30 to 150°C
Resolution: 0.1 μS, 1.0 μS, 0.01mS, 0.1°C
Accuracy: ±0.5% ±0.2μS, ±0.5% ±1.5% ±2μS, ±1.5% ±0.02 mS, ±0.5°C
Temperature Compensation: Automatic 0 to 50°C at 2%/°C
Cell Constant: Variable between 0.75 to 1.50
Power: 9V battery
Display: LCD
Size: 5.9″ × 2.4″ × 1″
Weight: 0.31 lb

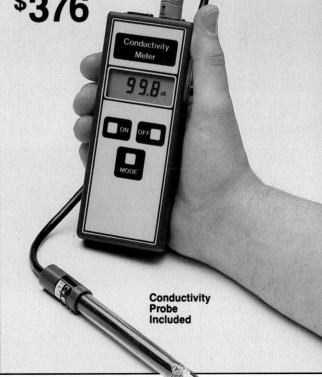

Model CDH-70

$**376**

Conductivity Probe Included

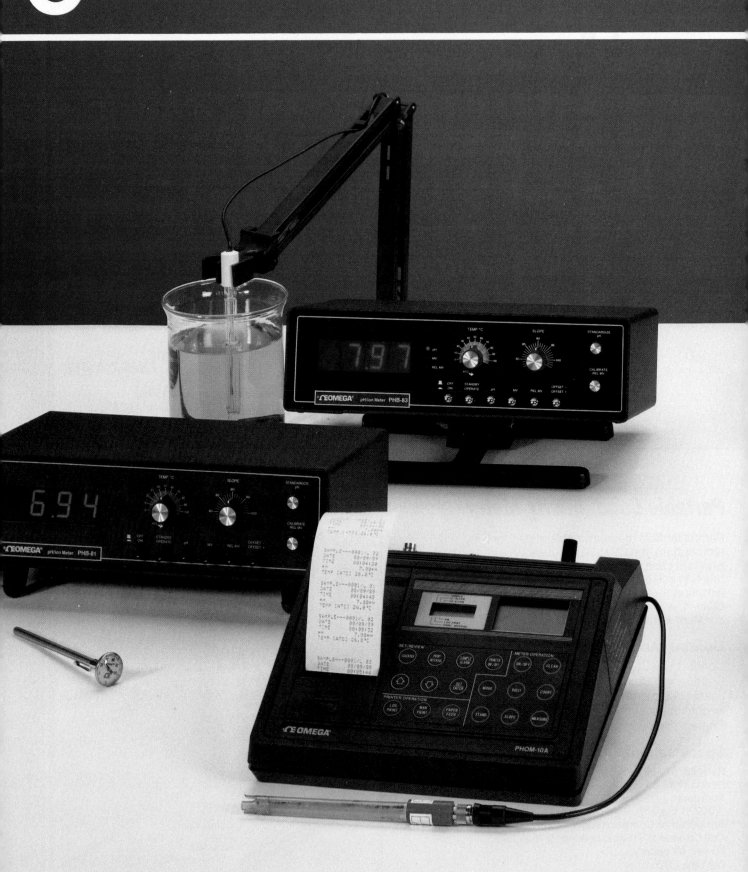

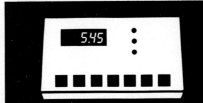
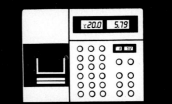
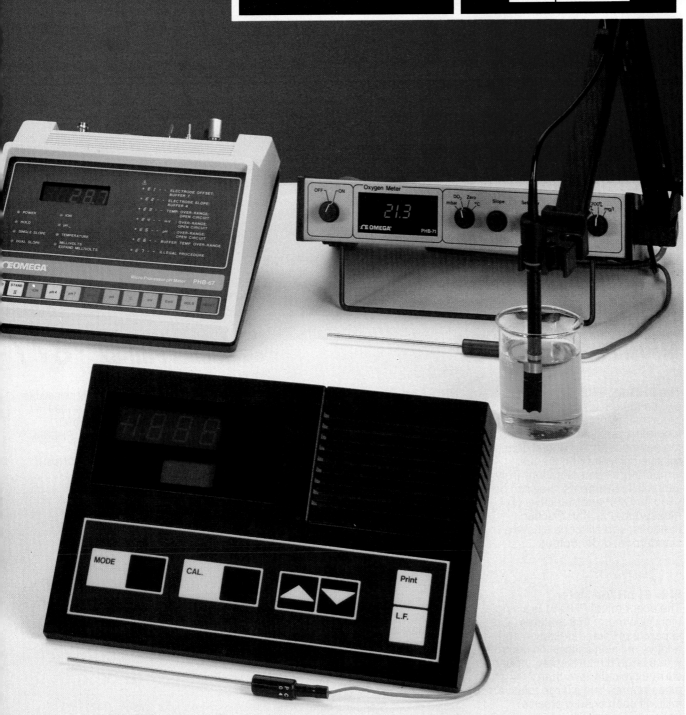

Digital pH/Ion Meters

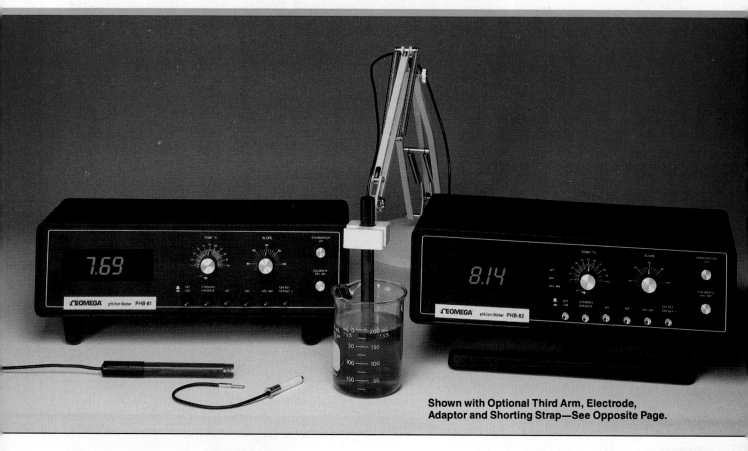

Shown with Optional Third Arm, Electrode, Adaptor and Shorting Strap—See Opposite Page.

Model PHB-81 $749*

The **PHB-81, PHB-82,** and **PHB-83** pH/ion meters are a sophisticated group of instruments for demanding laboratory applications. All three meters measure pH and absolute or relative millivolts with manual temperature compensation. Truly versatile instruments, they can be used for ORP and selective ion measurements, Karl Fischer titrations, and all models have a standard recorder output.

PHB-81 pH/Ion Meter

The economical PHB-81 is a single electrode meter that features separate pH standardization and relative millivolt calibration controls with a large digital display. Input bias current typically less than 2.0 picoamperes and a large relative millivolt span ensure precise accurate measurement.

PHB-82 pH/Ion Meter

If you require only a single electrode meter, the PHB-82 pH/Ion Meter offers the same specifications as the PHB-83. Both meters offer unsurpassed measuring capability in a laboratory instrument. Includes BCD output and adjustable tilt stand.

Specifications for PHB-81, PHB-82, PHB-83 and PHB-83-D:

Range: 0 to 14 pH; ±1999 mV; −6 to +106°C
Resolution: 0.01 pH; 1.0 mV
Accuracy: ±0.01 pH; ±1 mV
Input Impedance: $>10^{13}$ ohms
Temperature Compensation: 0 to 100°C (Manual)
Connector: PHB-81: BNC and U.S. Standard; PHB-82: BNC and U.S. Standard; PHB-83 and 83D: Input 1-BNC or U.S. Standard; Input 2-U.S. Standard

Model PHB-82 $877*

Power: 120/240 Vac internally selectable
Recorder Output: −1999 to +1999 mV, 100 mV per pH unit (0 to 1400 mV)
Digital Output: BCD PHB-82, PHB-83, PHB-83D
Relative Millivolt Span (Zero Offset): ±800 mV
Display: 0.8″ LED 3½ digit
Size: 5″ x 12 9/16″ x 7 7/8″
Weight: 9 lb

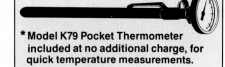

* Model K79 Pocket Thermometer included at no additional charge, for quick temperature measurements.

2 YEAR WARRANTY

Digital pH/Ion Meter

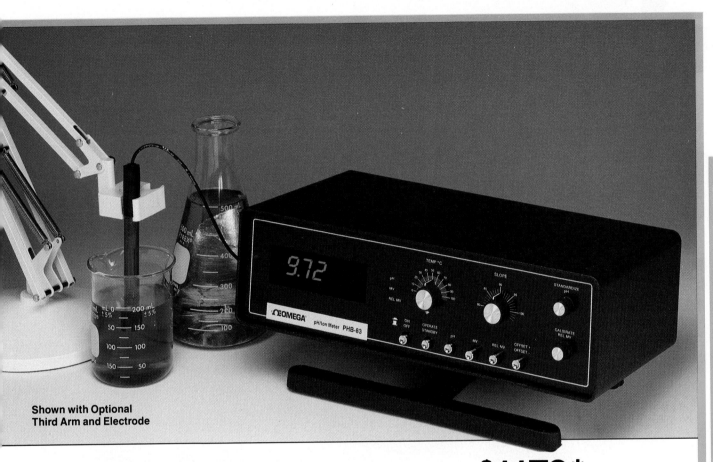

Shown with Optional Third Arm and Electrode

Model PHB-83 $1060*   Model PHB-83-D $1172*
(Not Shown)

PHB-83 pH/Ion Meter
The PHB-83 is like having two meters in one, a unique design that incorporates two high impedance inputs. By using two electrodes concurrently, both pH and ion levels can be measured in one simple step. Switching from pH to millivolt measurement is instantaneous with the touch of a button. By pressing the pH button, you get the pH readout from the pH electrode, assuring proper pH for the selective ion measurement. By pressing the millivolt or relative millivolt button, you get the millivolt readout from the selective ion electrode. Both measurements can be taken from the same solution or from separate solutions. It is not necessary to recalibrate when switching from one measurement to another. Because the PHB-83 has very low input bias (typically less than 0.075 pA), you are assured of precise readings.

PHB-83-D
pH/Ion Meter with Differential Input Option
Also available is the differential input that allows the substitution of a high impedance glass or selective ion electrode for the reference electrode. This avoids several problems such as variation of liquid junction potential and periodic refilling and contamination of sample with reference solution. Because high impedance inputs are isolated from ground loops and other electronic noise, more accurate measurements are possible especially when using external recorders or printers. In the differential mode, all three modes for measurement are useable (pH, mV and REL mV). The instrument user will need to interpret the meaning of the readout based on the nature of the experiment. The PHB-83-D can be used either for differential input or two separate inputs like the PHB-83.

Optional Accessories for PHB-81, 82, 83 and 83-D
Adjustable Third Arm **PHA-33 $73**
Shorting Strap **PHA-SS81 $16**
Combination pH Electrode Epoxy Body **PHE-1304 $33**
Adaptor to Convert U.S. Standard Meter to BNC Electrode
PHMA-UB $22

2 YEAR WARRANTY

Model PHB-62 Microprocessor Benchtop pH Meter

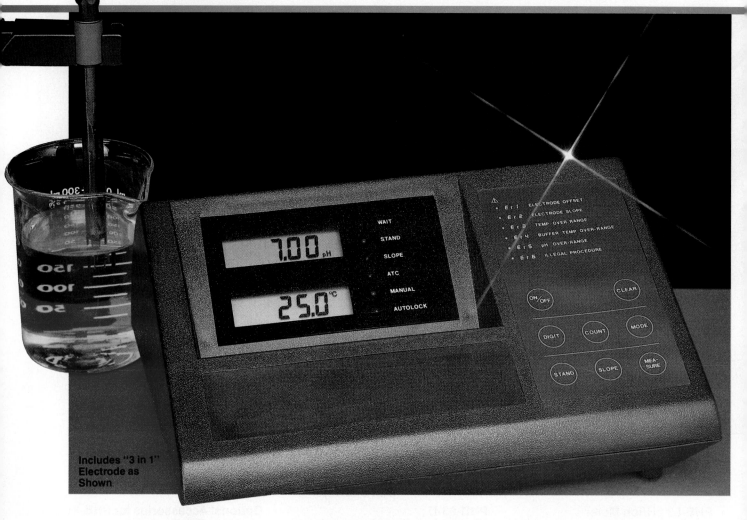

Includes "3 in 1" Electrode as Shown

$345*

- **Automatic Calibration**
- **Simultaneous pH and Temperature Readings**
- **Recorder Output**
- **Karl Fischer Output**
- **Uses Batteries or AC**

The PHB-62 is a microprocessor based pH meter for the measurement of pH, mV and temperature. The microprocessor stores, calculates and compensates for parameters such as temperature effects, slope deviations, buffer recognition etc. For versatility, the PHB-62 operates with ac adapter as well as internal batteries. The internal batteries also provide back up power to the processor memory to retain its calibration after the power is turned off. For ease of use, LED's guide the operator through set up and measurement. Two LCD's display temperature and pH simultaneously. An AUTOLOCK feature is provided for pH and millivolt measurements to enable the PHB-62 to automatically sense the endpoint and lock the display to indicate the endpoint value of a measurement. The PHB-62 comes with an ac adapter, "3 in 1" pH/ref/temp electrode and cable. The meter may be used with standard pH electrodes and optional ATC.

Optional Accessories:
Replacement "3 in 1" pH/Ref/Temp Electrode **PHE-1062** **$59**
ATC/Temp Probe: **PHAT-1050** **$39**

Specifications:
Range: −2.00 to 16.00 pH, 0 to 99.9°C, ±1999mV
Resolution: 0.01pH, 1 mV, 0.1°C
Accuracy: ±0.1% pH, ±0.1% mV, ±0.5°C
Input Impedance: > 10^{12} ohms
Temperature Compensation: Manual or automatic from 0 to 99.9°C
Connector: "3 in 1" electrode connector, BNC, reference pin, recorder banana plugs
Recorder Output: ±1000mV
Power: 110 Vac or 6 ea "AA" batteries
Dimensions: 11″ x 7.9″ x 4.7″
Weight: 2.6 lb

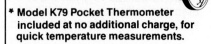

* Model K79 Pocket Thermometer included at no additional charge, for quick temperature measurements.

Laboratory Water Analyzer

- ✔ **Precise Readings of pH, Conductivity and ORP**
- ✔ **Measures Dissolved Oxygen, Temperature and Ionic Strength**
- ✔ **Conductivity Probe with ATC**
- ✔ **Swing Arm Electrode Holder**

The PHB-70X laboratory water analyzer offers complete and precise measurement of pH, conductivity, ORP, dissolved oxygen, ionic strength and temperature in most water and chemical samples. For unequalled versatility this meter combines all the features of the CDB-70 conductivity meter and the PHB-71 dissolved oxygen meter (see page C-8) with those of a precision lab pH meter. Includes conductivity probe (K=1) with ATC, glass combination pH electrode, temperature measurement probe, swing arm electrode holder and a pack of pH 4 and 7 buffers. (Dissolved oxygen probe sold separately.)

Optional Accessories:
Replacement temperature measurement probe **PHAT-70X $72.00**
Replacement conductivity probe with ATC (K=1) **CDE-70X-1 $128.00**
Replacement electrode **PHE-2111 $74.00**
Dissolved Oxygen Probe **PHOX-70 $180.00**
Replacement Membrane Electrolyte for Dissolved Oxygen Probe **PHAC-71A $70.00**

Specifications
Ranges: 0 to 14.000 pH; ±1999.9 mV; 0 to 100.0°C; Conductivity: 0 to 19.99 μS, 0 to 199.9 μS, 0 to 1999 μS, 0 to 19.99 mS; 0 to 199.9 mS; Dissolved oxygen 0 to 200%, 0 to 19.9 mg/L

Accuracy: pH ±0.005 pH, mV ±0.2 mV, Temp. ±0.5°C, Conductivity ±3% on 200 mS range, ±0.5% ±2 digits on all other ranges, Dissolved oxygen ±1%, ±0.2 mg/1

Model PHB-70X
$1430

Includes conductivity and temperature measurement probes, pH electrode, swing arm electrode holder and pH 4 and 7 buffers.

Resolution: pH 0.001, mV 0.1 mV, Temp. 0.1°C, Conductivity 0.01 μS, 0.1 μS, 1 μS, 0.01 mS, 0.1 mS, Dissolved oxygen 1%, 0.1mg/L

Recorder Output: 1 mV per digit

Connections: pH BNC; Temp., Cond., and DO_2 DIN, Ref, 2 mm pin jack

Conductivity Cell Constant: 0.75 to 1.5 user selectable

Conductivity Reference Temperature: 20 or 25°C switch selectable

pH Temperature Compensation: Automatic 0 to 100°C

Isopotential Adjustment: 6 to 8 pH

Input Impedance: 10^{13} ohms

Power: 115/230 Vac, 50/60 Hz

Size: 11.8″ x 7.1″ x 4.7″

Weight: 4.4 lbs.

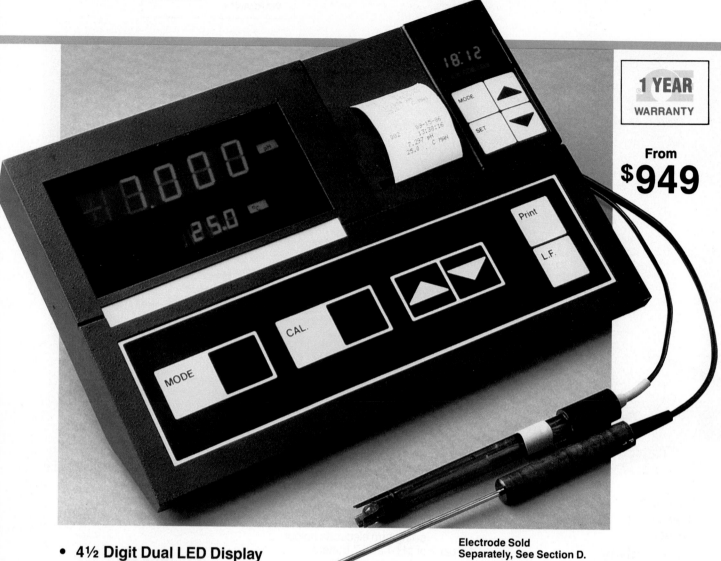

From $949

Electrode Sold
Separately, See Section D.

- **4½ Digit Dual LED Display**
- **Optional Printer with RS-232-C Output**
- **Microprocessor Recognizes Buffers**
- **Least Significant Digit Blanking**
- **Built-In Alarm**

The PHB-72 is a 4½ digit general purpose laboratory pH meter that measures pH, millivolts and temperature. The high resolution display makes the PHB-72 ideally suited to demanding analyses such as ion specific measurements. For ease of operation, a membrane keyboard accepts inputs for calibration and measurement. The microprocessor recognizes standard buffers and their individual temperature characteristics. Standard error indications are triggered if correct calibration procedure is not followed. For versatility, the PHB-72 has a separate temperature display for manual compensation or temperature measurement. It is possible to program a preset level via the membrane keyboard which is continuously monitored by the meter. If this level is reached, an audible alarm is sounded and an output is available at the rear of the unit. An optional printer and RS-232-C port is available to provide hard copy printout and data acquisition capability. Includes swing arm electrode holder, temperature/ATC probe and pH 4 and 7 buffer powders.

Specifications

Ranges: 0 to 14.000 pH, 0 to 1999.9 mV, −30 to 150°C

Resolution: 0.001 pH, 0.1 mV, 0.1°C
Accuracy: ±0.002 pH, ±0.1 mV, ±0.5°C
Input Impedance: 10 (13) ohms
Isopotential: 6 to 8 pH
Temperature Compensation: Automatic or manual 0 to 100°C
Buffer Recognition: 4.00, 7.00, 10.05
Outputs: 0.1 mV per digit, optional RS-232-C
Connector:
Size: 11.8″ × 7.1″ × 4.7″
Weight: 22 lb
Replacement Paper: PHB-72-RP $10

To Order:

Part No.	Option	Price
PHB-72	N/A	$ 949
PHB-72-P	Printer, Clock and RS-232-C Output	1467

Laboratory Conductivity, Dissolved Oxygen & Water Analyzers

Conductivity Meter
CDB-70

Model CDB-70
$680

The CDB-70 is designed for fast and accurate determinations of conductivity in the laboratory. It is a versatile instrument that can accept conductivity cells of any constant when the optional CDAT-70 ATC probe is used. The CDB-70 features direct setting and readout of cell constant, a linearized recorder output on all ranges, a swing arm electrode holder, and a 1.0 cell constant. With the optional probe PHAT-70A temperature can be displayed.

Optional Accessories:

Temperature measuring probe **PHAT-70A $72**
Automatic temperature compensator **CDAT-70 $67**
Conductivity cell 10.0 cell constant **CDE-70-10 $180**
Conductivity cell 0.1 cell Constant **CDE-70-01 $139**

Specifications:

Ranges: 0 to 19.99 μS, 0 to 199.9 μS, 0 to 1999 μS, 0 to 19.99 mS, 0 to 199.9 mS, −50 to +199.9°C
Accuracy: Conductivity ±0.5% ±1 digit, temperature ±1% ±1 digit
Resolution: 0.01 μS, 0.1 μS, 1 μS, 0.01 mS, 0.1 mS, 0.1°C
Cell Constant: Selectable 0.50 to 2.00
Recorder Output: 1 mV per digit
Power: 110/230 Vac switchable
Dimensions: 11.8″ × 7.5″ × 2.2″
Weight: 4 lb

Dissolved Oxygen Meter PHB-71

The PHB-71 dissolved oxygen meter is a high precision laboratory instrument that provides direct readout of oxygen concentration in both % and mg/L. To ensure repeatability of results, the instrument incorporates a variable barometric pressure control to compensate for the change in the solubility of oxygen in water relative to the change in atmospheric pressure. The PHB-71 is supplied with a rapid response dissolved oxygen sensor which is supplied with screw-on pretensioned membranes. In addition, the PHB-71 offers temperature readout, a linearized recorder output on all ranges and a swing arm electrode holder.

Optional Accessories:

BOD attachment ring **PHAC-71 $37**
Replacement membrane and electrolyte **PHAC-71A $70**

Specifications:

Range: 0 to 200%, 0 to 25.0%, 0 to 19.9mg/L, −50 to 199.9°C
Accuracy: mg/L range ±2% F.S. within ±10°C of calibration procedures, ±0.3°C
Resolution: 1%, 0.1%, 0.1 mg/L, 0.1°C
Automatic temperature compensation: 0 to 40°C
Barometric range: 800 to 1100 mbar
Recorder output: 1mV/digit
Power: 110/240 Vac user switchable
Dimensions: 11.8″ × 7.5″ × 2.2″
Weight: 4 lb

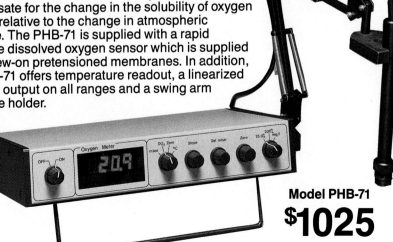

Model PHB-71
$1025

Conductivity Measurement with Computer Control

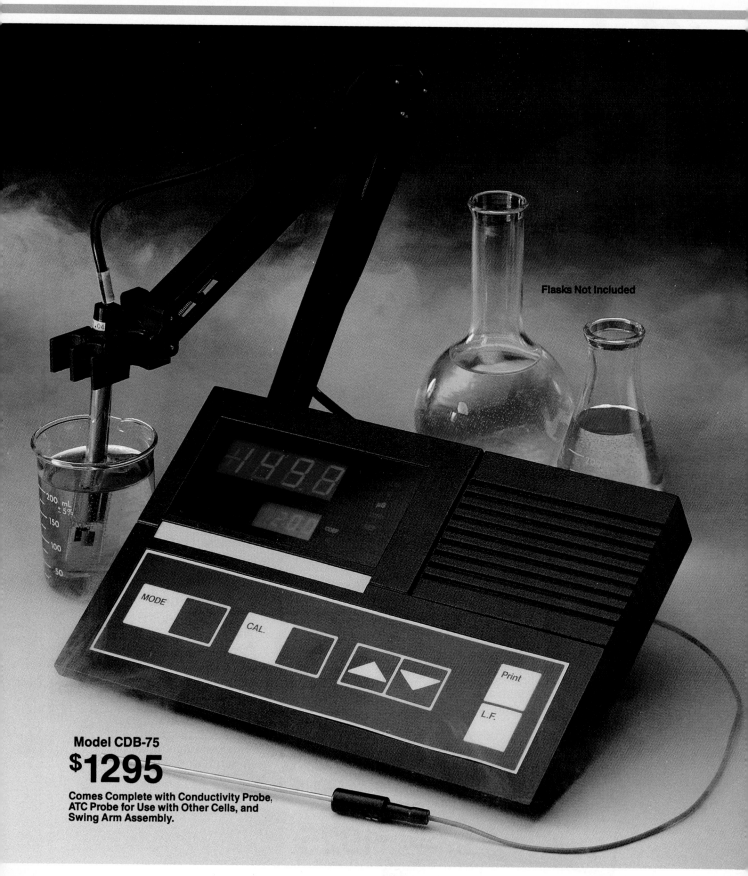

Flasks Not Included

Model CDB-75
$1295

Comes Complete with Conductivity Probe, ATC Probe for Use with Other Cells, and Swing Arm Assembly.

- ✓ **Simultaneous Display of Conductivity/Temperature**
- ✓ **Six Selectable Conductivity Ranges**
- ✓ **Temperature Compensation from 0 to 100°C**
- ✓ **Selectable Solution Temperature Coefficient from 0.5 to 4%/°C**
- ✓ **Automatic Excitation Frequency Compensation for Optimal Resolution**

The OMEGA CDB-75 is a sophisticated microprocessor conductivity meter which allows the user to select and set operating parameters for improved accuracy and resolution. It features six selectable conductivity ranges from 0 to 19.99 μS to 0 to 1000 mS, temperature compensation from 0 to 100°C, automatic excitation frequency compensation for optimal resolution, two audible alarm setpoints and a 1 mV/digit output. There are two LED displays: a 20 mm display for conductivity and a 10 mm display for temperature. Optional accessories include a factory fitted printer unit with a clock and RS232 output.

Specifications:

Range (Conductivity): 0 to 19.99 μS; 0 to 199.9 μS; 0 to 1999 μS; 0 to 19.99 mS; 0 to 199.0 mS; 0 to 1000 mS Temperature: 0 to 100.0°C
Resolution (Conductivity): 0.01μS; 0.1μS; 1μS; 0.01 mS; 0.1 mS; 1 mS; Temperature: 0.1°C
Accuracy (Conductivity): ±0.5% ±2 digits; ±2% on 1000 mS range; Temperature: 0.5°C
Temperature Compensation Range: 0 to 100°C
Slope Automatic Temperature Compensation: 0.5 to 4% per °C
Excitation Frequency: Automatically computer selected for optimal measurements
Reference Temperature: 0 to 100°C variable in 1°C steps
Cell Constant: 0.05 to 19.99 user selectable
Outputs: 1mV/digit (RS232 optional)
Display: Conductivity 20 mm LED, Temperature 10 mm LED
Power: 115/230 Vac ±10% 50/60 Hz
Size: 11.8"H × 7.1"W × 4.7"D
Weight: 4.4 lbs.

Model CDB-75-P
$1720
CDB-75 With Optional Printer

Comes Complete with Conductivity Probe, ATC Probe for Use with Other Cells, and Swing Arm Assembly.

To Order
(Specify Model Number)

Model No.	Price	Description
CDB-75	$1295	Conductivity meter with conductivity probe (K=1), automatic temperature compensator, and swing arm assembly
CDB-75-P	1720	Conductivity meter with printer unit, clock and RS232 output, conductivity probe (K=1), automatic temperature compensator and swing arm assembly
Replacement:		
CDE-75-1	145	Conductivity probe with ATC (K=1)
CDAT-75	69	Temperature compensator (for use with other cells)
Accessories:		
CDE-75-01	145	Conductivity probe with ATC (K=0.1)
CDE-75-10	194	Conductivity probe with ATC (K=10)

Microprocessor Benchtop pH Meters

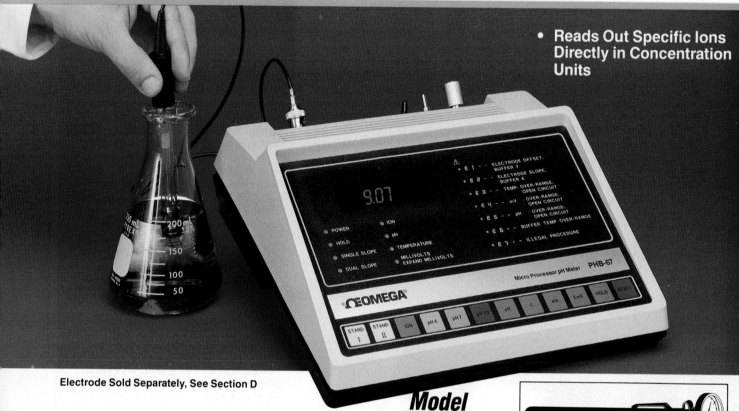

- **Reads Out Specific Ions Directly in Concentration Units**

Electrode Sold Separately, See Section D

- **Microprocessor Based**
- **Built-in Diagnostics**
- **High Resolution for Critical Analysis**
- **PHB-67 Reads Out Directly in Concentration Units**

1 YEAR WARRANTY

Model PHB-66
$449

Model PHB-67
$695 *

* **Model K79 Pocket Thermometer included at no additional charge, for quick temperature measurements.**

The PHB-66 and PHB-67 are versatile meters that measure pH, temperature, millivolts, and specific ion concentration. Both units have a splash proof front panel and touch key controls. A singleline keyboard with audio feedback controls calibration and mode changes. These microprocessor based meters recognize pH 4.01, 7.00, and 10.01 buffers and compensate for electrode offset and slope. High resolution readings are easily made, making these meters ideal for specific ion analysis. The PHB-67 provides a digital readout in any concentration unit (resolution to 0.5 units) after calibration.

Optional Accessory:
Automatic Temperature Compensation Probe
(100Ω Pt RTD)

PHAT-66 $69

Specifications: Models PHB66, PHB67

Range: 0 to 14 pH, −2047 to +2047 mV; −10 to +125°C
Resolution: 0.01 pH, 1.0 mV, 0.1 mV (expanded)
Accuracy: ±0.01 pH ±1 digit pH; ±2 mV ±1 digit, ±0.5°C
Input Impedance: > 10^{12} ohms
Temperature Compensation: Automatic (optional ATC probe) −10 to +125°C, manual: −5 to +110°C
Connector: BNC
Power: 115 Vac, 50/60 Hz, 230 Vac internally selectable
Display: 0.56″ LED with hold feature
Dimensions: 3.9″ H x 9.8″ W x 9.4″ D
Weight: 4¼ lb

Microprocessor pH Meter/Datalogger PHOM-10

1 YEAR WARRANTY

- **Measures pH/Temperature/Millivolts**
- **Built-In Printer**
- **Programmable Print Intervals from 10 Seconds to 20 Hours**
- **Audible High and Low Alarms**
- **Rechargeable Batteries for Field Applications**

The PHOM-10 is a versatile instrument that not only measures pH, temperature and millivolts, but also includes a built in printer for hard copy printouts of the data. User programmable print intervals may be selected from 10 seconds to 20 hours. In addition, the PHOM-10 is able to print sample and log numbers for easy sample identification. Measurements may be made without the printout if desired. Easy to use, the PHOM-10 features a membrane keyboard with audio feedback, user prompting, and the ability to print operation instructions and give the operator error indications should they occur. In the measurement mode, the PHOM-10 makes measurement quick and reliable with auto-lock, end point sensing and hold. For versatility of operation, the PHOM-10 includes rechargeable batteries for field operation. When the unit is shut off, a power down memory backup retains data. Includes a "3 in 1" pH/Ref/Temp electrode, cable and paper. Two output options are available: RS-232-C output and also an analog output of slope compensated pH and displayed mV.

Optional Accessories:
Replacement "3 in 1" pH/Ref/Temp Electrode **PHE-1062 $59**
Extension Cable for PHE-1062 **PHEC-1050 $20**
ATC/Temp Probe: **PHAT-1050 $39**
Replacement Paper, 4 Rolls: **PHOM-10-RP $10**

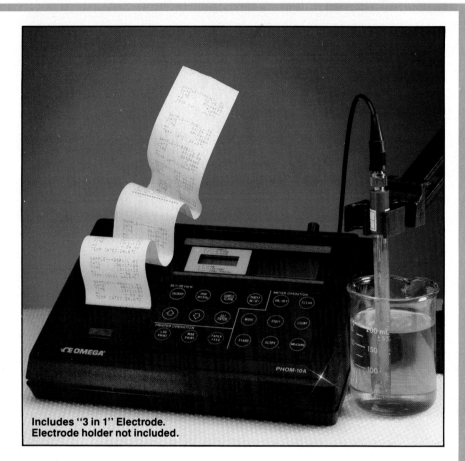

Includes "3 in 1" Electrode.
Electrode holder not included.

Specifications:
Range: −2.00 to 16.00 pH, ±999 mV, 0 to 100.0°C
Resolution: 0.01 pH, 1.0 mV, 0.1°C
Accuracy: (±1 digit) pH ±0.1%, mV ±0.1%, ±0.5°C
Buffer Recognition: pH 4, 7, 10
Temperature Compensation: Auto or manual from 0 to 100°C
Display: LCD
Input Impedance: $> 10^{12}$ ohms
Connector: "3 in 1" electrode connector, BNC
Optional Analog Output: 0.2% of slope compensated pH and displayed mV
Printer: thermal, dot matrix

Print Interval: 10 s to 10 h
High/Low Alarm Set: over measurement range
Power: 115/230 user selectable and rechargeable batteries (recharger included)
Battery Life: 10 hours typical
Size: 9.8″ x 9.5″ x 3.9″
Weight: 3.9 lb

From
$565

To Order:

Model No.	Output Option	Price
PHOM-10	N/A	**$565**
PHOM-10-A	Analog Output	615
PHOM-10-D	RS-232-C	615
PHOM-10-AD	Analog & RS-232-C	665

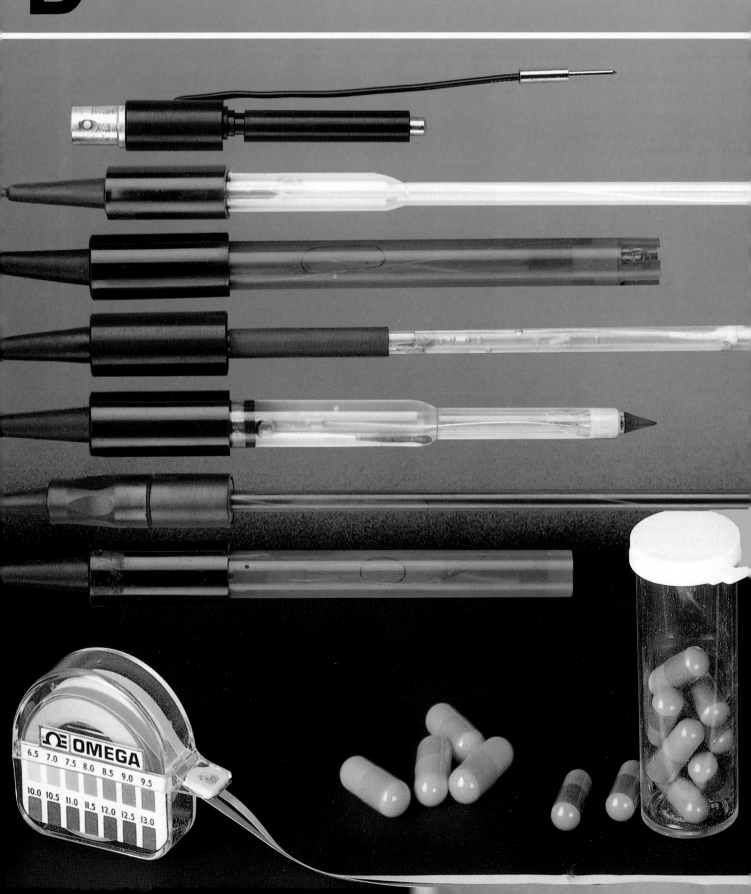

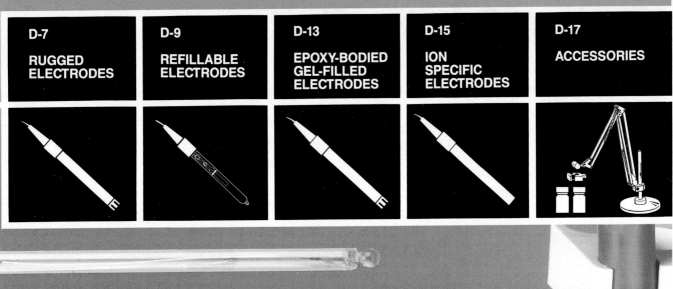

D-7	D-9	D-13	D-15	D-17
RUGGED ELECTRODES	REFILLABLE ELECTRODES	EPOXY-BODIED GEL-FILLED ELECTRODES	ION SPECIFIC ELECTRODES	ACCESSORIES

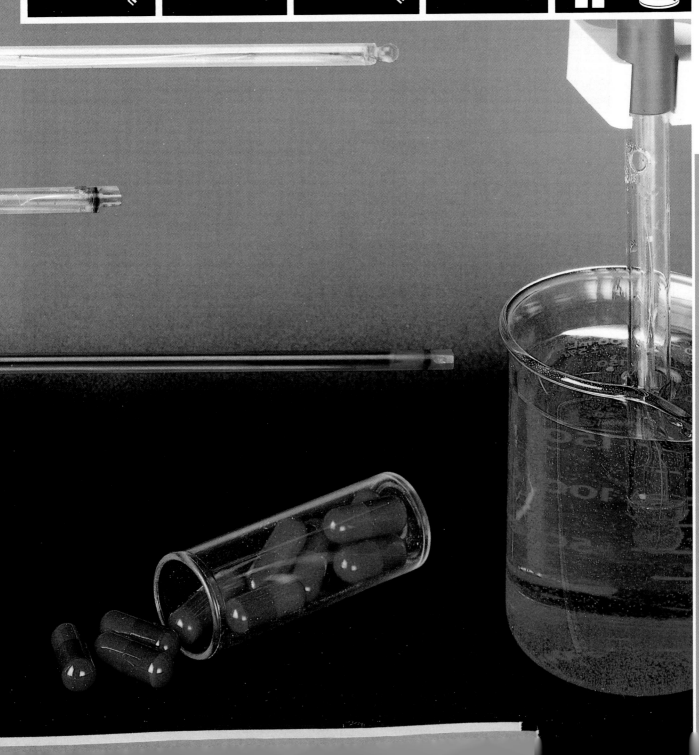

Electrode Selection Chart

In order to select the proper electrode for a particular application, the following parameters should be evaluated:

1.) Combination or Electrode Pair

Combination

Best electrode for most laboratory or field applications with exceptions noted below. Most popular type.

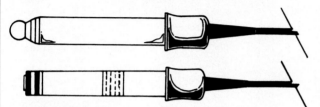

Electrode Pair

Best choice for following special applications:
1. Colloidal suspension
2. Iodides in sample
3. High solids
4. Viscous solutions
5. Specific Ion Determinations

2.) Fill Solution (Gel-Filled or Refillable)

Gel-Filled

Almost no maintenance. Polymer body for high durability. Moderate accuracy (±.05 pH units). Limited Life (6 mo.–1 year) Should not be immersed for long periods of time. Most often used for field or industrial applications.

Refillable

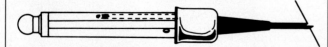

1. Higher maintenance
2. Typically glass body
3. High accuracy (±.01 pH unit)
4. Longer Life (1 yr. or more)
5. Most often used for laboratory applications.

3.) Junction Type

Single Junction Ag/AgCl

Best electrode for most laboratory or field applications with exceptions noted below.

Double Junction or Calomel

Used when samples can react with silver in Ag/AgCl electrode. Best choice for solutions containing:
1. Proteins, sulfide or heavy metal ions
2. Strong reducing ions
3. Tris Buffer

Calomel (Hg/HgCl) electrodes are often recommended in situations where the Ag/AgCl filling solution will interact with your sample. Calomel is a very stable reference at constant temperatures and is often used in laboratory applications. It has less temperature stability than Ag/AgCl and breaks down above 60°C. Ag/AgCl double junction electrodes now offer the same advantage as Calomel (Hg/HgCl) electrodes without heat stability limitations.

4.) Body Construction (Glass, Epoxy or Polymer)
Glass Body

Most often used in laboratory applications. Best choice for solutions containing:
1. Proteins and other compounds with high surface tension
2. Highly corrosive materials
3. Organics or solvents which might attack epoxy body

Epoxy or Polymer Body

More durable than glass. Best electrode for most field applications. Most often gel filled.

Electrode Selection

Considerations	Explanation
Physical Dimensions of Electrode and Bulb	Electrodes are available in various lengths and bulb shapes for different uses such as general purpose, test tubes, flat surfaces or puncturing soft moist surfaces.
Type of Sample	If sample will react with Ag/AgCl reference, Calomel or Double Junction reference should be used. When in doubt Double Junction should be used (Also see "Type of Liquid Junction").
Type of Liquid Junction	Any Ceramic or Teflon® junction can be used for most applications. Differences are as follows: Pin Ceramic—low junction flow rate. Annular or Coaxial Ceramic—higher flow rate with greater surface area to prevent clogging. Teflon® — higher flow rate, hard to clog. Sleeve junction—highest flow rate for hard to measure or easily clogging sample such as high purity water or dirty, viscous samples.
pH of Sample	At high pH (> 12) a special glass may be required to minimize error due to interference by sodium ions. This high pH glass can be used over the entire pH scale but has a higher resistance than the standard glass.
Resistance of Electrode	The higher the resistance of the electrode the more difficult it is to get a proper measurement. Meters with an input impedance of at least 10^{12} ohms should be used whenever possible. The input impedance of the meter should be greater than 1000 times the resistance of the electrode. Resistance of electrodes doubles for every 8°C drop in temperature, therefore at low temperatures this can become important.
Connector and Cable Length	Standard OMEGA® electrodes come with a BNC or U.S. standard connector and 3 ft of cable. Make sure this is compatible with the meter you are using. If not, adaptors and other cable lengths are available.

Ordering Information and Examples

Standard electrode configuration: 3 ft cable with either BNC type connector (ex. PHE-1311, $51) or U.S. standard connector (ex. PHE-1311-U, $51)

*To order electrodes with cables over 3 ft, add total desired length in ft to part no., and add $1 per each additional foot to base price (ex. PHE-1311-U-5, $53)

*To order electrodes with detachable cable connector, add suffix "D" to part no., and $5 to price (ex. PHE-1311-D, $56). See page D-6 for mating cables.

*To order electrodes for high pH ($>$pH12), add suffix "14pH" to part no. and $6 to price (ex. PHE-1311-14pH, $57)

*Longer production lead time is required for non-standard electrode configurations.

Introduction to Electrode Selection

With so many electrodes available, how do I select the one for my application?

One group or a few electrodes can not fill all the various applications that may be encountered.

The first question to ask is where the electrode will be used. Is it for the laboratory, the field or an industrial process environment? Once that is ascertained, then the physical dimensions of the electrode and the bulb style must be decided. Electrodes are available in various lengths and bulb shapes for different uses such as general purpose, test tubes, flat surfaces or puncturing moist surfaces. Also, if it is an industrial electrode, the proper mounting configuration must be chosen such as insertion or submersion.

What other parameters must I examine to choose the proper electrode?

The first choice to make is whether to use a combination electrode or an electrode pair.
A combination electrode is best for most laboratory or field applications with certain exceptions. It is the most popular type of electrode and the easiest to use. An electrode pair is the best choice for the following applications: 1) colloidal suspensions, 2) iodides in sample, 3) high solids, 4) viscous solutions, 5) specific ion determinations, 6) high purity water.

What is an electrode pair and a combination electrode?

An electrode pair consists of two electrodes, the reference electrode and the measuring electrode. A combination electrode combines these two elements into one electrode. All pH measurements are made using either the electrode pair or a combination electrode.

What are gel filled and refillable electrodes?

Electrodes are either refillable or gel-filled. Gel filled electrodes require almost no maintenance and their polymer bodies exhibit excellent durability. However, gel fills also have moderate accuracy (± 0.05 pH units) and a limited life span (6 month to 1 year). They should not be immersed for long periods of time. Refillable electrodes require periodic refilling with the appropriate fill solution. They have higher maintenance, typically glass bodies, but have higher accuracy (± 0.01 pH unit), longer life and are most often used for laboratory applications.

How do I select the electrode's body construction?

The glass body electrode is most often used in laboratory applications. It is the best choice for solutions containing proteins and other compounds with high surface tension, highly corrosive materials and organics or solvents which might attack a polymer body. Polymer bodied electrodes are more durable than glass. They are the best choice for field applications and are most often gel filled.

What is the junction of an electrode?

The junction of a reference electrode or combination electrode is a permeable membrane through which the filling solution escapes (called the liquid junction). The junction can come in several forms, but its principal function is to allow small quantities of the reference electrode's fill solution to slowly leak or migrate in to the sample being measured.

What are the types of junctions and how can I select them?

Junctions can be categorized by both number and type. Any ceramic or fluorocarbon polymer junction can be used for most applications. The differences are as follows: Pin ceramic- low flow rate. Annular or coaxial ceramic- higher flow rate with greater surface area to prevent clogging. Fluorocarbon polymer— higher flow rate, hard to clog. Sleeve junction— highest flow rate for hard to measure or easily clogging samples such as high purity water or dirty, viscous samples. Electrodes can use either single, double or triple junctions. Single junction electrodes with Ag/AgCl internal components are the best electrodes for many field or laboratory applications with the exceptions noted below. Double junction or triple junction electrodes provide protection when used with samples that can react with silver in Ag/AgCl electrodes. They are the best choice for solutions containing proteins, sulfides, heavy metal ions, strong reducing ions, or tris buffers. If in doubt, a double junction should be used.

What are calomel electrodes?

Calomel (Hg/HgCl) reference electrodes are often recommended in situations where the Ag/AgCl filling solution will interact with your sample. Calomel is a very stable reference at constant temperatures and is often used in laboratory applications. It has less temperature stability than Ag/AgCl and breaks down above 60°C. Ag/AgCl double junction electrodes offer the same advantage as calomel electrodes without the heat limitations.

How does the pH of the sample affect electrode selection?

At high pH (> 12), a special glass may be required to minimize error due to interference by sodium ions. This high pH glass can be used over the entire pH scale but has a higher resistance than the standard glass.

What are the various types of connectors that are available on electrodes?

The main connectors available are the BNC and the U.S. standard connectors. Make sure that these connectors are compatible with the meter that you are using. If not, adaptors for other connectors and meters are available.

Electrode Adaptors and Connectors

METER ADAPTORS

	Model No.	Converts Meter From:	To Electrode Type:	Price
A	PHMA-UB	U.S. Standard	BNC	$23
B	PHMA-BU	BNC	U.S. Standard	28
C	PHMA-RU	Radiometer	U.S. Standard	29
D	PHMA-RB	Radiometer	BNC	23
E	PHMA-CB	Corning 5 & 6	BNC	23
F	PHMA-CU	Corning 5 & 6	U.S. Standard	32
G	PHMA-UP	U.S. Standard	Pin Jack	29

Cables for Detachable Combination Electrodes

Used to adapt OMEGA detachable electrodes to meters with various types of connectors. 3 ft. cable length is standard. For extra cable, specify length and add $.50 per additional foot.

CABLE DESCRIPTIONS

	Model No.	Connector	Use w/Meter Types	Price
H	PHDC-B	BNC	Most U.S. field or industrial meters and many laboratory meters	$20
I	PHDC-U	U.S. Standard	PHR-501, PHR-811, PHR-611, PHR-601 & many U.S. lab meters	20
J	PHDC-CA	Miniature Phone A	Corning Models 5 & 6	20
K	PHDC-CB	Miniature Phone B	Corning Model 3	20
L	PHDC-RA	Radiometer (new)	Radiometers (post-1974)	28
M	PHDC-BP	Belling-Lee w/pin plug	EIL, PYE-Unicam (U.K.)	28
	PHDC-BB	Belling-Lee w/ban. plug	MECI pH meters (U.K.) (not shown)	28
N	PHDC-DA	DIN-19262	German, and new Polymetron, Metrohm Instrumentation Laboratory	28
	PHDC-DB	DIN-19262 w/ban. plug	German, and new Polymetron, Metrohm Instrumentation Laboratory (not shown)	28
	PHDC-E	Detachable	PHH-41 or as an extension for any detachable cable (not shown)	28
O	PHDC-SL	Spade Lugs	Industrial pH Meters	20
P	PHDC-RB	Radiometer (old)	Radiometers (pre-1974)	28
Q	PHDC-PV	Photovolt	Photovolt meters	28
R	PHDC-ME	Metrohm	Metrohm pH meters	28
S	PHDC-PL	Philips	Philips (Holland), Electrofakt (Denmark)	28
T	PHDC-LI	LEMO FS 00.250	Instrumentation Labs (Germany)	28
U	PHDC-LS	LEMO F 0.250	Seybold (Austria)	28
V	PHDC-LF	LEMO FE 1.275	Faxholm (Denmark)	28

All of these connectors can be used on standard OMEGA combination electrodes. Consult Sales for pricing and delivery.

Extension Cables for BNC Electrodes		
PHEC-B3	3 feet	$17
PHEC-B10	10 feet	$20

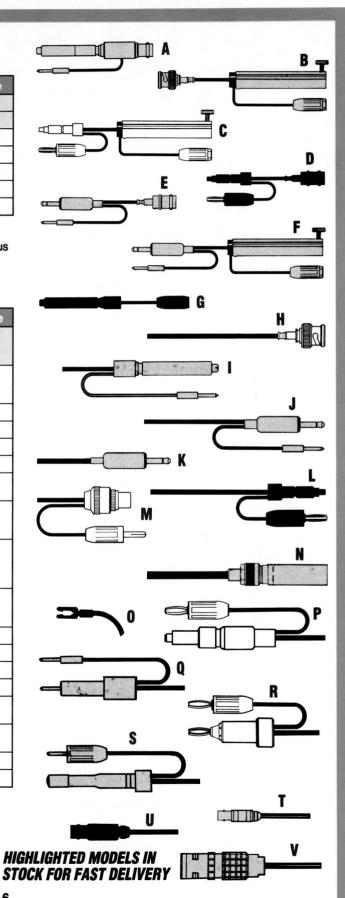

D

ELECTRODES AND ACCESSORIES

HIGHLIGHTED MODELS IN STOCK FOR FAST DELIVERY

Rugged Gel Filled Electrodes

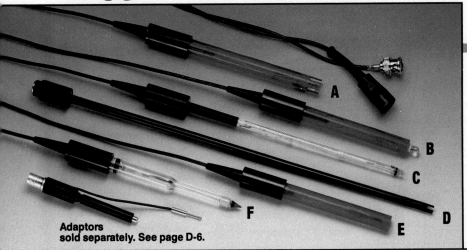

Adaptors sold separately. See page D-6.

	Part No. BNC	Part No. U.S. Std.	Application	Insertion Length (mm)	Diameter (mm)	pH Range	Temp. °C
A	PHE-1311	PHE-1311-U	General Purpose	110	12	0-12	−5 to 80
A	PHE-1411	PHE-1411-U	General Purpose for Samples Requiring Double Junction	110	12	0-12	−5 to 80
A	PHE-1511	PHE-1511-U	For use with sulfides or other contaminants found in plating baths and process streams	110	12	0-12	−5 to 80
B	PHE-1312	PHE-1312-U	General Purpose with removeable bulb guard	110	12	0-12	−5 to 80
B	PHE-1412	PHE-1412-U	Double junction design for use with interfering ions such as zinc, copper or sulfide.	110	12	0-12	−5 to 80
C	PHE-1332	PHE-1332-U	Test Tubes	180	6.5	0-12	−5 to 80
C	PHE-1432	PHE-1432-U	Test Tubes for samples requiring double junction	180	6.5	0-12	−5 to 80
D	PHE-1335	PHE-1335-U	Extra long Test Tubes (detachable style shown)	300	6	0-13	0-100
E	PHE-1371	PHE-1371-U	Measurement of flat, moist surfaces such as meat or paper	110	12	0-12	−5 to 80
E	PHE-1471	PHE-1471-U	Measurement of flat surfaces for samples requiring double junction	110	12	0-12	−5 to 80
F	PHE-2381	PHE-2381-U	Extra rugged puncture tip for meats, cheeses, fruits, leather	55	8	0-10	−5 to 100
F	PHE-2881	PHE-2881-U	Extra rugged puncture tip (Calomel)	55	8	0-10	−5 to 60
F	PHE-2481	PHE-2481-U	Extra rugged puncture tip for samples requiring double junction	55	8	0-10	−5 to 100
G	PHE-2385	PHE-2385-U	Rugged puncture tip for meats, cheeses, fruits, leather	55	8	0-13	0-100
H	PHE-1317	PHE-1317-U	Economical with removeable guard and Teflon® junction	110	12	0-13	0-100
H	PHE-1417	PHE-1417-U	Economical with double Teflon® junction	110	12	0-12	0-80
J	PHE-1304	PHE-1304-U	Economy	90	12.5	0-12	0-80
K	PHE-1301	PHE-1301-U	Economy	89	13	0-12	0-80
L	ORE-1311	ORE-1311-U	General Purpose-ORP	110	12	±5000 mV	−5 to 80
L	ORE-1411	ORE-1411-U	Dbl. junction for interfering ions such as zinc, copper or sulfide-ORP	110	12	±5000 mV	−5 to 80
L	ORE-1511	ORE-1511-U	For use with sulfides or other contaminants found in process streams-ORP	110	12	±5000 mV	−5 to 80

All electrodes supplied with 3 ft cable. For other configurations, see page D-4.
For additional lead length add desired length as suffix to electrode number and add $1 per additional foot.

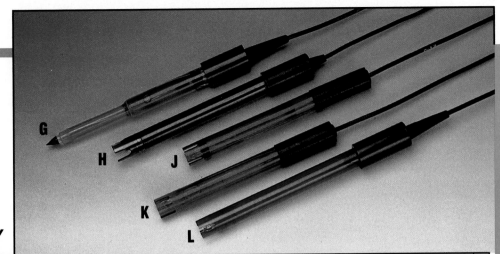

HIGHLIGHTED MODELS IN STOCK FOR FAST DELIVERY

Reference Type	Liquid Junction	Body Material	R (25°C) Megohms	Price	
Ag/AgCl	Coaxial w/Dual-pin Ceramic	Epoxy	80	$54	A
Ag/AgCl Double	Coaxial w/Dual-pin Ceramic	Epoxy	80	63	A
Ag/AgCl Triple	Coaxial w/Dual-pin Ceramic	Epoxy	80	95	A
Ag/AgCl	Coaxial w/Dual-pin Ceramic	Epoxy	80	60	B
Ag/AgCl Double	Coaxial w/Dual-pin Ceramic	Epoxy	80	67	B
Ag/AgCl	Dual-pin Ceramic	Epoxy	200	91	C
Ag/AgCl Double	Dual-pin Ceramic	Epoxy	200	101	C
Ag/AgCl	Annular Ceramic	Epoxy	200	86	D
Ag/AgCl	Dual-pin Ceramic	Epoxy	450	74	E
Ag/AgCl Double	Dual-pin Ceramic	Epoxy	450	93	E
Ag/AgCl	Annular Ceramic	Glass	500	91	F
Calomel	Annular Ceramic	Glass	500	98	F
Ag/AgCl Double	Annular Ceramic	Glass	500	107	F
Ag/AgCl	Annular Ceramic	Glass	150	82	G
Ag/AgCl	Annular Teflon®	Poly Ether Sulfone	60	48	H
Ag/AgCl Double	Annular Teflon®	Poly Ether Sulfone	60	58	H
Ag/AgCl	Annular Ceramic	Epoxy	50	33	J
Ag/AgCl	Dual-pin Ceramic	Epoxy	80	43	K
Ag/AgCl	Coaxial w/Dual-pin Ceramic	Epoxy	—	77	L
Ag/AgCl Double	Coaxial w/Dual-pin Ceramic	Epoxy	—	87	L
Ag/AgCl Triple	Coaxial w/Dual-pin Ceramic	Epoxy	—	112	L

D

ELECTRODES AND ACCESSORIES

pH Combination Electrodes
For Laboratory Use

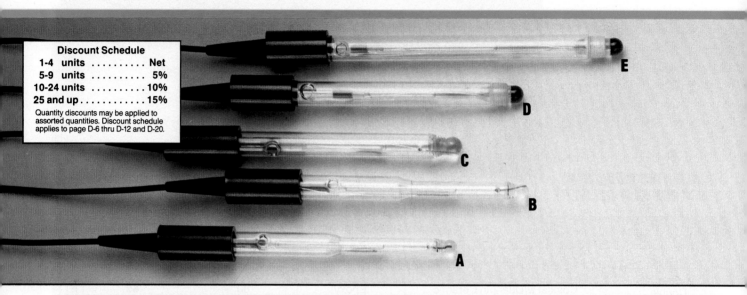

Discount Schedule

1-4 units	.... Net
5-9 units	.... 5%
10-24 units	.... 10%
25 and up	.... 15%

Quantity discounts may be applied to assorted quantities. Discount schedule applies to page D-6 thru D-12 and D-20.

	Part No. BNC	Part No. U.S. Std.	Application/Features	Length (mm) Insertion	Dia. (mm) Insertion	pH Range	Temp. °C
A	PHE-2121	PHE-2121-U	General Purpose Laboratory	55	8	0-12	0-100
A	PHE-2721	PHE-2721-U	General Laboratory with Calomel Reference	55	8	0-12	0-60
B	PHE-2122	PHE-2122-U	General Laboratory with removeable bulb guard	55	8	0-12	0-100
B	PHE-2722	PHE-2722-U	Calomel Reference for measurement of protein samples-removeable bulb guard	55	8	0-12	0-60
C	PHE-2111	PHE-2111-U	General Purpose with large spherical bulb for fast response	110	12	0-12	0-100
C	PHE-2711	PHE-2711-U	Calomel Reference with large spherical bulb for fast response	110	12	0-12	0-60
D	PHE-2114	PHE-2114-U	General Purpose large bulb	110	12	0-13	0-100
D	PHE-2714	PHE-2714-U	Calomel Reference large bulb, can be used for high-purity water	110	12	0-13	–5 to 60
D	PHE-2414	PHE-2414-U	Large bulb sealed double junction	110	12	0-13	0-110
D	PHE-2314	PHE-2314-U	General Purpose large bulb sealed	110	12	0-13	0-110
D	PHE-2214	PHE-2214-U	Sealed inner refillable outer junction	110	12	0-13	0-110
D	PHE-2319	PHE-2319-U	High pH sealed	110	12	0-14	5-110
E	PHE-2116	PHE-2116-U	Rugged bulb design	140	12	0-13	5-110
F	PHE-2131	PHE-2131-U	Test tubes, flasks	110	6	0-12	0-100
F	PHE-2731	PHE-2731-U	Test tubes, flasks for organics, proteins, metals	110	6	0-12	0-60
G	PHE-2123	PHE-2123-U	Large test tubes, flasks	120	8	0-12	0-100
G	PHE-2723	PHE-2723-U	Large test tubes, flasks for organics, proteins, metals	120	8	0-12	0-60
H	PHE-2124	PHE-2124-U	Extra long for measurement in narrow vessels	240	8	0-12	0-100
J	PHE-1477	PHE-1477-U	Flat surfaces, Teflon® double junction	127	12	1-10	0-60
K	PHE-2773	PHE-2773-U	Flat surfaces, Calomel, 6 mm tip	110	6	0-12	–5 to 60

All electrodes supplied with 3 ft cable. Combination electrodes available with detachable cable connector, see page D-4

HIGHLIGHTED MODELS IN STOCK FOR FAST DELIVERY.

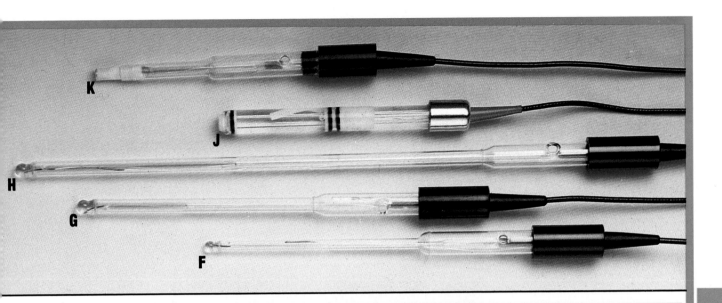

Reference Type	Liquid Junction	Body Material	Refillable or Gel	R (25°C) Megohms	Price	
Ag/AgCl	Pin Ceramic	Glass	Refillable	80	$61	A
Calomel	Pin Ceramic	Glass	Refillable	80	68	A
Ag/AgCl	Pin Ceramic	Glass	Refillable	80	63	B
Calomel	Pin Ceramic	Glass	Refillable	80	72	B
Ag/AgCl	Pin Ceramic	Glass	Refillable	50	74	C
Calomel	Pin Ceramic	Glass	Refillable	50	91	C
Ag/AgCl	Annular Ceramic	Glass	Refillable	50	68	D
Calomel	Annular Ceramic	Glass	Refillable	50	78	D
Ag/AgCl Double	Annular Ceramic	Glass	Gel	50	87	D
Ag/AgCl	Annular Ceramic	Glass	Gel	50	77	D
Ag/AgCl Double	Annular Ceramic	Glass	Gel/Refillable	50	87	D
Ag/AgCl	Annular Ceramic	Glass	Gel	250	82	D
Ag/AgCl	Annular Ceramic	Glass	Refillable	250	79	E
Ag/AgCl	Pin Ceramic	Glass	Refillable	90	82	F
Calomel	Pin Ceramic	Glass	Refillable	90	88	F
Ag/AgCl	Pin Ceramic	Glass	Refillable	80	79	G
Calomel	Pin Ceramic	Glass	Refillable	80	82	G
Ag/AgCl	Pin Ceramic	Glass	Refillable	80	91	H
Ag/AgCl Double	Teflon®	Poly Ether Sulfone	Gel	200	100	J
Calomel	Annular Ceramic	Glass	Refillable	300	122	K

Electrodes supplied with 3 ft. cable. For detachable cable and other configurations, see page D-4.

Laboratory pH Electrodes
Combination Electrodes, Sensing and Reference Half Cells

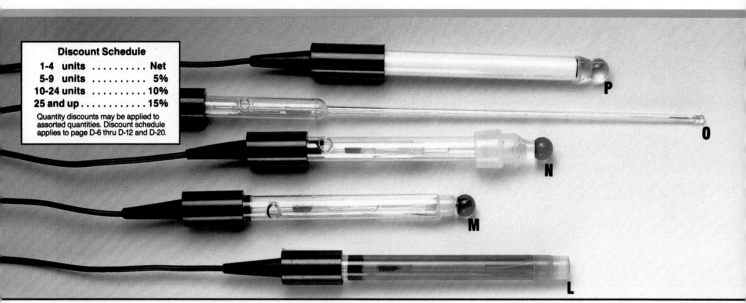

Discount Schedule
1-4 units	Net
5-9 units	5%
10-24 units	10%
25 and up	15%

Quantity discounts may be applied to assorted quantities. Discount schedule applies to page D-6 thru D-12 and D-20.

COMBINATION ELECTRODES

	Part No. BNC	Part No. U.S. Std.	Application	Length (mm)	Diameter (mm)	pH Range	Temp. °C
L	PHE-2171	PHE-2171-U	Flat surface for measurement of meats or agar plates	110	12	0-12	0-100
M	PHE-2161	PHE-2161-U	Soil pH measurements, directions included	110	12	0-13	0-100
N	PHE-2191	PHE-2191-U	High junction flow rate for difficult samples (slurries, emulsions, high-purity water)	130	14	0-13	0-110
N	PHE-2791	PHE-2791-U	High junction flowrate with Calomel reference	130	14	0-13	−5 to 60
N	PHE-2291	PHE-2291-U	High junction flowrate with double junction	130	14	0-13	0-110
O	PHE-2754	PHE-2754-U	Extra long 3.5 mm diameter for NMR tubes and small lab glassware	183	3.5	0-12	0-60

SENSING ELECTRODES

	Part No. BNC	Part No. U.S. Std.	Application	Length (mm)	Diameter (mm)	pH Range	Temp. °C
P	PHE-3011	PHE-3011-U	Fast response, ideal for measurement at low temperatures	110	12	0-12	−15 to 100
P	PHE-3018	PHE-3018-U	Fast response, low Na ion error	110	12	0-13	−5 to 100
P	PHE-3019	PHE-3019-U	High pH measurement	110	12	0-14	−5 to 100

REFERENCE HALF CELLS

	Part No.	Application	Length (mm)	Diameter (mm)	pH Range	Temp. °C
Q	PHE-3711	Calomel junction for protein substances and high-purity water	110	12	—	−5 to 60
Q	PHE-3111	General purpose reference half cell	110	12	—	−5 to 105
R	PHE-3291	High junction flow rate for low conductivity or dirty solutions	115	15	—	−5 to 105
R	PHE-3791	High junction flow rate with Calomel double junction	115	15	—	−5 to 60
S	PHE-3211	Double junction reference half cell with 10% KNO_3 salt bridge	110	12	—	−5 to 105
T	PHE-3217	Teflon® double junction reference, for difficult or dirty solutions	127	12	—	0 to 100

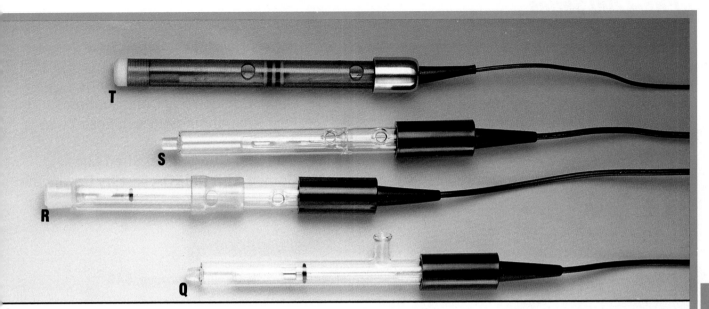

Reference Type	Liquid Junction	Body Material	Refillable or Gel	R (25°C) Megohms	Price	
Ag/AgCl	Annular Ceramic	Glass	Refillable	300	$100	L
Ag/AgCl	Annular Ceramic	Glass	Refillable	150	82	M
Ag/AgCl	Sleeve	Glass	Refillable	100	100	N
Calomel	Sleeve	Glass	Refillable	100	110	N
Ag/AgCl Double	Sleeve	Glass	Refillable	100	120	N
Calomel	Pin Ceramic	Glass	Refillable	500	141	O

—	—	Glass	—	40	$45	P
—	—	Glass	—	60	45	P
—	—	Glass	—	60	53	P

Calomel	Pin Ceramic	Glass	Refillable	—	$56	Q
Ag/AgCl	Pin Ceramic	Glass	Refillable	—	55	Q
Ag/AgCl Double	Sleeve	Glass	Refillable	—	110	R
Calomel Double	Sleeve	Glass	Refillable	—	112	R
Ag/AgCl Double	Pin Ceramic	Glass	Refillable	—	74	S
Ag/AgCl Double	Teflon®	Epoxy	Refillable	—	95	T

All electrodes supplied with 3 ft cable. Reference half cells have pin connector. Combination electrodes available with detachable cable connector, see page D-4.

D

ELECTRODES AND ACCESSORIES

Clear Epoxy-Bodied, Gel-Filled Combination Electrodes

PHE-4200 Series

From
$49

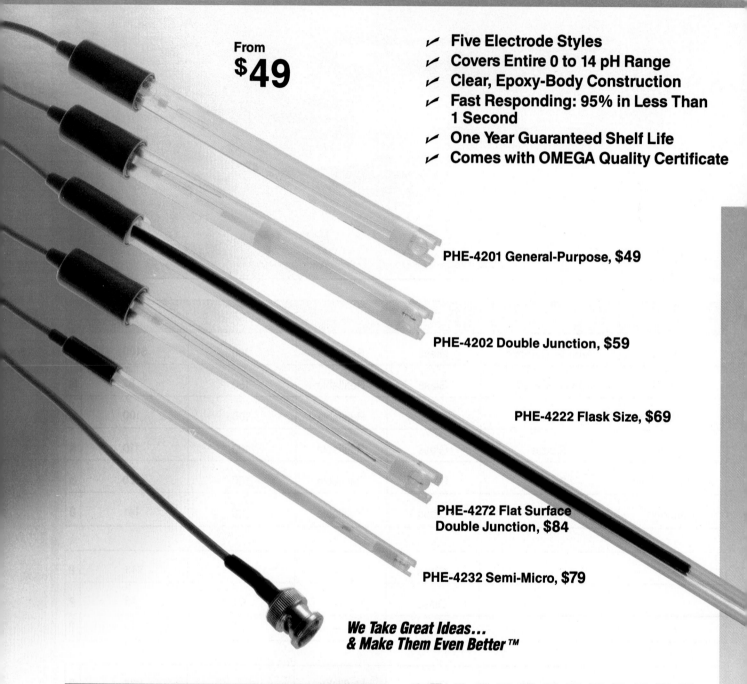

- ✔ **Five Electrode Styles**
- ✔ **Covers Entire 0 to 14 pH Range**
- ✔ **Clear, Epoxy-Body Construction**
- ✔ **Fast Responding: 95% in Less Than 1 Second**
- ✔ **One Year Guaranteed Shelf Life**
- ✔ **Comes with OMEGA Quality Certificate**

PHE-4201 General-Purpose, $49

PHE-4202 Double Junction, $59

PHE-4222 Flask Size, $69

PHE-4272 Flat Surface Double Junction, $84

PHE-4232 Semi-Micro, $79

We Take Great Ideas...
& Make Them Even Better ™

To Order (Specify Model Number)

Model No.	Description	Length mm	Dia. mm	R (25°C) MegΩ	Price
PHE-4201	Gen. purpose	150	12	50-80	**$49**
PHE-4202	Double junction	150	12	50-80	59
PHE-4222	Flask size	300	9.5	50-80	69
PHE-4272	Flat surface double junction	150	12	50-80	84
PHE-4232	Semi-micro	150	6	50-80	79

All electrodes are supplied with 3 ft of cable and BNC connector.

Certificate of Quality

This electrode has been manufactured to the most stringent quality control standards. It has been supplied in a special soaker/storage bottle to ensure its quality.

Your electrode has been 100% inspected prior to shipment and meets or exceeds all factory performance specifications.

OMEGA Engineering is pleased to offer a complete line of laboratory pH electrodes. The PHE-4200 Series are gel-filled, combination pH electrodes with a unique clear epoxy-body design. With five electrode styles to choose from, you're sure to find one suitable for your application.

The OMEGA PHE-4200 electrodes offer reliable quality at a reasonable cost. The electrodes measure the entire pH range from 0 to 14 pH units at 0 to 100°C and feature an Ag/AgCl reference and a polypropylene liquid junction. Each electrode comes in a soaker storage bottle to keep the electrode moist and ready for use. Shelf life is guaranteed for one year, and the OMEGA quality certificate provided assures that these electrodes meet the most stringent quality control requirements.

Compatible Meters from OMEGA

PHE-4200 electrodes are compatible with any handheld or benchtop meter that accepts a BNC connector. A few of the many compatible meters from OMEGA are shown below.

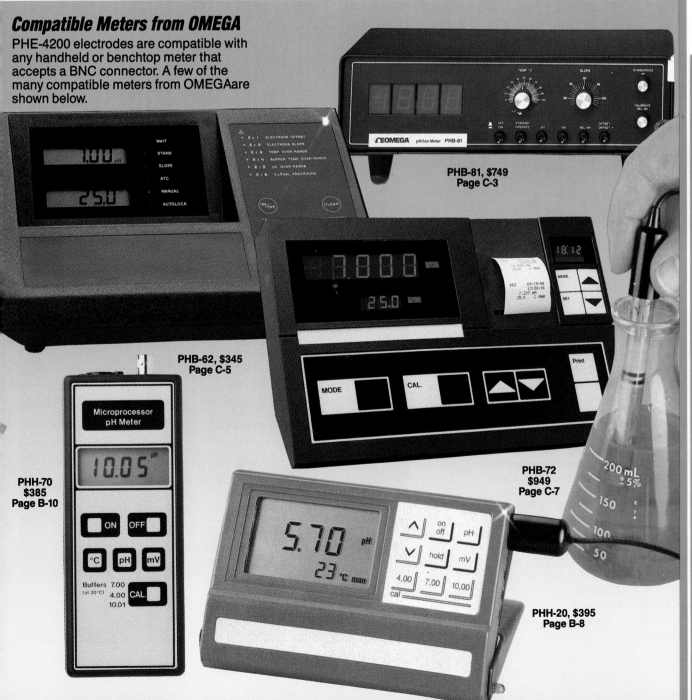

PHB-81, $749
Page C-3

PHB-62, $345
Page C-5

PHB-72
$949
Page C-7

PHH-70
$385
Page B-10

PHH-20, $395
Page B-8

D

ELECTRODES AND ACCESSORIES

Ion Selective Electrodes

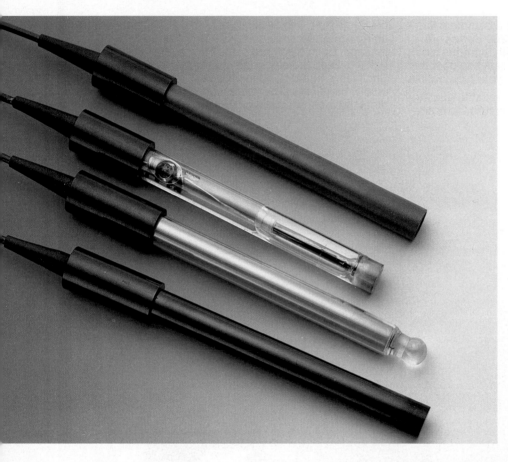

- **New Low Cost Design**
- **Extremely Sensitive Measurement of Both Cations and Anions**
- **Ideal for Field or Laboratory Usage**
- **Easy to Use and Saves Time Compared to Other Analytical Measurement Techniques**

From
$110

MADE IN
USA

The NEW OMEGA ISE-8700 series ion select electrodes offer a cost effective alternative for accurate selective ion measurement. Precise analytical evaluation of many substances including ions and dissolved gases can be achieved quickly and easily. Ionic concentrations can be displayed directly on a specific ion meter, or indirectly in millivolts using any mV meter and calculated from a calibration curve. There is a vast assortment of applications for these portable electrodes, ideally suiting them for field or laboratory use.

Applications Include:
- Water Treatment
- Food Processing
- Medical Research
- Fuels and Refining
- Agriculture

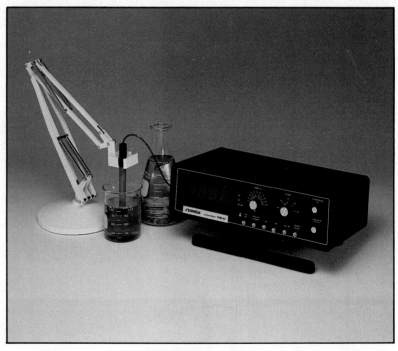

Electrode	Part Number	Type	Concentration Range (M) ppm	Temp. Range	Interferences	Suggested Reference Electrode	Price
Ammonia (NH$_3$) [Ammonium (NH$_4$+)]	ISE-8710	Gas-sensing	(1.0 to 5 $\times$ 10^{-7}) 17,000 to 0.01	0 to 50°C	Volatile amines	N/A	$275.00
Bromide (Br$^-$)	ISE-8720	Solid-state	(1.0 to 5 $\times$ 10^{-6}) 79,900 to 0.40	0 to 80°C	S^{-2}, I$^-$, CN$^-$, high levels of Cl$^-$ and NH$_3$	PHE-3211	198.00
Cadmium (Cd^{+2})	ISE-8730	Solid-state	(10^{-1} to 10^{-7}) 11,200 to 0.01	0 to 80°C	Ag$^+$, Hg^{+2}, Cu^{+2} high levels of Pb^{+2} and Fe^{+2} interfere	PHE-3211	220.00
Calcium (Ca^{+2})	ISE-8740	Polymer Membrane	(1.0 to 5 $\times$ 10^{-7}) 40,100 to 0.02	0 to 40°C	Pb^{+2}, Na$^+$, Hg^{+2}, H$^+$, Sr^{+2}, Fe^{+2}, Cu, Ni^{+2}, NH$_4$$^+$, Tris$^+$, Li$^+$, K$^+$, Ba^{+2}, Zn^{+2}, Mg^{+2}	PHE-3211	275.00
Carbon dioxide [carbonate (CO$_3$$^{-2}$)]	ISE-8750	Gas-sensing	(10^{-2} to 10^{-4}) 440 to 4.4	0 to 50°C	Volatile weak acids	N/A	275.00
Chloride (Cl$^-$)	ISE-8760	Solid-state	(1.0 to 5 $\times$ 10^{-5})	0 to 50°C	OH$^-$, S^{-2}, Br$^-$, CN$^-$	PHE-3211	165.00
Chloride (Cl$^-$)	ISE-8770	Combination	(same as above)	(Same)	(Same as above)	N/A	220.00
Cyanide (CN)	ISE-8780	Solid-state	(10^{-2} to 8 $\times$ 10^{-6}) 260 to 0.2	0 to 80°C	S^{-2}, I$^-$, Br$^-$, Cl$^-$	PHE-3211	165.00
Fluoride (F$^-$)	ISE-8790	Solid-state	(Saturated to 10^{-6}) Saturated to 0.02	0 to 80°C	OH$^-$	PHE-3217	198.00
Fluoride (F$^-$)	ISE-8795	Combination	(Same as above)	(same)	(Same as above)	N/A	242.00
Iodide (I$^-$)	ISE-8715	Solid-state	(1.0 to 5 $\times$ 10^{-8}) 127,000 to 5 $\times$ 10^{-3}	0 to 80°C	S^{-2}, CN$^-$, NH$_3$, S$_2$O$_3$$^{-2}$	PHE-3211	165.00
Lead (Pb^{+2})	ISE-8725	Solid-state	(0.1 to 10^{-6}) 20,700 to 0.2	0 to 80°C	Ag$^+$, Hg^{+2}, Cu^{+2} high levels of Cd^{+2} and Fe^{+2}	PHE-3211	165.00
Nitrate	ISE-8735	Polymer Membrane	(1.0 to 7 $\times$ 10^{-6}) 14,000 to 0.1 as N	0 to 40°C	ClO$_4$$^-$, I$^-$, ClO$_3$$^-$, CN$_2$$^-$, Br^{-4}, NO$_2$$^-$, HS^{-3}, CO$_3$$^-$, HCO$_4$$^-$, H$_2PO_4$$^-$, OAc F$^-$, SO$_4$$^{-2}$	PHE-3211 with 3M (NH$_4$)$_2$ SO$_4$ Outer Fill Solution	275.00
Potassium (K$^+$)	ISE-8745	Polymer Membrane	(1.0 to 10^{-6}) 39,000 to 0.04	0 to 40°C	C$_S$$^+$, NH$_4$$^+$, Tl$^+$, H$^+$ Ag$^+$, Tris$^+$, Li$^+$, NA$^+$	PHE-3211 with 1M NaCl Outer Fill Solution	220.00
Silver/Sulfide (Ag$^+$/S$^-$)	ISE-8755	Solid-state	(Ag$^+$: 1.0 to 10^{-7}) 107,900 to 0.01	0-80°C to	Hg^{+2} 10^{-7}M	PHE-3211	165.00
Sodium (Na$^+$)	ISE-8765	Combination	(Saturated to 10^{-6}) Saturated to 0.02	0 to 80°C	Ag$^+$, H$^+$, Li$^+$, Ca$^+$; K$^+$, Tl	N/A	193.00
Sodium (Na$^+$)	ISE-8775	Glass	(Same as above)	(same)	(Same as above)	PHE-3211 with 0.1M NH$_4$ Cl Outer Fill Soln	110.00

ISE Standard Solutions and Accessories

**Ion Selective Electrodes
Shown on Page D-16**

ION SELECTIVE ELECTRODE STANDARDIZING SOLUTIONS (475 mL)

Part No.	Description	Electrode	Price
ISE-8710-S1	0.1M NH$_4$Cl	Ammonia	$ 34
ISE-8710-S2	NH4Cl, 1000 ppm as N		30
PHFS-8710	Internal Fill Solution, 0.1M NH$_4$Cl (50 mL)		16
ISE-8720-S1	0.1M NaBr	Bromide	34
ISE-8720-S2	NaBr, 1000 ppm as Br$^-$		30
ISE-8740-S1	0.1M CaCl$_2$	Calcium	34
ISE-8740-S2	CaCl$_2$, 1000 ppm as Ca^{+2}		34
ISE-8730-S1	0.1M Cd(NO$_3$)$_2$ 4H$_2$O	Cadmium	34
ISE-8730-S2	Cd(NO$_3$)$_2$ 4H2O, 1000 ppm as Cd^{+2}		34
ISE-8750-S1	0.1M NaHCO$_3$	Carbon Dioxide	34
ISE-8750-S2	Carbon Dioxide Std., 1000 ppm as CO$_2$		34
PHFS-8750	Internal Fill Solution for ISE-8750 (50 mL)		30
ISE-8770-S1	0.1M NaCl	Chloride	34
ISE-8770-S2	NaCl, 1000 ppm as Cl$^-$		30
ISE-8780-S1	Cyanide Activity Solution, 1000 ppm as CN$^-$ (10 x 50mL bottles)	Cyanide	90
ISE-8790-S1	0.1M NaF	Fluoride	26
ISE-8790-S2	NaF, 100 ppm as F$^-$		22
ISE-8715-S1	0.1M NaI	Iodide	34
ISE-8715-S2	NaI, 1000 ppm as I$^-$		34
ISE-8725-S1	0.1M Pb(ClO$_4$)$_2$	Lead	34
ISE-8725-S2	Pb(ClO$_4$)$_2$, 1000 ppm as Pb^{+2}		34
ISE-8735-S1	0.1M NaNO$_3$	Nitrate	34
ISE-8735-S2	NaNO$_3$, 1000 ppm as NO$_3^-$		30
ISE-8745-S1	0.1M KCl	Potassium	34
ISE-8745-S2	KCl, 1000 ppm as K$^+$		34
PHFS-8745	1M NaCl, Fill Solution for outer junction (125 mL)		8
ISE-8755-S1	0.1M AgNO$_3$	Silver/ Sulfide	30
ISE-8755-S2	AgNO$_3$, 1000 ppm as Ag$^+$		30
ISE-8765-S1	0.1M NaCl	Sodium	27
ISE-8765-S2	NaCl, 1000 ppm as Na$^+$		18

IONIC STRENGTH ADJUSTORS AND REAGENTS (475 mL)

Part No.	Description	ION Selective Electrode	Price
ISE-8720-R1	5M NaNO$_3$	Br$^-$	$ 30
ISE-8730-R1	5M NaNO$_3$	Cd^{+2}	30
ISE-8770-R1	5M NaNO$_3$	Cl$^-$	30
ISE-8715-R1	5M NaNO$_3$	I$^-$	30
ISE-8755-R1	5M NaNO$_3$	Ag$^+$/S$^-$	30
ISE-8710-R1	5M NaOH/0.05M Disodium EDTA/10% Methanol with color indicator	NH$_4^+$	30
ISE-8740-R1	4M KCl	Ca^{+2}	30
ISE-8750-R1	Carbon Dioxide Buffer	CO$_3^{-2}$	30
ISE-8735-R1	2M(NH$_4$)$_2$ SO$_4$	NO$_3^-$	30
ISE-8765-R1	NH$_4$Cl/NH$_4$OH	Na$^+$	18
ISE-8790-R1	TISAB-1	F$^-$	16
ISE-8790-R2	TISAB-2	F$^-$	16
ISE-8725-R1	5M NaClO$_4$	Pb^{+2}	34

REFERENCE FILL SOLUTIONS (125 mL)

Part No.	Description	Price
PHFS-NO$_3$	1M KNO3 Salt Bridge Solution	$8
PHFS-KCL	Saturated KCl/AgCl Reference Fill Solution	8

REPLACEMENT MEMBRANE KITS

Part No.	Description	Price
ISE-8710-KIT	Ammonia Membrane Kit, 10 membranes and spare ''O'' rings	$40
ISE-8750-KIT	Carbon Dioxide Membrane Kit, 5 membranes and spare ''O'' rings	40

pH Buffers and Indicator Papers

Buffers

A. Color Coded Buffer Capsules

For quick preparation of fresh buffer solutions, these color coded buffer capsules make 100 mL of standard buffer solution accurate within ±0.02 pH. Available in three pH ranges, each package contains five vials with ten capsules in each.

Model No.	Color	Value	Price
PHA-94	Red	pH 4	$30/pkg
PHA-97	Green	pH 7	$30/pkg
PHA-100	Blue	pH 10	$30/pkg

B. Buffer Pack

This color coded buffer pack has two vials each containing ten capsules of different pH value, four each of pH 4.0 (red), four each of pH 7.0 (green) and two each of pH 10.0 (blue). All values accurate within ±0.02 pH.

Model No.	Description	Price
PHA-85	Two Vial Set	$18/set

Non-Color Coded Buffer Sets (not shown)

This set contains five vials with ten capsules in each. Available in 1 pH steps from pH 2 to 12, each capsule makes 100 mL of standard buffer solution accurate within ±0.02 pH.

Model	Description	Price
PHA-99(*)	5 Vial Pack	$25/set

* Insert pH value desired

Triple-Check Buffer Sets (not shown)

Triple-check buffer sets contain three pH values, pH 4.0, 7.0 and 10.0 accurate to ±0.02 pH. Available in

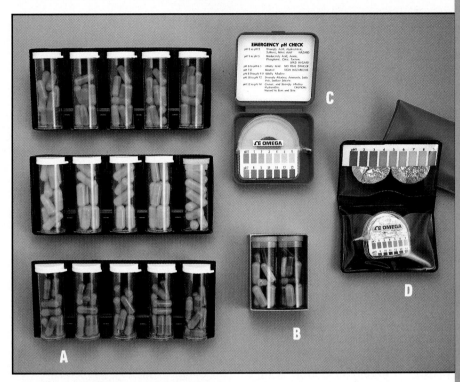

color coded and non-color coded sets, each set contains one vial of each pH value with ten capsules per vial. Each capsule makes 100 mL of buffer solution.

Model No.	Description	Price
PHA-89	Non-Color Coded	$18/set
PHA-79	Color Coded	$25/set

Indicator Papers

C. Jumbo pH Paper Dispenser (½" tape)

The dispenser contains one 50 ft roll of pH paper and a color comparison chart, measures pH from 0 to 13.

Model PHA-90 $7.50

D. Dual pH Paper Pouch Set

The PHA-91 Pouch Set contains two different dispensers of pH paper-one with 1.0 pH resolution for pH range 1 to 14, the other covers the pH 0 to 13 range with a 0.5 pH resolution. All papers in 15 ft spool, 5/16" wide.

Model PHA-91 pH Pouches $17/pair

D

ELECTRODES AND ACCESSORIES

OMEGA pH Buffer Solutions

Formulated to provide precise pH determinations, these buffer solutions which are standardized against N.B.S. certified reference samples, are ideal for calibrating electrodes and pH meters. The buffers are color coded to avoid error and are accurate to ±0.02 pH at 25°C. Each buffer contains a preservative/mold inhibitor and a shrink sealed cap to prevent contamination and leakage.

Temperature compensation charts are included with each buffer solution.

475 mL / plastic bottles.

Model No.	Color	Value	Price
PHA-4	Red	4.01	$4.80
PHA-7	Yellow	7.00	4.80
PHA-10	Blue	10.01	4.80

15% discount when purchasing 6 or more buffer solutions of the same type.

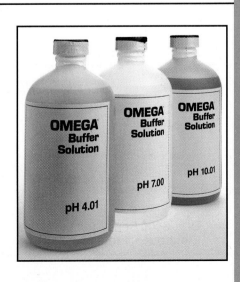

pH Accessories

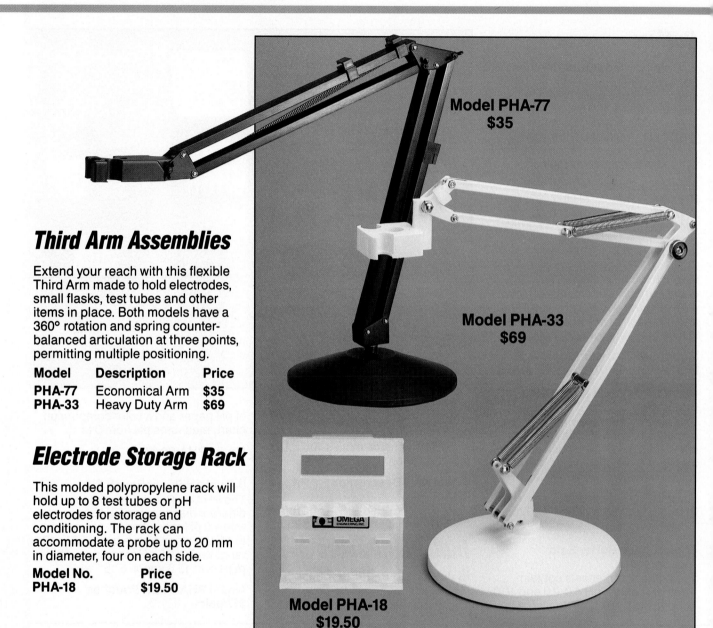

Third Arm Assemblies

Extend your reach with this flexible Third Arm made to hold electrodes, small flasks, test tubes and other items in place. Both models have a 360° rotation and spring counterbalanced articulation at three points, permitting multiple positioning.

Model	Description	Price
PHA-77	Economical Arm	$35
PHA-33	Heavy Duty Arm	$69

Electrode Storage Rack

This molded polypropylene rack will hold up to 8 test tubes or pH electrodes for storage and conditioning. The rack can accommodate a probe up to 20 mm in diameter, four on each side.

Model No.	Price
PHA-18	$19.50

Model PHA-77
$35

Model PHA-33
$69

Model PHA-18
$19.50

For Industrial Electrodes, See Section E.

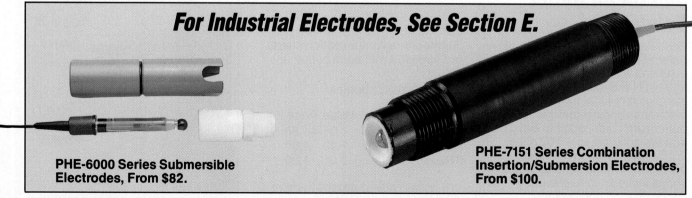

PHE-6000 Series Submersible Electrodes, From $82.

PHE-7151 Series Combination Insertion/Submersion Electrodes, From $100.

Conductivity Solutions and Fill Solutions For pH Electrodes

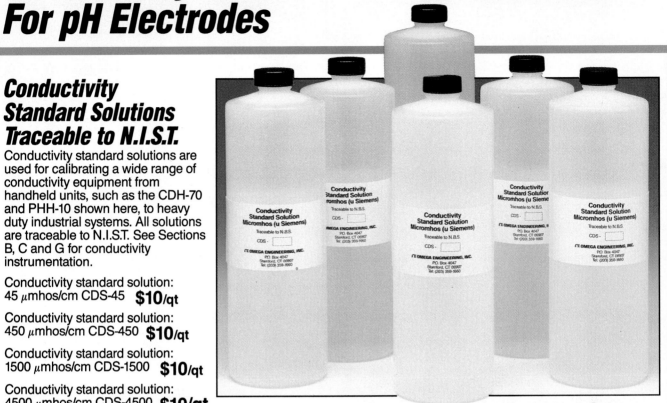

Conductivity Standard Solutions Traceable to N.I.S.T.

Conductivity standard solutions are used for calibrating a wide range of conductivity equipment from handheld units, such as the CDH-70 and PHH-10 shown here, to heavy duty industrial systems. All solutions are traceable to N.I.S.T. See Sections B, C and G for conductivity instrumentation.

Conductivity standard solution:
45 μmhos/cm CDS-45 **$10**/qt

Conductivity standard solution:
450 μmhos/cm CDS-450 **$10**/qt

Conductivity standard solution:
1500 μmhos/cm CDS-1500 **$10**/qt

Conductivity standard solution:
4500 μmhos/cm CDS-4500 **$10**/qt

D

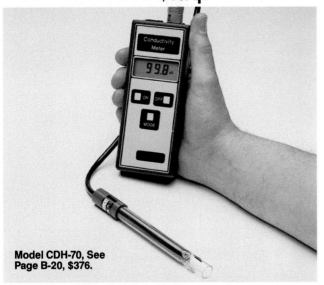

Model CDH-70, See Page B-20, $376.

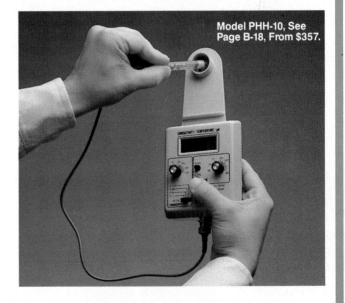

Model PHH-10, See Page B-18, From $357.

Fill Solutions for Electrodes

Description	Uses	Part No.	Price
KCl/AgCl solution, 500 mL bottle with spout	Fill solution for Ag/AgCl reference 3.8 M KCl saturated with Ag $^+$	**PHFS-A500**	**$20**
KCl/AgCl solution, 250 mL bottle with spout		**PHFS-A250**	15
10% KNO_3 solution, 250 mL bottle with spout	Fill solution used as salt bridge in some double junction electrodes	**PHFS-B250**	15
3.8M KCl solution, 500 mL bottle with spout	Fill solution for Calomel electrode and used as salt bridge in some double junction electrodes.	**PHFS-C500**	20
3.8M KCl solution, 250 mL bottle with spout		**PHFS-C250**	26

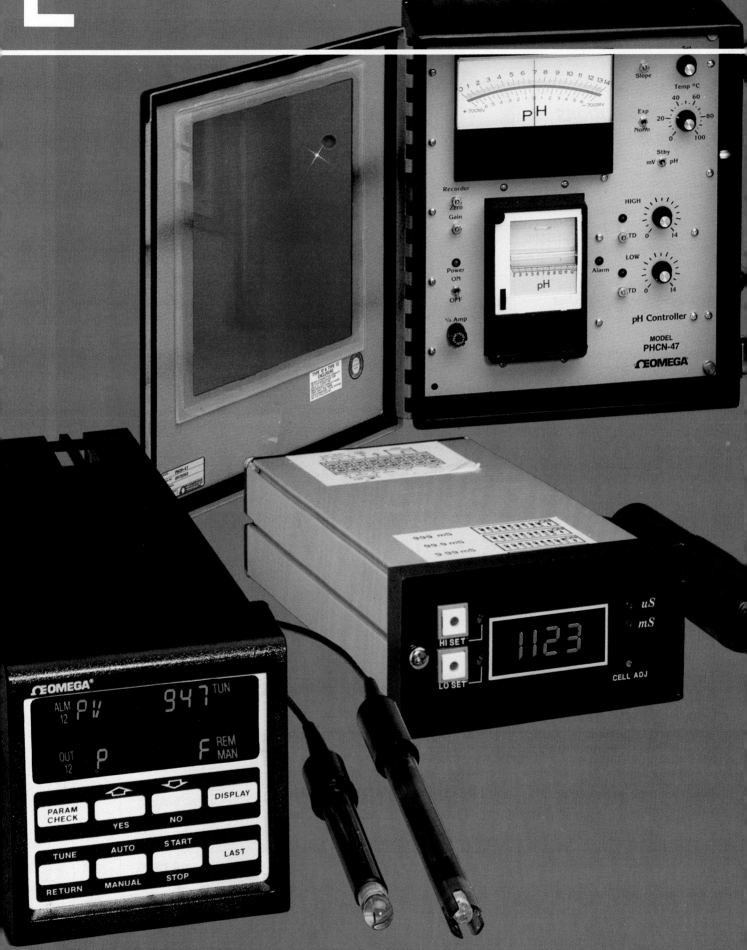

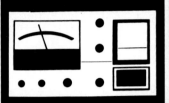

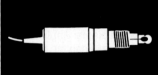

pH Control

Accurate measurement and control of pH is a common requirement in industrial plants. Applications include monitoring of cooling tower water, boiler feedwater, process steam, waste treatment, and plant effluent. Control of pH is dependent on measurement reliability, and proper measurement requires an understanding of the basic principles.

By definition, pH is the logarithm of the expression 1/(hydrogen-ion concentration). The concentration is expressed in moles per liter.

The linear scale for pH is not linear with concentration because it is a logarithmic relationship. A change of one pH unit represents a tenfold change in the effective strength of an acid or base.

Control Factors—Normally, one of two conditions exists when controlling pH: either the solution is too acidic and a base must be added to reach a specified higher pH, or the solution is too alkaline and an acid must be added to lower the pH. In both cases, the corrective medium (called a reagent) must be added at a controlled rate.

A key objective in designing pH control systems is to minimize the amount of required reagent. But determining and feeding the exact amount can be difficult because of the logarithmic relationship. Overshooting pH limits by adding more than the correct amount of reagent is easy to do if the control system is improperly designed.

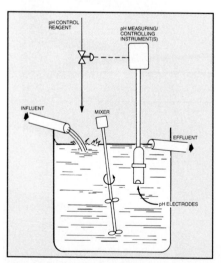

Figure 1. Batch control of pH is normally used when solution volumes are relatively small. Efficient mixing and proper location of pH electrodes is critical to ensure accurate results.

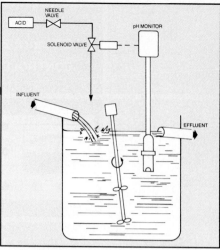

Figure 2. Continuous control of pH involves constant flow of solution in and out of treatment tank.

Control Techniques—Basically, pH control involves supplying the proper amount of reagent to bring the pH to the desired value. Control can be performed on either a batch or continuous basis.

Batch control is normally used when the total volume of the solution to be treated is relatively low, such as in waste treatment processes where liquids can be collected efficiently and treated in tanks. The amount of reagent required for neutralization can be determined from a titration curve, tank volume, and reaction time. Slow reagent addition rates and good stirring permit more accurate control with less likelihood of pH overshooting.

In the batch process shown in Fig. 1, the tank inlet and reagent feed point are shown located away from the pH electrodes and effluent discharge pipe. This separation is necessary to ensure proper mixing of reagent before measurements are made. Immersed electrodes near the outlet ensure rapid sensor response.

Continuous control is similar to batch control except that there is a continuous flow of influent and treated effluent, Fig. 2. A proportional controller may be required to regulate reagent flow rates if influent pH varies widely, Fig. 3.

Electrode Assembly Placement—An improperly placed electrode assembly can cause excessive deadtime for control action and result in cyclic control and wasted reagent. Deadtime is defined as the elapsed time between reagent addition and the first measureable pH change resulting from the addition. Ideal deadtimes range from 5 to 30 sec. Excessive deadtime can often be avoided by locating the electrode assembly close to where the reagent is added.

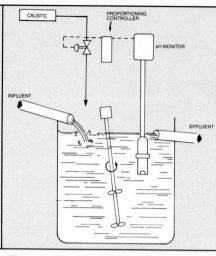

Figure 3. Proportioning controller is used to adjust pH with caustic on this system where influent's pH fluctuates greatly. Throttling valve automatically regulates reagent flow.

Vertical mounting of electrodes is preferred, and they should always be exposed to a representative sample of the process solution. The entire assembly should remain wet at all times to keep the electrodes from drying out.

Because pH is a high-impedance measurement, it is best to utilize a controller, preamplifier or signal conditioner as close to the electrode as possible. The preamplifier converts a high-impedance signal to a low-impedance signal, making it less susceptible to noise and signal loss on transmission back to the receiving instrument over unshielded wire.

Maintenance—A regularly scheduled maintenance program must be enacted to keep electrodes clean and calibrated. Electrode assemblies should be equipped with an ultrasonic cleaning device if solutions contain high levels of suspended solids that are fibrous or crystalline in nature.

Some solutions will chemically attack the electrodes and/or electrode housing material. For example, at elevated temperatures, highly alkaline (pH above 12) solutions can damage glass electrodes or cause significant sodium-ion errors. Fluoride solutions with a pH below 4 will quickly dissolve glass membranes. Process solutions above 230°F will significantly reduce electrode life. Maximum life is normally achieved at ambient temperatures. Coolers are recommended for extremely hot sampling situations.

Based on the article "Understanding pH Measurement and Control" from PLANT ENGINEERING Magazine. Used with permission.

Factors in Assessing pH System Requirements

1. **The solution requiring pH adjustment must be thoroughly evaluated. Some of the factors to consider are:**

   a. Are there any stray currents in the solution? This could disrupt the signal from the sensing device to the controller.

   b. What is the temperature of the solution? High temperatures may require special materials of construction. The housing and material inside the probe itself would need to be designed for higher temperature applications. Also, temperature has a bearing on the life of the probe. The specially designed units are filled with materials to improve on the lifetime of the probe.

   c. Knowing if the solution contains solvents or fluorides is important for chemical compatibility. Solvents affect the probe housing and require a material like Kynar®. Fluorides attack glass, which prevents the use of glass probes. A special probe is available for these types of applications.

2. **The installation of probes is also important to the success of the operation of a pH system.**

   a. A pH probe is always installed vertically. In any other position an air bubble may prevent the solution, to be adjusted, from entering the tiny pin hole at the end of the probe. Therefore, improper sensing can occur.

   b. It is critical to prevent moisture at the cable connections to the probe and the controller. The greatest opportunity for such moisture is at the probe. This could short out the probe. The probe holder, for immersion applications, is designed to mate to a female, ¾" NPT fitting. The threading should always be Teflon® taped. A damp-proof connector should be used for the cable-to-controller connection, where the environment of the controller is such that spray/mist may be in the air (this can include high humidity areas).

   c. The location of probes in solution can assist in the success of your pH system. First, the probe is always placed downstream of the chemical injection point. The solution being measured should have proper mixing, in order to get proper pH levels sensed and controlled. The probe, however, should not be near the turbulent mixing point. Air bubbles affect the proper sensing of the solution, and cause the readings from the controller to wander back and forth. However, it would be incorrect to locate the probe in a totally dead area (little to no circulation) as you would not get a represenative reading. A depth of between 1-2' from the bottom of the tank is suggested for immersion applications.

   d. Cleaning of the probe is very important. Probes get coated, even in very clean solutions. Each application will determine how frequently the probe needs to be cleaned. To have an effective pH control system, it is a must to consider this a part of your preventative maintenance schedule. Some applications may require cleaning only once a month or more, others once a week. The pH of the solution should be monitored to corroborate that the probe controlling the solution is still functioning correctly. Litmus paper or a portable, battery-operated, pH meter can verify the main systems probe. The needed accuracy from the system suggests which corroborating device to use.

      1) Design plumbing so that it is easy to get at the probe. Hard to get at objects are forgotten more than they are remembered.

      2) The probe must be calibrated to the controller, each time the probe is cleaned or replaced. Keep a record of the shelf life of the reagents used to calibrate.

3. **The cable connecting the probe to the controller should also receive attention during installation:**

   a. A general rule of thumb is that cable should be kept as short as possible. No longer than 30' is preferrable. Beyond this, test to see if signal strength is sufficient. For long runs, a preamplifier may be needed to boost the signal.

   b. Proximity to mechanical devices emitting AC power and closeness to fluorescent lighting are other factors that can effect the signal passing through the cable, causing the pH readout to jump about. If the cable is to run parallel to AC power, place it in a conduit at least six (6") inches away from the AC power line. If crossing the AC power line, do so at 90°. If the cable has to run close to a fluorescent light, then a conduit might have to be considered. A triaxial cable can be provided as an option to the standard cable, which provides increased shielding for the signal.

   c. A cable can be broken. Treat accordingly. An indication of a broken cable is that the pH readout drifts, even after the controller has been checked out okay.

These guidelines are designed to minimize potential problems. **Œ**

OMEGA ENGINEERING, INC. gratefully acknowledges Prominent Fluid Controls, Inc. for permission to use portions of the article "Factors in Assessing pH System Requirements".

E

INDUSTRIAL EQUIPMENT

pH Control Systems

This technical article describes six basic types of pH control systems. It will help you identify the correct application and choice of pH instrumentation.

BATCH PROCESSING (System A)

This type of system uses an ON/OFF relay controller for "batch" processing. The system operates as follows:

1. Process solution is pumped into a tank until it is full.
2. Agitation or mixing commences and chemical is added until desired pH is reached. The relay controller turns on/off the chemical addition pump (or solenoid valve).
3. Process then flows out or is pumped out of tank.

In this system, level sensing of some type is very desireable to signal when the tank is full and empty, and to lock out the mixer and pH control when solution is not at the proper level. If mixing is poor, a repeat-cycle timer is recommended. The OFF time of the cycle will give the system some time to mix and reduce any eventual overshoot.

When sizing the final control element, note that there will be some delay between adding chemical and sensing the resulting pH change. If the final control element is oversized, the system will have unacceptable overshoot. The faster the mixing in the system, the less the delay and/or overshoot will be.

This simple system has one disadvantage; it does not easily handle a continuous flowing process.

CONTINUOUS WITH TANK (System B)

This type of system is very similar to SYSTEM A, but allows for continuous input. With continuous process input, an ON/OFF relay controller with latching or deadband is required. The deadband will hold the final control element on for a longer time than without deadband. This results in smooth operation without rapid cycling.

SYSTEM B does not require as much level control and monitoring as SYSTEM A, since the reaction tank outlet can be sized large enough and placed in the tank wall to make tank overflow unlikely.

The final control element can be a pump or an ON/OFF valve. Sizing of the final control element is complicated and depends on many factors. This is one situation where a titration curve can be invaluable. In many cases, it may be necessary to use two final control elements, each delivering different amounts of chemical and having different setpoints. For example, one valve may deliver 1 GPM of caustic below 3 pH and another may deliver 0.1 GPM of caustic below 4 pH.

Good mixing is very important in these systems and the mixer or agitation method should not be undersized. The retention time of the system (tank volume divided by GPM inflow) should be greater than 10 minutes. If it is much longer, a repeat-cycle timer may reduce overshoot.

This type of system can be fairly accurate, but in general it does not produce smooth outputs. The pH will tend to cycle between levels.

CONTINUOUS WITH TANK (System C)

This type of system uses a PROPORTIONAL GAIN controller with TIME PROPORTIONING (% CYCLE) OUTPUT for applications like those of SYSTEM B, except that the delay time between chemical addition and sensing is at least one minute. This might occour where the solution flows through a long tank, a trough or series of tanks.

The time proportioning (% cycle) output is a switch closure that activates a solenoid valve or pump. The controller analog output is fed to an electronic "percent of cycle timer" to electrically adjust the "ON" time from 0 to 100%. The time base of the cycle timer is electrically adjustable from a few seconds to a few minutes. The chemical delivery to the system is a series of "shots" of chemical. If not enough chemical is being added, the controller output will affect the cycle timer to lengthen the "ON" time and shorten the "OFF" time.

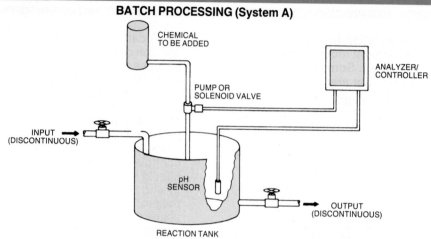

BATCH PROCESSING (System A)

CHEMICAL TO BE ADDED

ANALYZER/CONTROLLER

PUMP OR SOLENOID VALVE

INPUT (DISCONTINUOUS)

pH SENSOR

OUTPUT (DISCONTINUOUS)

REACTION TANK

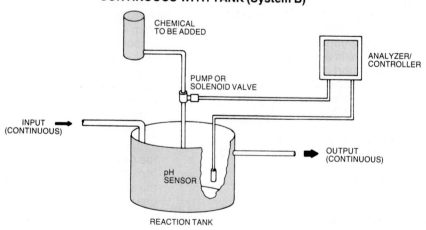

CONTINUOUS WITH TANK (System B)

CHEMICAL TO BE ADDED

ANALYZER/CONTROLLER

PUMP OR SOLENOID VALVE

INPUT (CONTINUOUS)

pH SENSOR

OUTPUT (CONTINUOUS)

REACTION TANK

CONTINUOUS WITH TANK (System C)

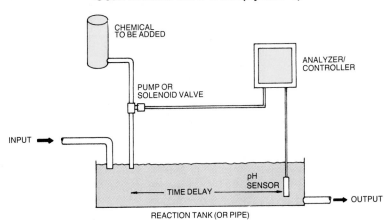

CHEMICAL TO BE ADDED

ANALYZER/ CONTROLLER

PUMP OR SOLENOID VALVE

INPUT →

pH SENSOR

← TIME DELAY →

→ OUTPUT

REACTION TANK (OR PIPE)

The cycle time should usually be less than the delay time of the system so that a series of shots are in the tank and gradually mixing. By the time chemical reaches the sensor, it should be mixed enough so that the sensor does not measure large variations in pH.

The final control element should be sized so that it cannot deliver more than five times the amount of chemical required at the maximum system load.

CONTINUOUS, ON-LINE CONTROL (System D)

This type of system uses a PROPORTIONAL GAIN controller with an ANALOG OUTPUT for two general types of pH control where the pH is to be adjusted only slightly or to a value away from 7 pH (less than 4 pH or more than 10 pH). The system consists of the following elements:

1. A pH sensor which senses the pH of the final product.

2. An analyzer/controller which provides an analog control signal.

*3. A transducer that produces a pneumatic signal proportional to the analog control signal.

*4. A pneumatic valve which delivers reagent to the process.

5. A mixing device placed between the chemical delivery point and the pH sensor.

* The transducer and pneumatic valve may be replaced by an electrically controlled pump or valve.

Two very important points of this system are the mixing and the delay

time between adding chemical and sensing the result of the addition. The mixing must be thorough and the delay time should not be more than a few seconds. A long delay time will result in the process pH cycling back and forth about the desired setpoint.

When solution is flowing through a pipe, an excellent mixing device to consider is a "static mixer". This device provides good mixing in a very short time. By injecting chemicals at the mixer input and placing the pH sensor at the mixer output, the two most significant problem areas of this type of system are eliminated.

An inherent characteristic of this system is that the actual controller pH setpoint will not be the same as the desired process pH value. The difference may not be large, but there will be some difference.

SYSTEM E

This type of system is the same as SYSTEM D except that it uses a

TWO-MODE controller in place of the proportional gain controller. The two-mode controller is much more complex than the proportional gain (one-mode) controller and should be used if there is doubt about the proportional gain controller's performance.

The integral (reset) function of the two-mode controller will try to adjust the process to the desired setpoint if it is physically possible to do so.

The two-mode controller also has a sample/hold feature (transit time) that allows it to control a process with as much as 8 minutes of delay time from chemical addition point to actual sensing.

SYSTEM F

This type of system uses the two-mode controller of SYSTEM E with the ON/OFF control element of SYSTEM C. This hybrid system is recommended for applications where accuracy of control is important, process delay times of 1 to 8 minutes exist and the chemical to be added is abrasive or tends to clog small openings (lime slurry, for example). For this reason, an ON/OFF valve is preferred over the proportional valve to avoid erosion of its internal parts and to provide more reliable reagent addition.

OMEGA ENGINEERING, INC. gratefully acknowledges Great Lakes Instruments, Inc. for permission to reprint the bulletin "pH Control Systems".

CONTINUOUS, ON-LINE CONTROL (System D)

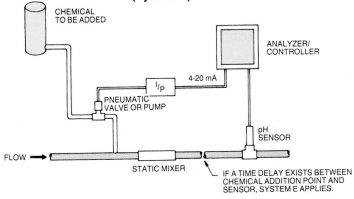

CHEMICAL TO BE ADDED

ANALYZER/ CONTROLLER

4-20 mA

I/P

PNEUMATIC VALVE OR PUMP

pH SENSOR

FLOW →

STATIC MIXER

IF A TIME DELAY EXISTS BETWEEN CHEMICAL ADDITION POINT AND SENSOR, SYSTEM E APPLIES.

E

INDUSTRIAL CONTROL SYSTEMS

pH Controller/Recorders and Recorders

MADE IN USA

1 YEAR WARRANTY

Model PHCN-54-ORP

$1102

Shown

Signal Conditioner Transmitter Included with All Models

- **LCD Display and Digital Set Point Switches**
- **Includes Two-wire 4 to 20 mA Transmitter Signal Conditioner**
- **Accepts either pH Electrode Input or 4 to 20 mA Input**
- **Adjustable Deadband 1% to 50%**
- **Time Delay Option**
- **NEMA-4X Enclosure**

The PHCN-50 Series of pH recorders and controllers provides a low cost and versatile method of measuring, controlling and recording pH levels of various industrial and chemical processes. Featuring an extensive list of standard features, the PHCN-50 series includes a digital pH display, digital switches for alarm set points, remote or integral mounting of pH signal conditioner/transmitter, 10 amp relays, and front panel adjustable deadband pots. The signal conditioner/transmitter module may be mounted inside the recorder controller or it may be mounted externally in the waterproof enclosure provided.

Specifications
Display

Range: 0 to 14 pH available, see optional accessories
Resolution: 0.01 pH, 1 mV
Accuracy: ±0.01 pH, ±1 mV
Repeatability: ±0.01 pH, ±1 mV
Display: ½" 3½ digit LCD

Controller

Set point accuracy: 1.5% of span

Set point resolution: 0.1 pH, 10.0 mV
Contact rating: SPST, 10 A, 117 V ac
Deadband range: 1% to 50% of span, adjustable
Time delay: 1 to 11 min.
Power: 120/240 V ac
Automatic Temperature Compensaton: 1000 ohm Pt RTD

Recorder

Ranges: 2 to 12 pH or 0 to 14 pH, 0 to 1000 mV
Resolution: 0.1 pH per minor lateral division, 10 mV per minor lateral division
Accuracy: ±0.2 pH
Response time: 1 s

All models shown on Pages E-7 and E-8 include the Model K79 Pocket Thermometer at no additional charge, for quick temperature measurements.

E-7

Model PHCN-53

$1139
Shown

**Electrodes Sold Separately
Beginning on Page E-25.**

PHCN-50 pH Recorder   **$744**
The pH recorder includes digital display, recorder calibration adjustment. Accepts one electrode input. pH range is 2 to 12. (Not Shown)

PHCN-51 pH Controller   **$745**
A basic pH controller, it includes a digital display, 2 digital setpoints for high/low alarm, adjustable deadband, two 10A relays. Accepts one electrode input. pH range 2 to 12. (Not Shown)

PHCN-52 Controller/Recorder $1065
The PHCN-52 is a combination of the PHCN-50 and 51 in one instrument. It accepts one electrode that drives the recorder, controller and digital display. (Not Shown)

PHCN-53 Controller/Recorder $1139
This instrument combines the features of the PHCN-52 and

additionally accepts two independent pH electrodes that perform separate functions. One electrode input drives the digital display and controller, the other drives the pH recorder. The recorder electrode may be placed downstream from the control point to record the adjusted values.

PHCN-54 Dual pH Controller $1102
A very versatile unit, the PHCN-54 can accept two separate electrode inputs and can adjust pH at two separate locations. When one of the two controllers is configured with the ORP option, it may be used for cyanide destruction or chrome reduction.

PHCN-55 Battery Powered Recorder   **$930**
Perfect for use in hostile environments and remote locations, the battery powered pH recorder is enclosed in a NEMA 4X enclosure. It

uses a 6V rechargeable battery that may be left unattended for about 2 weeks. (Not Shown)

Optional Accessories

Time Delay—Add the suffix "TD" to part number. A safety feature that warns the operator of system malfunction when pH is not adjusted in predetermined time limit. The timer is adjustable from 1 to 11 minutes.   **$93**

ORP Option—Add suffix "ORP" to part number. The ORP option allows the PHCN-50 series to accept an input from an ORP electrode. The measuring range is 0 to 1000 mV and digital setpoints are adjustable from 0 to 99% of the 1000 mV span.   **$42**

0 to 14 pH Option—Add the suffix "-14" to the part number   **$42**

**Replacement chart paper
PHCN-45 CHART**   **$10**

Versatile Microprocessor-Based pH Controller

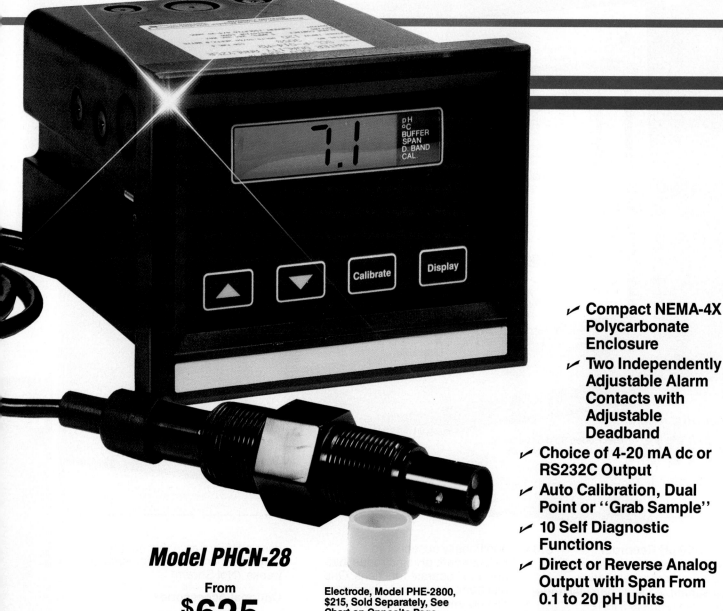

Model PHCN-28

From

$625

Electrode, Model PHE-2800, $215, Sold Separately, See Chart on Opposite Page.

✔ **Compact NEMA-4X Polycarbonate Enclosure**
✔ **Two Independently Adjustable Alarm Contacts with Adjustable Deadband**
✔ **Choice of 4-20 mA dc or RS232C Output**
✔ **Auto Calibration, Dual Point or "Grab Sample"**
✔ **10 Self Diagnostic Functions**
✔ **Direct or Reverse Analog Output with Span From 0.1 to 20 pH Units**
✔ **CSA Approved**

The OMEGA PHCN-28 microprocessor pH controller features auto buffering, solution temperature compensation, self-diagnostics and communication capabilities. Designed with the end-user in mind, this controller is user friendly and easy to operate. Four tactile membrane keypads allow for the selection and input of set-up parameters, input of calibration data and alarm setpoint adjustments. The two 5 A, 230 Vac relays can be configured as high/low, high/high or low/low.

The PHCN-28 is offered with a choice of an isolated 4-20 or 0-20 mA dc output (field selectable) or an RS232C interface with a non-isolated 0-5 V analog output. The analog output is flexible enough to be used as either a proportional control output or recorder output. The self-diagnostics of the PHCN-28 can alert the user to such conditions as internal circuitry malfunction, pH out of range, pH slope out of normal range, ATC short or open, or electrode failure to stabilize in buffer. The unit also employs a "watch-dog" timer which prevents memory loss in the event of a power surge.

The PHCN-28 has an integral pre-amplifier and is designed for use with the PHE-2800 gel filled, double junction combination electrode with ATC. For locations where the electrode and controller must be separated by more than 50 ft, the PHCN-28-PA external pre-amplifier should be considered. The unit features a rugged NEMA-4X polycarbonate enclosure. If an application requires an electrode other than the PHE-2800, then the PHCN-28-PA must be used. In this case a Pt100 is necessary for ATC (see page E-25).

NEW!

Pre-Amplifier, Model PHCN-28-PA, Sold Separately, $319, See Chart Below.

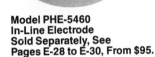

Pumps, PHP-200/210 Series, Sold Separately, See Pages H-3 and 4, From $512

Model PHE-6510 Submersible Electrode Sold Separately, See Pages E-28 to 30, From $95.

Model PHE-5460 In-Line Electrode Sold Separately, See Pages E-28 to E-30, From $95.

Model PHE-4580 Bypass Electrode Sold Separately. See Pages E-28 to 30, From $95.

Specifications

Ranges: −4 to 16 pH, −100 to 200°C
Resolution: 0.01 pH, 0.1°C
Temperature Compensation: Automatic
0 to 100°C, Pt100 ohm RTD
pH Accuracy: ±0.02 pH over range, −4 to 16 pH
Temp Accuracy: ±0.25°C over 0 to 100°C
Stability: ±0.01 pH, ±1 mV ORP over 30 days non-cumulative
Sensitivity: ±0.01 pH, ±1 mV ORP
Repeatibility: ±0.01 pH, ±1 mV ORP
Ambient Temperature Coefficient: ±0.002 pH/°C
Power Input: 120 V 50/60 Hz 8 Watts, 240 V 50/60 Hz 8 Watts, jumper selectable (requires fuse change)
Outputs: 4-20 mA dc isolated, RS232C with 0-5 V non-isolated
Output Span: Any 0.1 to 20 pH span
(0.1 pH increments) selectable reverse or direct acting
Alarms: 2 SPST electromechanical relays rated 5 A 230 Vac, resistive load; supplied as normally open; alarms can be configured H/H, H/L, L/L; alarm deadband fully adjustable over pH span
Dimensions: 4.45"H × 5.75"W × 6.95"D (113 x 146 x 177 mm)
Weight: 3 lbs (1.35 kg)

The PHCN-28 pH Controller Features Rugged NEMA-4X Enclosure for Panel or Wall Mounting

To Order *(Specify Model No.)*

Model No.	Price	Description
PHCN-28	$625	pH controller w/isolated 4-20 or 0-20 mA dc output
PHCN-28-D	730	pH controller w/RS232C interface and 0-5 V analog output (software available)
PHE-2800	215	Combination gel filled, double junction electrode w/ATC (integral Pt100); Kynar body construction; 1″ MNPT connections at both ends for insertion or submersion, max pressure 100 PSIG at 65°C. Overall electrode length 5.67″, insertion length 2.52″
PHCN-28-PA	319	Pre-amplifier for distances >50 ft or for use w/electrodes other than PHE-2800; NEMA-4X enclosure (6.94″ × 5.25″ × 3.25″)

E

INDUSTRIAL pH EQUIPMENT

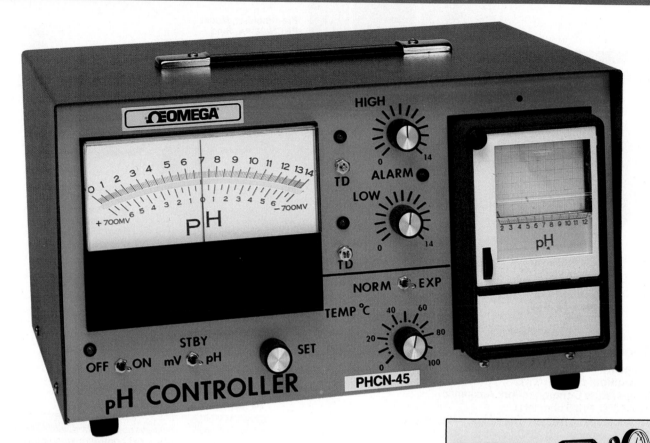

Model PHCN-45
$925*

* **Combines pH Measurement, Recording, and Controlling in One Unit**
* **Built-in 30 Day Chart Recorder**
* **High and Low Set Points**
* **Time Delay Safety Feature**
* **On/Off Control**

PHCN-45
The PHCN-45 combines pH measurement, recording and controlling in a single compact unit. pH and millivolt readings are displayed on a 6″ mirrored meter and the built-in chart recorder provides a 30 day record. In the standard mode, accuracies as great as ±0.05 pH and ±5 mV can be

achieved. If increased accuracy is required, a 10X scale expansion is provided. Easy to use front panel controls can set both the high and low limits for pH control function to within 0.1 pH and activate a visual alarm when the limits are exceeded. If desired, an adjustable Time Delay Safety Feature will shut off power to the output if the pH does not return to the control point within set time (0-10 minutes). This can prevent over addition of neutralizing chemicals due to probe or meter malfunction. A pulsed 5 VDC alarm output is available to drive a DC solid state relay to indicate this condition.

Optional Accessories:

Replacement chart paper
PHCN-45-CHART — $10
Suggested Electrodes: In-line
Disposable **PHE-5311-10** — $100
Submersible Disposable
PHE-6354-10 — $105

*Model K79 Pocket Thermometer included at no additional charge, for quick temperature measurements.

Specifications:

Accuracy: ±0.01 pH, .001 expanded
Meter Resolution: 0.1 pH, .01 expanded
Recorder Resolution: 0.2 pH, .02 expanded
Ranges: 0 to 14 pH, ±700 mV; (expanded 1.4 pH/±70 mV)
Temperature Compensation: Manual, 0 to 100°C
Connector: BNC or U.S. Standard
Adjustable Time Delay: 0 to 10 min
Power: 110 Vac, 50/60 Hz
Output Control Capacity: Two each 4 amp
Size: 7″ x 6″ x 4″ (PHCN-45)
Weight: 4 lb (PHCN-45)
Size: 12″ x 14″ x 6″ (PHCN-47 and 48)
Weight: 25½ lb (PHCN-47 and 48)
Recorder Specifications: 30 day chart, 1 inch/hour
Chart Width: 2½ in.
Chart Range: pH 2 to 12
Chart Accuracy: ±2% Full Scale
Chart Response: 1 second full scale

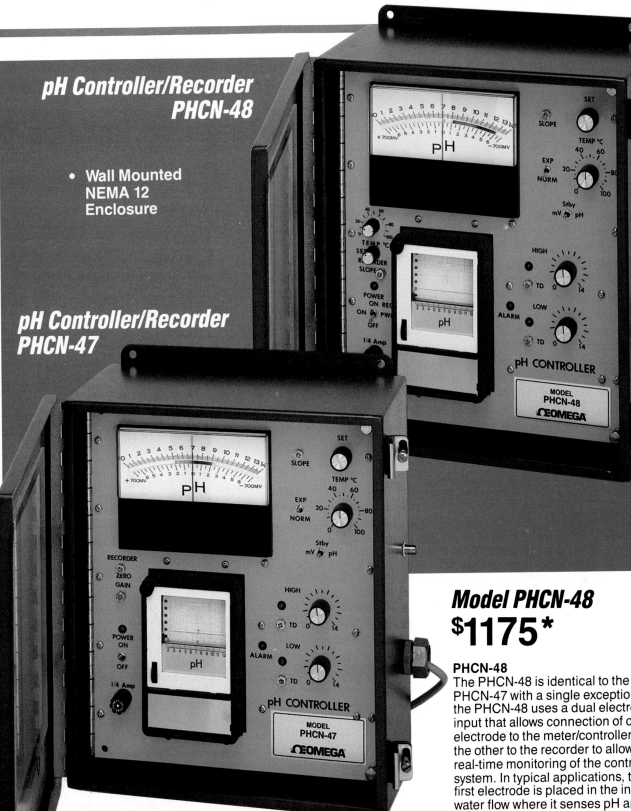

pH Controller/Recorder PHCN-48

- Wall Mounted NEMA 12 Enclosure

pH Controller/Recorder PHCN-47

Model PHCN-48
$1175*

Model PHCN-47
$1045*

PHCN-47
The PHCN-47 is a single electrode input model that combines the same functions as the PHCN-45 in a NEMA 12 type cabinet that may be used in a harsh environment.

PHCN-48
The PHCN-48 is identical to the PHCN-47 with a single exception: the PHCN-48 uses a dual electrode input that allows connection of one electrode to the meter/controller and the other to the recorder to allow real-time monitoring of the control system. In typical applications, the first electrode is placed in the input water flow where it senses pH and activates the control system. A second electrode located downstream drives the recorder to provide a continuous record of the pH of the effluent from the control system.

Microprocessor Based pH Controller PHCN-30

- **Monitors pH, Millivolts and Temperature**
- **On/Off or Proportional Control**
- **Optional Pulse Output**
- **Isolated 4 to 20 mA Output**
- **Direct Calibration from Front Panel Membrane Keyboard**
- **Memory Backup for Power Line Failures**
- **LOCK Feature prevents parameter changes**
- **¼ DIN Panel Mount**

From

$395

An excellent cost-effective pH controller, the PHCN-30 features a built-in microprocessor that stores, calculates and compensates for pH related measurement parameters. It recognizes electrode slope and offset, performs automatic slope calculations, and automatic temperature compensation.

For ease of operation, data is inputted directly from a front panel membrane keyboard that has audio feedback. Stored buffer values, a special data LOCK key and backup battery project the set up parameters.

5A relays are provided that incorporate high and low setpoints for on/off control or other equipment. In addition, a reversible 4 to 20 mA current output can be used to drive recorders or proportionally control auxiliary equipment.

An optional pulse output is available to drive equipment such as chemical feed pumps for proportional control applications.

Mounting and connecting the PHCN-30 is easy. It fits in a ¼ DIN panel cutout and connections are made via rear panel screw terminals and BNC connector.

Specifications:

Range: 0 to 14.00 pH, ±1,999 mV, −20 to 130°C
Accuracy: ±0.01 pH, ±0.1% mV, 0.5°C
Resolution: 0.01 pH, 1.0 mV, 0.1°C
Input Impedance: > 10^{12} ohms
Display: 0.5″ LCD

Power: 115/230 Vac, user selectable. 50/60 Hz
Temperature Compensation: automatic, 100 ohm Pt RTD, −20 to 130°C
Relay Output: 5A at 115 Vac, 2.5A at 230 Vac, 2 ea. SPDT
Set Point Hysteresis: ±0.1 pH
Current Output: 4 to 20 mA isolated
Input Connector: pH-BNC; all other connections—screw terminal
Dimensions: 3¾″ square panel cutout, ¼ DIN, 3.75″ deep
Weight: 1.75 lb

How To Order

Model No.	Options	Price
PHCN-30	—	$395
PHCN-31	Pulsed Output to Drive Pump	445

pH/ORP Controllers

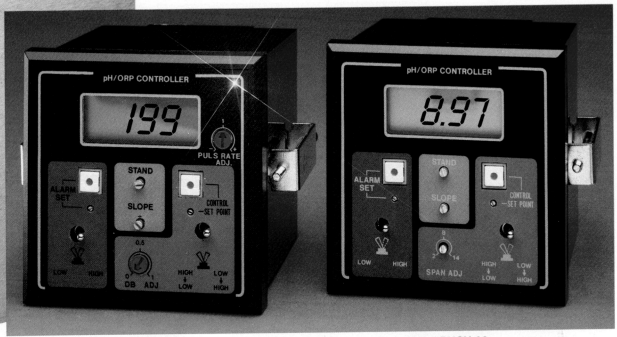

Model PHCN-33
$359

1 YEAR WARRANTY

Model PHCN-32
$295

Model PHCN-32

- **Isolated 4 to 20 mA Output**
- **Dual On/Off Relays**
- **Output Current Direction Switching**
- **User Selectable ORP/pH**

Model PHCN-33

- **Pulse Frequency Output Proportional to Ion Concentration**
- **Compatible with PHP-90 Series Pumps**
- **Output Current Direction Switching**
- **Dual On/Off Relays**
- **User Selectable ORP/pH**

The PHCN-32 and PHCN-33 are ¼ DIN panel mounted controllers for both pH and ORP applications. The PHCN-32 features both dual on/off relays and a 4 to 20 mA output, and an independent front panel selectable high/low alarm. For ease of operation, the output current span may be adjusted from the front panel. A large LCD display indicates setpoint and reading. Control direction (acid to base or base to acid) may also be selected via a front panel toggle switch. For versatility, the PHCN-32 is user switchable for either pH or ORP applications.

For precise pH control, the PHCN-33 features a pulse frequency proportional output that is exponentially scaled over 2 pH units. The PHCN-33 will directly control the PHP-90 Series pumps to form a proportional control chemical metering system. A deadband adjust is provided for manual reset control of the proportional bandwidth of 2 pH units. For conditions requiring alarm capability, a front panel selectable high/low control is provided. Control direction selection and easy switching of pH/ORP assures that the PHCN-33 will function in a wide range of control environments. In addition to the pulse output, a pair of relays is provided for on/off control.

Common Specifications:

Range: pH 0 to 14.00, ±1999 mV
Resolution: 0.01 pH, 1.0 mV
Accuracy: 0.01 pH, 0.1% mV
Input Impedance: > 10^{12} ohms
Temperature Compensation: 100 ohm Pt RTD, Auto 0 to 100°C
Connections: pH- BNC, ATC- stripped leads, relays- stripped leads
Relays: 2 ea. SPDT relays, rated 5 A at 115 Vac, 2.5 A at 230 Vac
Power: 115/230 Vac switchable
Size: 3.8″ x 3.8″ x 4.3″ (¼ DIN)
Weight: 2 lb

PHCN-32
Current Output: Isolated 4 to 20 mA over span
Load Resistance: 600 ohms minimum
Isolation Voltage: 500 Vdc minimum

PHCN-33
Dead Band (Reset) Adjustment Range: 0.05 to 1 pH, 5 mV to 100 mV
Proportional Bandwidth: 2 pH, 200 mV
Output Pulse Frequency: 60 to 120 pulses/min.

MICROPROCESSOR pH CONTROLLER
PHCN-2031

PHE-8000 Sensor sold separately.

From

$585

- **Accepts 4 to 20 mA Input**
- **Easy Operation With User Prompting**
- **Three Region Proportional Control**
- **Wide Variety of Output Options**
- **User Programmable for Acid and Base Feed Control**
- **Provides 24 Vdc for Transmitters**

For the optimum in pH control, the PHCN-2031 is a versatile user programmable on/off or proportional controller. The PHCN-2031 employs a three region "notch gain" technique to compensate for the wide range typical of pH control systems. Three region control means closer tracking of the non-linear pH gain so process control with the PHCN-2031 is much more precise than with single gain control systems. For maximum flexibility, models with the solid state relay output can be used in the following configurations: acid or base on/off, acid or base time proportioning, acid or base solid state relay pulsed output. The PHCN-2031 can be used with pulse metering or proportional type chemical feed equipment. When selected with the 4 to 20 mA output option, the outputs are acid or base 4 to 20 mA. The voltage output option selection

is acid or base 0 to 5 Vdc. Finally, the open collector output option may be used as acid or base open collector control. Adjustable transfer delay is available to minimize reagent waste by preventing transfer between feeders until after a selectable timed interval. Two electromechanical alarm/timer relays are also included. For ease of programming, the PHCN-2031 has a color coded vacuum fluorescent alphanumeric display and eight key touchpad operator interface. In addition to numerical operating information, this unique display shows key words to prompt, inform, direct and query the operator. All key strokes show immediate response on the display. Structured display sequences ensure correct and complete calibration, tuning and operation. Colored status, alarm and output indicators on the display keep the operator informed at all times.

Specifications:

General Accuracy: ±0.01 pH
Repeatability: ±0.01 pH
Resolution: 0.01 pH
Operating Temperature: 40 to 130°F
Input: 4 to 20 mA from pH transmitter
Power: 117 Vac ±10%
Memory Protection: 10 year life lithium battery

CONTROL

On/Off Deadband: Selectable at 0.25, 0.50 or 1.00 % of span
Cycle Time: 1 to 60 s, 1 s resolution

Reset (Integral): 0.01 to 20.00 rpm, 0.01 rpm resolution
Anti-Reset Windup: standard, inhibits automatic reset when the pH input is outside of the proportional band
Rate (derivative): 0.01 to 5.00 min., 0.01 min. resolution
Gain Breakpoints: set to same precision as pH setpoint
Pulse Frequency: 0 to 200 pulse/min
Transfer Delay: 0 to 60 s, 1 s resolution
Auto/Manual: bumpless transfer standard. Each output settable in 1% increments, 0 to 100%

OUTPUT

Independent Control Outputs for Acid and Base Feed.
Solid State Relay: optically isolated SPST contacts, 0.03 to 1.0 amp at 90 to 240 Vac resistive
Open Collector: optically isolated SPST contacts. 80 Vdc max.
Current Output: 4 to 20 mA in 750 ohm max. load.
Voltage Output: 0 to 5 Vdc into 1000 ohm min load
Alarm/Timer Relays: two independent electromechanical. SPDT contacts rated 1 A at 120 Vac. Process and deviation alarms settable in display unit increments. Timer alarms can be on/off acting
Ramp and Soak Program: up to 8 ramp and soak segments of up to 100 h Auto repeat and assured soak included.

To Order:

Model No.	Price	Description
PHCN-2031	$585	Single Output
PHCN-2032	615	Dual Output

Dimensions

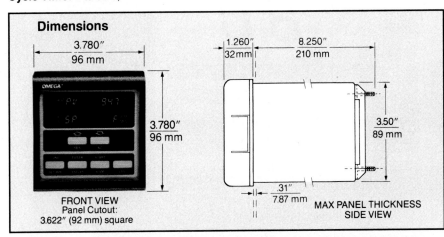

3.780″ / 96 mm
3.780″ / 96 mm

FRONT VIEW
Panel Cutout:
3.622″ (92 mm) square

1.260″ / 32 mm
8.250″ / 210 mm
3.50″ / 89 mm
.31″ / 7.87 mm

MAX PANEL THICKNESS
SIDE VIEW

Output Options (no additional charge)

Type	Ordering Suffix	
	Output 1	Output 2*
S.S. Relay	Standard	Standard
4 to 20 mA	-F1	-F2
0 to 5 Vdc	-DC1	-DC2
Open Collector	-OC1	-OC2

PHCN-2032 Only

Communications Options

Ordering Suffix	Price	Description
-D1	$ 50	Remote Analog Setpoint
-D2	195	RS-232-C Non-isolated
-D3	195	RS-232-C Isolated
-D4	195	RS-422 Non-isolated
-D5	195	RS-422 Isolated
-D6	50	Remote Start/Stop

Ordering Example:

Model PHCN-2032-F2-D3
Price: $580 + $195 = $775
Description: Dual Output Controllor with solid state relay and 4 to 20 mA outputs, and RS-232-C isolated communication option

PARAM CHECK
Advances all subroutines other than DISPLAY, one step at a time, in order to tune the controller, set ramp and soak intervals, or enter multi-setpoints.

DISPLAY
Advances the DISPLAY subroutine one step at a time, to show the present control parameters.

UP/YES
Increases displayed variable (i.e., set point) or is a positive response to displayed question.

DOWN/NO
Decreases displayed variable, or is a negative response to displayed question.

TUNE/RETURN
Calls up TUNE subroutine, or will return program to DISPLAY mode.

AUTO/MANUAL
Transfers control of outputs to and from automatic or manual control.

START/STOP
Turns the outputs on or off. Does not affect power to controller.

LAST
Allows user to back up within a sub-routine to review or modify previously set variables.

E — INDUSTRIAL EQUIPMENT

Microprocessor pH Controllers and Sensors

PHCN-80

$750
Isolated
4-20 mA Output

PHCN-80A

$650
Non-isolated
4-20 mA Output

✔ **Frequency Output**
✔ **Built-In Diagnostics**
✔ **One-touch Calibration of Standardization, Slope**
✔ **Easy Access High/Low Alarms**
✔ **4-20 mA Recorder Output**

Combining microprocessor efficiency, the ease of touch-sensitive control, and the flexibility for system expansion, the PHCN-80 is designed to give precise pH control for a broad range of applicatons. Pressure-sensitive switches allow instant checking of pH, mV and temperature, as well as "one-touch" calibration of standardization and slope. In addition, electrode degradation can be easily checked by actuating the mV switch while the sensor is in a 7 pH buffer solution, yielding an up-to-the minute indication of aging.

The unit's built-in diagnostic routines immediately alert you to pH and temperature malfunctions. The instrument's alarm relays

automatically activate pumps, valves or audible alarms. The on/off Control can be used for adding reagents to control pH in single-tank processing or, for continuous in-line or tank processing, you can change to (or add) single band proportional control without the need for an additional controller.

pH Sensors Sold Separately, See Chart Below.

Specifications:
Range: 0 to 14.0 pH, ±413 mV, 0 to 100°C
Accuracy: ±0.1 pH, ±1 mV, ±1°C
Repeatability: ±0.1 pH, ±3 mV, ±1°C
Resolution: 0.1 pH, ±3 mV, ±1°C
Input Impedance: 10^{12} ohms
Display: 3 digit LCD
Power: 110 Vac
Backup Battery Power: 3 Vdc Lithium Cell; lasts 2 years in ac source Power-down mode
Temperature Compensation: Automatic 0 to 100°C
Ambient Operating Temperature Range: 0° to 50°C
Alarm Relays: Dual SPDT, rated 3 A at 250 Vac or 3 A at 30 Vdc
Dimensions: 5.5″ × 5.5″ × 5.1″
Weight: 2.5 lb

Optional Accessory:
Pulse/Relay Module (required when pulse drives metering pump)
PHCN-81   **$150**

To Order *(Specify Model Number)*

Model	Price	Description	Cable
PHCN-83	$375	General Purpose pH Sensor for submersion with built-in preamp, ¾″ NPT	25 ft
PHCN-84	375	General Purpose pH Sensor in-line with built-in preamp, 1¼″ NPT	25 ft
PHCN-85	450	General Purpose pH Sensor (CPVC) for submersion with remote preamp (for use above 80°C),¾″ NPT	25 ft
PHA-86	40	Pipe Adaptor for in-line sensors	—

Microprocessor-Based Controllers

 MADE IN USA

 NEW!

pH CONTROLLER

From $675

✔ **Proportional 4-20 mAdc Output for Recording or Control**

✔ **Optional (Field Installable) Proportional Pulse Output for Chemical Metering Pumps**

✔ **Selectable Readouts of pH, mV and Temperature**

Housing is Molded, Glass-Filled Polypropylene. Electrode Rated to 100 PSI at 25°C, 25 PSI at 100°C

The PHCN-86 is the perfect controller for a variety of applications including waste-water treatment, plating, and food processing. The tactile feedback keypad allows access to readouts for pH, temperature and millivolts. Other features include sensor diagnostics, automatic temperature compensation, and dual alarms with adjustable hysteresis. Additionally, the controller has a current output of 0-20 mA or 4-20 mA for input to recorder, computer or other control device.

An optional plug-in circuit board, PHCN-88, offers a proportional pulse output to interface directly with chemical metering pumps.

pH Sensor

PHCN-87 Electrode $225

Alarm Hysteresis: Adjustable from 0.1 to 2.5 pH units
Alarm Relays: Dual SPST; 5A @ 250 Vac; 5A @ 30 Vdc
Power Requirements: 120/240 Vac ±10% 50/60 Hz
Output PHCN-86A: 4-20 mA, non-isolated (450 Ω max load)
Output PHCN-86: 4-20 mA, isolated (700 Ω max. load)
Input Isolation: 600V RMS
Enclosure Dimensions: 5.5"H × 5.5"W × 7.4"D
Materials: ABS
Rating: NEMA 4X (watertight corrosion resistant)
Optional Pulse Output: Dual (acid, base) selectable 0-100, 0-50, 0-25 ppm to drive pumps

To Order (Specify Model Number)

Model No.	Price	Description
PHCN-86A	$675	pH controller, non-isolated 4-20 mA output
PHCN-86	750	pH controller, isolated 4-20 mA output
PHCN-87	225	High range pH sensor, with internal temp. compensating element (5-100°C) and integral pre-amp, in-line 1¼″ NPT

Order controller and electrode separately; use PHCN-87 electrode only.

Accessories

Model No.	Price	Description
PHCN-86S	$25	Submersion adaptor kit, requires ¾″ NPT pipe (customer supplied) and special coax cable
PHAC-86-(**)	25	pH coax cable
PHCN-88	150	Pump pulser board

** Specify length in feet (from 4 to 12 feet).
Ordering Example: *PHAC-86-8 indicates 8 ft coax cable, $25.*

Specifications
Reference Operating Conditions: 25°C; 10-30% RH; 120 Vac
Display: 3½ digit LCD, .7″ characters
Display Range: 0 to 14 pH, ±500 mV, −10 to 100°C
Accuracy, FS: ±0.02 pH, ±6 mV, ±1.0°C
Repeatability: ±0.01 pH, ±0.3 mV, ±0.1°C
Temp Compensation: Automatic from 0 to 100°C 3KΩ resistive sensor
Alarm: Programmable; 0 to 14 pH

Four Channel Microprocessor pH Controller and Sensor

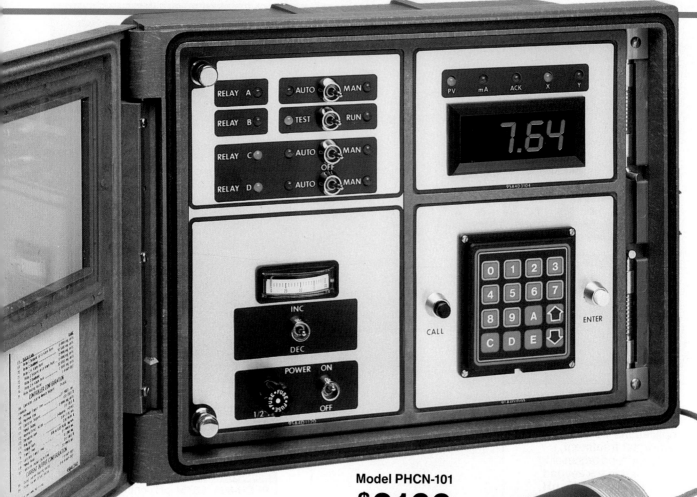

Model PHCN-101

$2160

Encapsulated pH Sensor with Integral Two-Wire Transmitter

- **Differential Electrode Technique Minimizes Errors Caused by Ground Loop Currents, Reference Electrode Contamination and Precipitate Build-up**
- **Integral Two-Wire Transmitter**
- **Complete Encapsulation Eliminates Moisture Problems**
- **Automatic Temperature Compensation**
- **Convertible for Flow-Through or Submersion**

The PHE-8000 is an industrial pH sensor that utilizes a unique differential electrode measurement. The sensor is comprised of two sensor circuits whose voltages are measured and transmitted by amplifiers. A temperature sensitive resistor in the unit automatically compensates for process temperature variations. To further enhance the PHE-8000's capabilities, a 4 to 20 mA transmitter is built in to allow remote sensing without any additional equipment.

Model PHE-8000

$490

Specifications:

Range: 0 to 14 pH
Wetted Materials: vinyl ester body
Temperature Range: −5 to 80°C in steel fitting; −5 to 95°C in CPVC fitting
Max Pressure: 100 PSIG in plastic fitting, 75 PSIG in steel fitting
Max Flow Rate: 10 fps
Sensitivity: < 0.005 pH
Output Span: 0.95 mA per pH
Connector: stripped leads, 10 feet cable
Threads: 1½″ NPT both ends
Power Required: 24 to 40 Vdc
Dimensions: 7⅞″ long

relays with auto/manual switches which allow the operator to disable or manually activate each relay and two control relays without the switches. Dual alarm phasing may be selected to operate the relay in response to increasing, decreasing and increasing and decreasing values. Each relay has an adjustable setpoint and deadband and a repeat cycle timer.

Specifications

Display: alphanumeric, ½″ four character LED

Scale: 0 to 9999 engineering units for each input channel

Operating Conditions: −30 to 50°C

Control Setpoints and Deadbands: 0 to 100%; 0.5 to 50% of full scale

Relays: 3 A continuous, SPST solid-state

Power: 115 V ac, 230 V ac available

Analog Inputs: 24 V dc power supply to drive four two-wire transmitters which produce 4 to 20 mA output or the unit can accept four 0 to 20 or 4 to 20 mA signals (isolated) 50 ohm input impedance, 1100 ohms max. per channel Switch closure input: SPST

Analog Outputs: two voltages, four current signals (isolated)
0 to 5 V dc, 50 K ohms min. load
0 to 1 mA, 100 ohms max. load
1 to 5 V dc, 50 K ohms min. load
0.2 to 1.0 mA, 100 ohms max. load
0 to 20 mA, 500 ohms max. load
4 to 20 mA, 500 ohms load

Scale Expand: analog output signals can represent a selected portion of the input signal. This must be greater than 5% of the input span and may be established anywhere in that span.

Controller Outputs: Current; one isolated 0 to 20 or 4 to 20 mA signal (user selectable), 500 ohms max load % cycle; one switched signal solid state relay output; 3 A rating

Pulsed; one switched signal, 30 to 600 pulses per minute, solid state relay output, 3 A rating

General: Sensitivity: 0.05% of span; Stability: 0.05% of span per 24h, non-cumulative
Non-linearity: 0.05% of span (electrical)
Repeatability: 0.05% of span
Temp. Drift: Zero, 60 ppm/°C; Span, 90 ppm/°C
Response time: 2s
Weight: 12 lb

Microprocessor Based Controller PHCN-101

- **NEMA-4X Mounted PID Controller with Differential Algorithm for pH Control**
- **16 bit Microprocessor**
- **Pushbutton Calibration and Range Expand**
- **Four DC mA and Two DC Voltatge Output Signals Standard**
- **Software Stored in Field-Replaceable EPROMs**
- **Supplies Power (24 V dc) to Four Current Loops**
- **Relays for Control or Alarms with Repeat Cycle**

The microprocessor based PHCN-101 Controller is a versatile instrument which can be used to monitor and control up to four 4 to 20 mA process variables with three non-linear and one linear input. For pH control, a PID control with a differential algorithm allows up to 16 points to characterize a neutralization curve. In addition, the PHCN-101 can be used to control a number of processes thanks to adaptive gain, PID and a flow scaled output.

Program software is stored in a convenient field replaceable module and the PHCN-101 features a battery backup memory in case of lost instrument power. To ensure long operating life in field conditions, the controller is housed in a NEMA 4X universal mount enclosure and the modular electronics swing out for easy servicing. Four solid state relays are provided: two control

pH and Conductivity Controller/Analyzer

PHE-8000 sensor sold separately.

Model PHCN-105
$710

Process Controller/Analyzer

- **Quick Field Configurability to Change Measurement Parameters**
- **Digital and 20 Segment Bargraph Display**
- **Accepts 4 to 20 mA Signal and Provides 24 Vdc for Transmitters**
- **Two Control Relays with Adjustable Deadband**
- **Non-isolated 0 to 1 mA, 0 or 4 to 20 mA, 0 to 5 Vdc Outputs**
- **NEMA 4X Enclosure**
- **On/Off or Proportional only Control with Selectable Current or Pulse Output**

The PHCN-105 is a unique instrument that combines the functions of a controller and an analyzer. For versatility, the PHCN-105 features quick field configurability with programmable jumpers to change measurement parameters and easy access controls for calibration, range expansion, relay control and alarms. It can accept any 4 to 20 mA transmitter signal and display the signal in engineering units with a measuring scale span of 100 to 1999 counts and provide 24 Vdc to power a two wire transmitter. For at-a-glance monitoring, the PHCN-105 features a 3½ digit LCD display with a 20 segment analog display bargraph. Designed for use in harsh environments, the controller is housed in a NEMA 4X housing with brackets that allow surface, panel or horizontal pipe mounting. Two control relays are provided with an adjustable deadband, outputs are non-isolated 0 to 1 mA, 0 to 20 mA, 4 to 20 mA and 0 to 5 Vdc.

Specifications:
Display: 3½ digit LCD 0.7″ with annunciators for engineering units and relay status; and 20 segment bargraph to simulate analog display.

Display Span: for 4-20 mA input, ±1999 counts

Display Units: C, ppm, pH, Mohm/cm, mS/cm, mV; (user selectable)

Enclosure: NEMA 4X, ½ DIN

Sensitivity: 0.1% of span

Stability: 0.1% of span per 24 h

Repeatability: 0.05 mA

Inputs: 4 to 20 mA

Outputs: Non expandable, non-isolated 0 to 1 mA, 0 to 5 V dc, 0/4 to 20 mA

Range Expand: Analog outputs can be made to represent a selected part of the input current. This must be greater than 1.6 mA.

Relays: Control setpoints—adjustable 0 to 100% f.s., Control deadbands—adjustable 0 to 50% f.s., Contact rating—SPDT, 5 A 115/220 Vac, 5 A at 30 Vdc resistive

Dimensions: 5.67″ x 5.67″ x 5.37″ 5.43″ square cutout

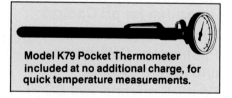

Model K79 Pocket Thermometer included at no additional charge, for quick temperature measurements.

Options:
Pulse converter card PHCN-106 $175
Converts 4 to 20 mA output to 0 to 100 pulses/minute, compatible with PHP-90 Series Pumps page F-10.

Analog To Frequency Converter/Controller
Model PHCN-20

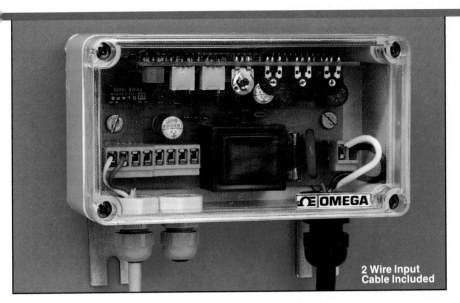

2 Wire Input Cable Included

The PHCN-20 accepts an analog 4 to 20 mA signal and converts it into a switch selectable proportional or inversely proportional variable frequency pulse train, which can be used to control OMEGA® PHP-90 Series Solenoid-Operated Metering Pumps. The PHCN-20 is designed for applications where a frequency signal is needed to drive a metering pump, or where the pulse output is started/stopped automatically when the input passes a preselected setpoint, such as:

- pH proportional injection of acids in effluent treatment to achieve a pre-selected pH, using a pH transmitter or meter with an analog current output

- Turbidity control of flocculants in waste water treatment

The PHCN-20 converter comes in a NEMA 4X enclosure, which may be wall or panel mounted for convenience.

Specifications:
Power: 110 Vac, +20 −15%, 45 to 62 Hz
Power Rating: 5W
Input Signal: 4 to 20 mA STD; 0 to 20 mA, 0 to 1 V or 0 to 10 Vdc also available; consult Sales for ordering information
Input Impedance: 33 ohms, proportional; 39 ohms inversely proportional
Output: Dry contact to activate PHP-90 Series Solenoid-Operated Metering Pump in external control mode
Contact Load: 24 Vdc max., resistive load only
Maximum Frequency: 65 to 120 pulses per minute, adjustable
Control Action: Proportional or inversely proportional, switch selectable
Setpoint: Adjustable between 1 and 100% of input signal; pulse output starts/stops automatically when input level passes setpoint
Non-linearity: 1%
Protection: NEMA 4X
Dimensions: 3¾″ H x 5⁵⁄₁₆″ W x 2¹³⁄₁₆″ D
Weight: 0.9 lb

Model PHCN-20

$418

1 YEAR WARRANTY

Pulse Frequency pH Controller
Model PHCN-23 $1533

1 YEAR WARRANTY

The PHCN-23 pH Controller features two exponentially scaled pulse frequency outputs, which control two PHP-90 series chemical metering pumps (for an acid and base) to precisely control pH level. Both setpoints are independently adjustable, and the frequency output signal is scaled over an adjustable bandwidth of 1 to 3 pH units. The PHCN-23 has a splashproof, gasketed, glass fiber reinforced Noryl® case, which can be either wall or panel mounted. The PHCN-23 also has an analog current output, 4 to 20 mA, proportional to the 0 to 14 pH range.

Specifications:
Accuracy: ±0.03 pH
Resolution: 0.01 pH
Display: LCD, 0.00 to 14.00 pH
Control Range: 0 to 14 pH
Pulse Frequency Outputs: Two each, potential free contact outputs for control of two PHP-90 Series Chemical Metering Pumps; Frequency from 10 to 100 pulses/min., exponentially scales over an adjustable bandwidth of 1 to 3 pH units; control direction opposite to each other (one each for acid and base)
Setpoints: Independent, adjusted over full 0 to 14 pH range
pH Electrode Connection: BNC
Input Impedance: $>5 \times 10^{12}$ ohms
Temperature Compensation: Fixed at 25°C or automatic with 100 ohm Pt RTD
Analog Output: 4 to 20 mA, isolated, scaled to 0 to 14 pH
Size: 5¾″ x 7″ x 5″

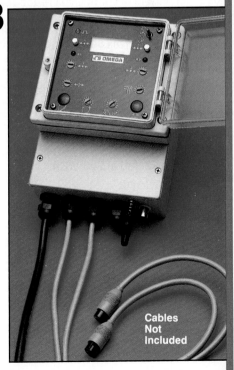

Cables Not Included

Waterproof and Panel Mount pH Meters

Model PHW-71
with Alarms
$780
Shown

Model PHW-70
$590
Not Shown

Waterproof pH Meters

The PHW-70 and PHW-71 Waterproof pH Meters have been developed for use in damp and dirty environments and are housed in chemically resistant polycarbonate cases waterproofed to IP54 standard. All inputs and outputs from the units are through waterproof compression glands and access to the instrument controls is via a hinged clear front panel. In addition, the Model PHW-71 has two independent alarm points each having its own relay and front panel LED indicator. The relay contacts are rated at 240V/2A. Both models measure pH and millivolts, and in the pH mode automatic temperature compensation is provided.

Specifications

Ranges: 0 to 14.0 pH, 0 to 14.00 pH, ±1999 mV
Accuracy: ±0.02pH, ±0.1 pH, 1 mV
Resolution: 0.1 pH, 0.01 pH, 1 mV
Automatic Temperature
Compensation: 0 to 100°C, 100 ohm Pt RTD
Input Impedance: 10^{13} ohms
Recorder Output: 4-20 mA
Power: 110/240 V ac user switchable
Dimensions: 8.9″ × 8.7″ × 4.9″
Weight: 4.4 lb

1 YEAR
WARRANTY

Model PHPM-70
$489
Not Shown

Panel Mounted pH Meters

The PHPM Series of panel mounted pH meters offer user selectable pH or millivolt readouts enabling them to be used for a wide variety of pH and redox measurements. The units are housed in rugged steel panel mounting DIN sized case and are installable from the front to allow fitting in limited access areas.
To prevent accidental adjustment of the buffer and slope controls, they are recessed on the front panel. The instruments have automatic temperature compensation from 0 to 100°C. In addition, the PHPM-71 features a Hi/Lo alarm system that consists of two totally independent alarm points, each having its own relay and front panel LED indicator. The relay contacts are rated at 240 V/2 A.

Specifications

Ranges: 0 to 14.00 pH, ±1999 mV
Accuracy: ±0.02 pH, ±0.1 pH, 1 mV
Resolution: 0.01 pH, 0.1 pH, 1 mV
Automatic Temperature
Compensation: 0 to 100°C, 100 ohm Pt|RTD
Input Impedance: 10^{13} ohms
Recorder Output: 4 to 20 mA
Power: 110/240 V ac user switchable
Dimensions: 3.8″ × 3.8″ × 5.9″
Weight: PHPM-70 2.4 lb, PHPM-71 3.3 lb
Connector: Stripped Leads

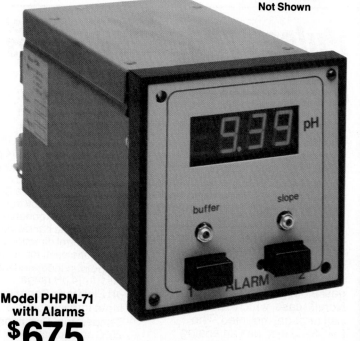

Model PHPM-71
with Alarms
$675
Shown

Digital Panel pH Controller
Model PHCN-36

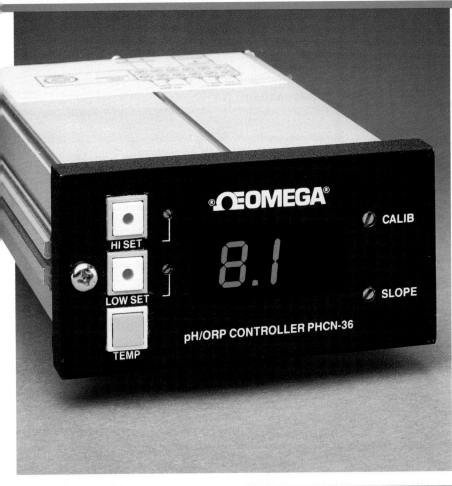

- ✔ **High and Low Setpoints**
- ✔ **Compact 1/8 DIN Panel Mount**
- ✔ **Internal Switching for pH or ORP**
- ✔ **8 Amp Relay Capacity**

The PHCN-36 is a compact 1/8 DIN panel mount controller that features automatic pH temperature compensation from 0 to 100°C with high and low setpoints on the front panel. Internal switching allows selection of pH or ORP measurements. To ensure reliability, the PHCN-36 utilizes a low power consumption design that increases reliability through reduced internal heating. Outputs are provided for a recorder and an 8A capacity relay. Temperature or pH may be read on the panel display.

Model PHCN-36

$216

PHE-1311 Gel Filled Electrode $54

Optional Accessories:
Suggested Electrodes (See electrode specifications Section E):
Submersible Disposable Electrode
PHE-6351-10-PT100   **$150**
In-line Disposable Electrode
PHE-5311-10-PT100   **$130**

Specifications:

Range: 0 to 14 pH, ±1990 mV, 0 to 100°C

Resolution: 0.1 pH, 10 mV, 1°C

Accuracy: 0.1 pH ±1 digit, 10 mV, 1°C

Recorder Output: 1400 mV, ±1990 mV, 1000 mV

Input Impedance: $>10^{12}$ ohms

Automatic Temperature Compensation: 0 to 100°C, requires 100 ohm Pt RTD

Connector: pH—BNC, Temperature — miniature phone jack

Control Output: Dual point, on/off for high and low setpoints

Deadband: ±0.1 pH for each setpoint

Relay Capacity: 2 ea. 8A at 117 Vac, 4A at 230 Vac, SPDT

Power: 115/230 Vac, 50/60 Hz

Size: 3.9″ x 2″ x 7″

Weight: 1.5 lb

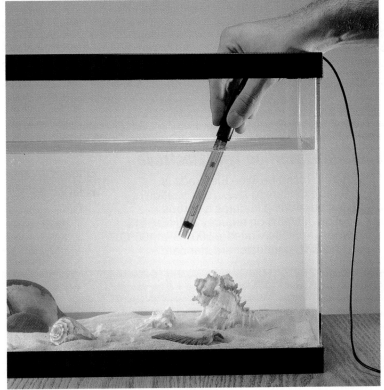

Industrial Electrodes

How to Order

Ordering Example:

PHE-6354	—	10	PT100
1		**2**	**3**

1) **Electrode part number**

2) **Cable length:**
   Standard cable length in feet shown in part number. For non-standard length, add $1 per foot. Maximum 50 feet.

3) **Temperature Compensation** (if required)
   See chart for available types.

   Termination for temperature compensator: Spade lugs standard.

4) **Standard connector:** BNC. Stripped leads available; add suffix "ST"

ATC Information

Temperature Compensator (ATC)	Add to Part Number	Used With	Page
100 ohm Platinum RTD	PT 100	PHTX-92 PHCN-36	F-6 E-24
1000 ohm Platinum RTD	PT1K	PHTX-1	F-5
700 series thermistor	TH700	PHTX-11	F-5
3000 ohm resistive sensor	R3K	PHTX-20SC	F-12

Submersible Disposable Electrodes

Submersible Disposable Electrodes are combination electrodes that are permanently potted into a 36" or 42" pipe. Ideally suited for measuring pH in drums, tanks and open streams, the electrode features an annular ceramic reference junction and is supplied with 10 foot cable with BNC connector.

HIGHLIGHTED MODELS IN STOCK FOR FAST DELIVERY

	Part No.	Length (inches)	Dia. (inches)	Body Mat'l.	pH Range	Temp. °C	R (megohms) at 25°C	Description	Price	Price w/ATC*
A	PHE-6354-10	42	1	CPVC	0-13	– 5 to 80	80	CPVC Body General Purpose ¾" CPVC Pipe (Schedule 80)	$105	126
A	ORE-6354-10	42	1	CPVC	± 5000 mV	– 5 to 80	—	ORP Pt Band General Purpose	137	—
B	PHE-6351-10	36	1¹⁄₁₆	ABS Pipe	0-13	0 to 80	50	ABS Body General Purpose	110	150
B	PHE-6352-10	36	1¹⁄₁₆	ABS Pipe	0-14	0 to 80	200	ABS Body High pH	110	150
B	PHE-6451-10	36	1¹⁄₁₆	ABS Pipe	0-13	0 to 80	50	ABS Body Double Junction	130	170
B	PHE-6452-10	36	1¹⁄₁₆	ABS Pipe	0-14	0 to 80	200	ABS Body Dbl. Junction High pH	130	170

* To order an electrode with automatic temperature compensation, see "ATC Information" chart at top of page.
Ordering Example: PHE-6354 indicates an electrode with ATC, 100 ohm Platinum RTD, **$126.**

High Temperature Insertion Type Electrode

The High Temperature Insertion Type Electrode is designed for periodic exposure to steam sterilization or continuous high temperature. It features a porous Teflon® liquid junction. Installation requires a PHEH-51S mounting gland which is pressure rated to 500 PSI at 100°C. 10ft cable length and BNC connector are standard

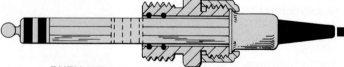

PHEH-51S
316SS — ¾" MNPT Mounting Glands **$100**
10 ft cable length and BNC connector are standard

Part No.	Length (inches)	Dia.	pH Range	Temp. °C	Reference Type	Body Material	R Megohms at 25°C	Application	Price	Price w/ATC*
PHE-5431-10	5"	12 mm	0-14	– 5 to 135°C	Ag/AgCl Double	Polyether Sulfone	150	General Purpose Steam Sterilizable	$102	$142
ORE-5431-10	5"	12 mm	—	– 5 to 135°C	Ag/AgCl Double	Polyether Sulfone	—	ORP (Redox)	117	157

* To order an electrode with automatic temperature compensation, see "ATC Information" chart at top of page.
Ordering Example: PHE-5431 indicates an electrode with ATC, 100 ohm Platinum RTD, **$142.**

Insertion/Submersion Combination Electrodes

The PHE-7151 series combination electrodes are ruggedly constructed; the outer body is ABS with ¾" MNPT threads at both ends. The maximum insertion length is 1.25". Electrodes are annular Teflon® liquid junction refillable and include 15 ft cable with BNC connector. For applications with temperatures up to 120°C, units are available in polyphenylene sulfide (PPS).***

HIGHLIGHTED MODELS IN STOCK FOR FAST DELIVERY

Part No.	Length (inches)	Dia. (inches)	pH Range	Temp. °C	Refill. or Gel	R (megohms) at 25°C	Description	Price	Price w/ATC*
PHE-7151-15	5.5	1.16	0-12	0 to 80	Refill.	400	Refillable General Purpose**	$100	$175
PHE-7351-15	5.5	1.16	0-12	0 to 80	Gel	400	Sealed General Purpose	90	175
PHE-7152-15	5.5	1.16	0-14	0 to 80	Refill.	1000	Refillable High pH Applications**	130	175
ORE-7151-15	5.5	1.16	—	0 to 80	Refill.	—	General Purpose Refillable ORP**	143	—

*Specify type of temperature sensor. See page E-25 for ordering information. **Model PHEH-71-4   48 inch extension for above ABS $30**

**Refill Solution PHFS-7151-4 4 oz Bottle $5
PHFS-7151-16 16 oz Bottle $12

***For polyphenylene sulfide body add the suffix "-PPS" to the part number and $50 to the price.
Ordering Example: *PHE-7151-15-PT100-PPS* indicates a refillable general purpose electrode, 15 ft cable with BNC connector, 100 ohm Platinum RTD, and polyphenylene sulfide body. Price: $175 + 50 = $225.

Inline Disposable Electrodes

OMEGA® inline combination electrodes mount on standard pipe tees for continuous pH or ORP monitoring. The electrode is constructed in a Kynar® housing with ½" MNPT threading. Probe insertion length is 1" and is able to withstand pressure up to 150 psi. 10 ft. cable length and BNC connector are standard. Dimensions: 127 × 25 mm.

CPVC Inline Disposable pH Electrodes

Also available, the CPVC Inline Disposable Electrode is ruggedly constructed to withstand up to 100 psi. Probe insertion length is 2" with ¾" diameter. A ¾" MNPT fitting is standard and is supplied with 10 ft. cable and a BNC connector. Dimensions: 168 mm × 25 mm

A

B

	Part No.	pH Range	Temperature Range	Notes	R Megohms at 25°C	Price	Price with ATC
A	PHE-5311-10	0-13	−5 to 100°C	General Purpose	50	$ 90	$130
A	PHE-5312-10	0-14	0 to 100°C	High pH	200	92	132
A	PHE-5411-10	0-13	−5 to 100°C	Double Junction	50	115	155
A	PHE-5412-10	0-14	0 to 100°C	Double Junction High pH	200	120	160
A	ORE-5311-10	ORP	−5 to 100°C	Platinum Band	—	105	—
A	ORE-5411-10	ORP	−5 to 100°C	Platinum Band Double Junction	—	114	—
A	ORE-5419-10	ORP	−5 to 100°C	Gold Disc Double Junction for Cyanide Applications	—	120	—
B	PHE-5316-10	0-13	−5 to 80°C	Sealed Ag/AgCl	50	80	120

*See page E-25 for ordering information. Automatic Temperature Compensation is not required with ORP (Redox) electrodes.

Heavy Duty Extension Cables For Industrial Electrodes

Part No. BNC to BNC	Length (feet)	Price
PHEC-B10HD	10	$34
PHEC-B25HD	25	50
PHEC-B50HD	50	76

E INDUSTRIAL EQUIPMENT

Industrial Electrodes

Twist Lock Industrial Electrodes and Adaptors

Specially designed to withstand harsh industrial environments, the twist lock style combination electrode features a non-fouling annular ceramic junction and an electrode housing of Kynar® construction with 316 SS locking pins. Dual "O" rings (1 EPR, 1 Viton®) are supplied to prevent process contact with potting epoxy. A choice of PVC or Kynar® adaptors are available with ¾" or 1" NPT threading.

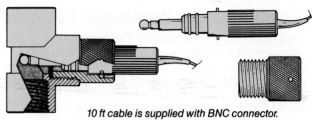

10 ft cable is supplied with BNC connector.
Withstands pressure up to 150 PSI.

ELECTRODES

HIGHLIGHTED MODELS IN STOCK FOR FAST DELIVERY

Part No.	pH Range	Temp. °C	R Megohms at 25°C	Notes	Price	Price w/ATC*
PHE-5321-10	0 to 13	−5 to 110	50	General Purpose	$110	$150
PHE-5421-10	0 to 13	−5 to 110	50	Double Junction	130	170
PHE-5322-10	0 to 14	0 to 110	200	High pH	135	175
ORE-5421-10	ORP Platinum	−5 to 110	—	ORP General Purpose	130	—
ORE-5329-10	ORP Gold	−5 to 110	—	ORP with Cyanide Present	140	—

*See page E-25 for ordering information.

PIPE TEES

Part No.	Fitting	Material	Max. Temp. °C	Price
PHEH-34TP	¾" MNPT	CPVC	66°C	$20
PHEH-1TP	1" MNPT	CPVC	66°C	20
PHEH-34TK	¾" MNPT	Kynar®	110°C	40
PHEH-1TK	1" MNPT	Kynar®	110°C	40

TWIST LOCK ADAPTORS

Part No.	Fitting	Material	Max. Temp. °C	Price
PHEH-34AP	¾" MNPT	CPVC	66°C	$40
PHEH-1AP	1" MNPT	CPVC	66°C	40
PHEH-34AK	¾" MNPT	Kynar®	110°C	50
PHEH-1AK	1" MNPT	Kynar®	110°C	50

Rebuildable Submersible Electrode Assemblies

OMEGA® Submersible Electrode Assemblies are intended for use in industrial and process ORP/pH measurement applications. For versatility, modular construction allows quick removal of the sealed combination electrode and easy mounting onto ¾" pipe. The CPVC or Kynar® housings permit use in hostile environments. The electrodes utilize annular non-fouling reference junctions.

Electrode holder

Electrode

Inline housing

Submersion assembly

Optional In-line Housing
½" MNPT Kynar®
Rated to 100 PSI
PHEH-66K $40

Electrode Part No.	Length mm	Dia. mm	pH Range	Temp. °C	R Megohms at 25°C	Application	Price	Price w/ATC*
PHE-6361-3	80	12	0-13	−5 to 100	50	General Purpose	$ 74	$114
PHE-6362-3	80	12	0-14	0 to 110	200	High pH	79	119
PHE-6461-3	80	12	0-13	−5 to 100	50	Double Junction	99	139
PHE-6462-3	80	12	0-14	0 to 110	200	Double Junction High pH	104	144
ORE-6361-3	80	12	ORP Pt	−5 to 110	—	ORP General Purpose	96	—
ORE-6461-3	80	12	ORP Pt	−5 to 110	—	ORP Double Junction	101	—
ORE-6469-3	80	12	ORP Gold	−5 to 110	—	ORP Dbl. Junc. for Appl. w/Cvanide	130	—

*Specify type of temperature sensor. See page E-25. Order electrode and housing separately.

Submersion Assy.	Len. ft	Dia. in	Material	Temp °C	Price	Price/Add'l. ft
PHEH-63P-3	3	¾	CPVC	−5 to 80	$154	+ $5/ft
PHEH-63K-3	3	¾	Kynar®	−5 to 110	248	+ $5/ft

Replacement Elec. Holder	Material	Temp. °C	Price
PHEH-64P	CPVC	−5 to 80	$88
PHEH-64K	Kynar®	−5 to 110	170

Flat Surface pH/ORP Industrial Electrodes
Self Cleaning, Abrasion Free

MADE IN
USA

- ✔ **Special Design for Difficult Applications**
- ✔ **Self Cleaning**
- ✔ **Abrasion Free**
- ✔ **Reduced Breakage, Extended Performance**

Model PHE-5460
$95
Page E-30

9.58
pH/ORP CONTROLLER PHCN-36

Controller Model PHCN-36
Sold Separately.
From **$216**
Page E-24.

Model PHE-4580
$95
Page E-29

Model PHE-6510
$95
Page E-30

E

INDUSTRIAL pH EQUIPMENT

Flat Surface pH/ORP Industrial Electrodes

✔ **Flat Surface Design**
✔ **100 PSIG to 76°C, 50 PSIG to 100°C**

Priced From $95

OMEGA's line of self-cleaning/abrasion free pH and ORP electrodes are designed for applications in which fouling or coating can present a problem. The electrode has a non-protruding, flat surface design which minimizes coating and helps eliminate electrode breakage. It is this same design which utilizes flow sweeping past the electrode to scrub the electrode clean. The flat glass surface also prevents particles moving past the electrode from impinging upon its surface thus eliminating abrasion and extending electrode life.

OMEGA offers an in-line electrode, PHE/ORE-5460 and assembly PHEH-54-10, a submersible electrode PHE/ORE-6510 and mounting assembly PHEH-65-10, and a side-stream mounting design for lines with flows between 3 and 5 GPM, PHE/ORE-4580 and flow cell and cable assembly, PHEH-45-10. All electrodes are constructed from CPVC and are supplied with sealed, gel filled double junction references. They are rated for pressures up to 100 PSIG at up to 76°C or 50 PSIG at 100°C and are available with temperature compensation. Easy to use and install the electrodes are compatible with most pH equipment. Designed for such difficult applications as oily waste water, emulsions, lime slurries and flocculant coagulation, they may be the solution to your application problems.

Specifications (General):
Materials: CPVC, gel filled, double junction combination
pH Range: 0 to 14
Temperature Range: 10 to 100°C
Pressure Rating: 100 PSIG @ 76°C
50 PSIG @ 100°C
Impedance: Less than 300 megaohms @ 25°C

Cable

Flow Cell

By-pass PHE/ORP-4580 Flow Electrodes

From $95

The OMEGA PHE/ORE-4580 by-pass flow pH system has a modified CPVC tee and cable assembly matched to the flat surface pH and ORP electrodes. Each GPM flowing through the tee results in a 2 ft/sec velocity which performs the self-cleaning action. No moving parts, liquid jets or power are required. Electrodes can be used in applications in which emulsions, slurries, oily waste-water and other difficult flowing samples are present. Continuous self-cleaning affords uninterrupted readings. Automatic temperature compensation is available as an option.

Self Cleaning, Abrasion Free

NEW!

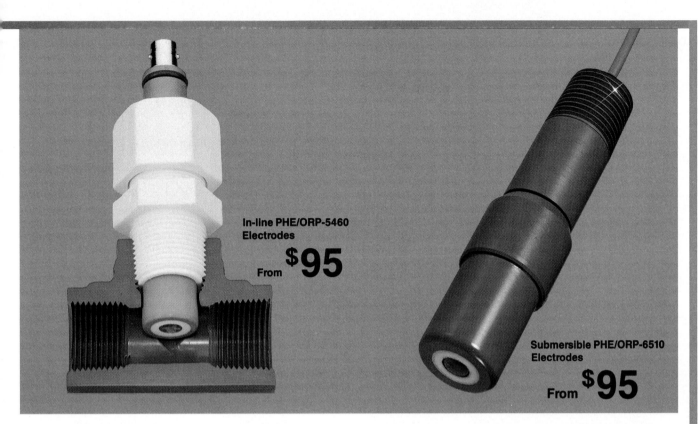

In-line PHE/ORP-5460 Electrodes
From **$95**

Submersible PHE/ORP-6510 Electrodes
From **$95**

The OMEGA PHE/ORE-5460 in-line pH and ORP electrodes feature a flat self-cleaning abrasion-free surface. Turbulence causes the scrubbing action. The electrodes can be used in applications with 0-100°C temperatures, pressures up to 100 PSIG and 0-14 pH measurement range (without sodium ion error). Having fresh material sweeping past the electrode's surface improves response time as well as accuracy, especially for the measurement of oily waste fluids, lime slurries, flocculants and emulsions. The electrodes accept a cable assembly with a gland mounted in a ¾″ NPT tee.

The OMEGA PHE/ORE-6510 submersible electrodes are designed for use in drums, open tanks and streams, etc. The flat sensing surface is surrounded by a porous polyethylene reference junction which minimizes fouling. Installation is as easy as connecting a coupling and pipe to the electrode's cable assembly cap with a simple ¼ turn. The cable assembly cap is ½″ MNPT (¾″ with ATC) that attaches to a support pipe. The resulting assembly is lightweight for convenient handling when maintenance is needed. ATC is available.

To Order *(Specify Model No.)*

Model No.	Price	Description
PHE-4580	$ 95	By-pass flow pH electrode
ORE-4580	115	By-pass flow ORP electrode
PHE-5460	95	In-line pH electrode
ORE-5460	115	In-line ORP electrode
PHE-6510	95	Submersible pH electrode
ORE-6510	115	Submersible ORP electrode
PHEH-45-10	126	Flow cell and cable with manual temperature compensation for PHE/ORE-4580
PHEH-45-10-(*)	198	Flow cell and cable with ATC for PHE/ORE-4580
PHEH-54-10	51	Mounting assembly with manual temperature compensation for PHE/ORE-5460
PHEH-54-10-(*)	148	Mounting assembly with ATC for PHE/ORE-5460
PHEH-65-10	41	Mounting assembly with manual temperature compensation for PHE/ORE-6510
PHEH-65-10-(*)	118	Mounting assembly with ATC for PHE/ORE-6510

*Specify ATC sensor: 'PT100' for 100 ohm platinum RTD or 'PT1K' for 1000 ohm platinum RTD. Note: temperature compensation is not required with ORP electrodes. Ordering Example: PHEH-45-10-PT100 indicates flow cell and cable with ATC sensor, 100 ohm platinum RTD, $198.

E — INDUSTRIAL pH EQUIPMENT

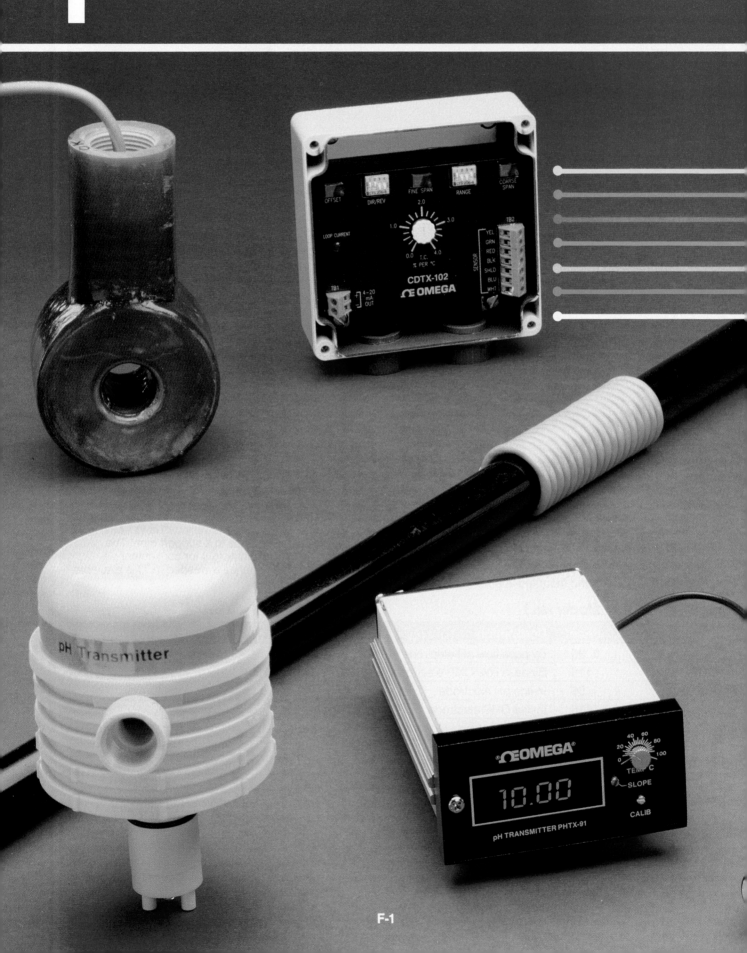

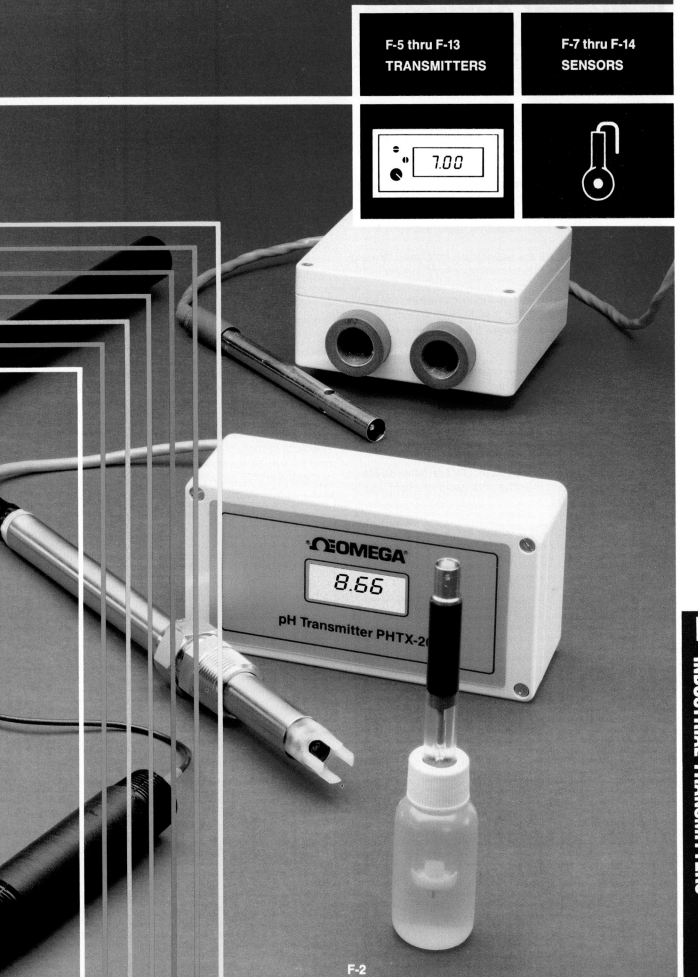

F-5 thru F-13
TRANSMITTERS

F-7 thru F-14
SENSORS

7.00

OMEGA

8.66

pH Transmitter PHTX-20

F
INDUSTRIAL TRANSMITTERS

Industrial Application of Two-Wire Transmitters

TRANSMITTER INTRODUCTION

Two-wire transmitters have been in use for temperature and flow measurements in the process industries for several years. In the past 6 to 8 years many end-users have requested transmitters for the majority of analytical instrumentation found in chemical process plants. Why two-wire? There are several reasons that their use is almost exclusively in hard industrial applications:

1. Two-wire transmitters are specifically designed for field remote installations that cannot supply AC power.

2. Two-wire transmitters can be located in a hazardous area (Division I or II). Using a safety barrier to limit the voltage signals the system can be made intrinsically safe.

3. 24 V dc power supplies are standard in plants with large amounts of instrumentation.

4. As well as reducing the number of wires required for signal transmission, the cost of the wire is also reduced by no longer requiring shielded coax cable.

5. Industrial environments are typically corrosive so the transmitter housing must be both weather-proof and corrosion-resistant.

6. Grounding practices in process plants require input/output isolation in most applications.

TWO WIRE THEORY

An increasing number of modern industrial processes are being monitored or controlled by remote signals. In many cases, a transducer must transmit its signal a considerable distance back to the control room or computer terminal. As this distance increases, the signal handling problems can multiply rapidly. System costs increase in direct proportion to the distance over which a signal must be transmitted. Long signal transmission lines are highly susceptible to noise pick-up unless relatively expensive, shielded cable is used. A significant portion of the transmitted signal voltage can be absorbed in the resistance (R_0) of such long lines; and the longer the line, the greater the possibility for large differences in ground potentials (V_g) between signal source (V_s) and load (V_1).

Assuming that the system is not battery-powered, at least one additional line is required to furnish power to the transmitter (fig. 2a). However, if the signal and the power supply line are combined (one wire serves a dual function), then the number of lines can be held to the absolute minimum of two (fig. 2b). *Only the power supply and its ground return are required; the actual signal is transmitted as a change in power supply current.*

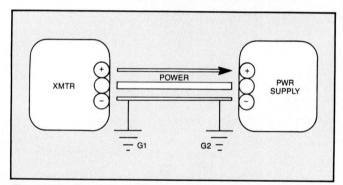

Figure 2A: *An additional line is required to furnish power to the transmitter.*

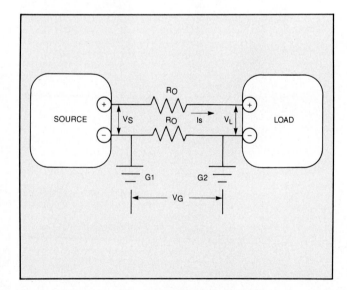

Figure 1: *The minimum requirement for remote signal transmission in most hard wired systems is two wires: a signal line and a ground-return line.*

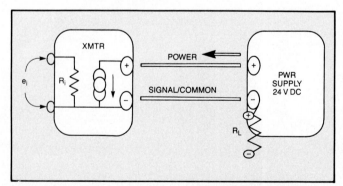

Figure 2B: *If the signal and power to the transmitter are combined (one wire serves a dual function) then the number of lines can be held to the minimum of two.*

In most process control systems, the signal current is 4-20 mA or 10-50 mA; an output voltage (e_O) is developed from this signal current by connecting a load resistor (R_1) in series with the power supply return line. In the case of a 4-20 mA signal, $I_O = 4$ mA; the remaining signal (up to 16 mA) is generated in direct proportion to the input voltage (e_i).

A two-wire transmitter requires that the input signal be supplied from a "floating" sensor. This is what is traditionally referred to as "input isolation", where the input voltage is referenced to one of its two lines, not to its own separate "ground" reference. In applications using two separate "grounds", the typical end-user will encounter a "ground-loop error" where current flow between the two ground connections develops a voltage error on the load resistor (R_1) in addition to any error in the desired output voltage (e_O).

In addition to reducing the number of wires required to signal transmission, the cost of the wire can also be reduced when using two-wire transmitters. Signal transmission from a pH sensor, a conductivity sensor or almost any other type of transducer requires the use of "shielded cable" to minimize pick up of ambient electrical noise from AC power mains, arching electrical equipment and other similar sources of interference. In order to reduce errors from signal voltage drops in line resistance, expensive, heavy gauge wire is frequently installed on applications that require long cable runs. Typically, the longer the line, the greater the error in signal due to line voltage drop.

Transmitter current output signals (4 to 20 mA) are relatively immune to noise voltage pick up and are not degraded by long distance transmission, even over small diameter wire. As long as the combined value of line resistance plus load resistor does not exceed the current generator's driving capability, signal transmission suffers no degradation from source to load. Current receivers such as remote panel meters, controllers, recorders, etc., have input resistances of 50 to 250 ohms. For example, the resistance of 3 miles of 20 gauge wire is approximately 160 ohms per wire or 340 ohms per loop. Using a two wire transmitter capable of driving a nominal 700 ohm load (@24 Vdc), one can obviously transmit a very accurate signal over a large distance with a simple twisted pair of 20 or 22 gauge wires.

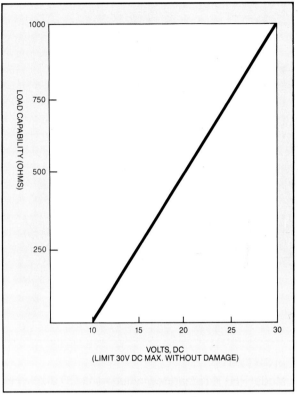

Figure 3: *Load driving capability versus voltage for 4 to 20 mA loop. Do not exceed 30 Vdc.*

By reducing the number of lines required to transmit a signal, the two-wire transmitter also reduces installation costs, power requirements and the possibility of error. You get a better signal at a lower cost.

A single pair of wires perform two functions—the same two lines that power the transmitter also carry the output signal several thousand feet or more, and you get a highly accurate measurement because the two-wire transmitter converts relatively weak electrical signals into high-level direct current, which is immune to noise. Therefore, your signal can be transmitted over a long distance with no loss of accuracy.

Two-wire transmitters provide a 4-20 mA output for signal transmission to a wide variety of process instrumentation including chart recorders, data loggers, panel meters, multiplexers, controllers and computers. ΩE

OMEGA ENGINEERING, INC. gratefully acknowledges Signet Scientific for permission to reprint the bulletin "Industrial Applications of Two-Wire Transmitters."

pH Two-Wire Transmitters

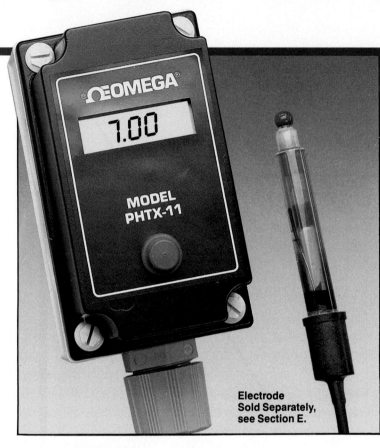

Electrode
Sold Separately,
see Section E.

- Isolated
- 4 to 20 mA Output
- Manual or Automatic Temperature Compensation
- High Accuracy ±0.01 pH

Model PHTX-11
$575

Specifications:
Range: 0 to 14 pH
Span: Any 1 to 14 pH unit; selectable with internal DIP Switch (Example: 4 to 20 mA could represent 6 to 8 pH)
Accuracy: ±0.01 pH
Input Impedance: > 10^{13} ohms
Temperature Compensation: Manual using fixed resistor; automatic using a 700 Series thermistor
Operating Temperature: −10 to +60°C
Connector: BNC
Power: 12 to 80 Vdc, requires U24Y100 power supply, see section F.
Output: 4 to 20 mA
Dimensions: 4.92″ H x 2.92″ W x 3.92″ D
Display: 3½ digit LCD

Optional Accessories:
See Section E for complete selection of Industrial Electrodes, including electrodes with automatic temperature compensation.

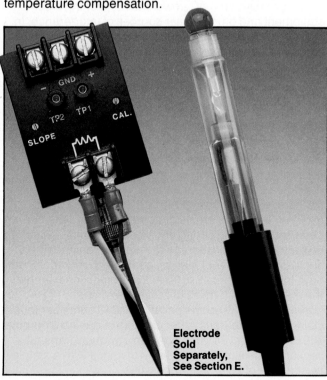

Electrode
Sold
Separately,
See Section E.

Model PHTX-11
The Model PHTX-11 features include an LCD display for a continuous pH reading or for a direct corresponding readout in milliamps, a convenient pushbutton switch is provided. The 4 to 20 mA output signal can be easily scaled to meet specific pH ranges (see specifications). Temperature compensation is manual using a fixed resistor or automatic with any 700 Series thermistor. An NEMA 4X enclosure is standard with the PHTX-11.

Model PHTX-1
The PHTX-1 pH two wire transmitter is designed to provide a standard 4 to 20 mA current output which is proportional to the pH being measured. Its small size and encapsulated construction allow for easy installation and will accommodate any pH electrode with a BNC connector. Temperature compensation is either manual or automatic with use of any 1000 ohm Platinum RTD.

- **Non Isolated**

Model PHTX-1
$225

Specifications:
Range: 0 to 14 pH
Span: 0 to 14 pH
Accuracy: ±0.01 pH
Input Impedance: > 10^{13} ohms
Temperature Compensation: Manual using fixed resistor; automatic using a 1,000 ohm Platinum RTD
Operating Temperature: −25 to +70°C
Connector: BNC
Power: 12 to 80 Vdc; requires U24Y100 power supply, see section F.
Output: 4 to 20 mA, non isolated
Dimensions: 2″ H x 1.5″ W x .95″ D

Digital Panel pH Transmitters
PHTX-91 and PHTX-92

Model PHTX-91

- ✓ Manual Temperature Compensation
- ✓ LED Display
- ✓ 4-20 mA Output Scaled to 0-14 pH or to Any 2 pH Unit Span

Model PHTX-92

- ✓ Automatic Temperature Compensation
- ✓ LCD Display
- ✓ 4-20 mA Output Scaled to 0-14 pH

The PHTX-91 and PHTX-92 four-wire transmitters provide panel-mounted displays of pH and 4 to 20 mA dc outputs representing pH 0 to 14 pH. Other features include modular design, an aluminum 1/8 DIN standard case and bezeled front panel for quick installation. The PHTX-92 does not have manual temperature compensation.

Specifications:

Range: 0 to 14 pH
Accuracy: 0.02 pH ±1 digit (relative) when standardized within 2 pH units
Resolution: 0.01 pH
Input Impedance: > 10^{12} ohms
Temperature Compensation: PHTX-91: Manual 0 to 100°C; PHTX-92: Automatic, requires 100 ohm Pt RTD
Current Output Span: PHTX-91: Isolated 4 to 20 mA dc for 0 to 14 pH Normal; 4 to 20 mA dc for any 2 pH span, in Expanded Mode; PHTX-92: Isolated 4 to 20 mA dc for 0 to 14 pH
Current Accuracy: ±0.3%
Connector: BCN; Screw terminals for ATC on PHTX-92
Power: 115 Vac, 230 Vac, ±15% 50/60 Hz
Display: PHTX-91: Red 0.56" super efficient LED; PHTX-92: LCD
Dimensions: 3.9" × 2" × 7"; Weight: 1.3 lb

Model PHTX-92 **$215**   Model PHTX-91 **$215**

Unregulated Power Supply

Model U24Y100

U24Y100

24 Volt dc, 1000 mA unregulated power supply
−10°C to +65°C operating range
110 V ac input power
3.71" Sq. x 4.5" W

Model U24Y100

$110

Non-Indicating Two-Wire Resistivity Transmitter

1 YEAR WARRANTY **MADE IN USA** **CARE**

Model RSTX-201-202

The OMEGA RSTX-201-202 non-indicating two-wire transmitter for use with a matching conductivity sensor requires only two wires for output and power transmission. Current to operate the transmitter is provided by a two-wire receiver, such as the OMEGA PHCN-105 (see page E-21), or by an appropriate DC power supply. This controlled current loop has high noise immunity, permitting use of a simple twisted pair of wires. Since current is used instead of voltage, the resistance of the wire does not affect accuracy.

The transmitter electronics are fully encapsulated. Terminal strips are provided for field connections. The transmitter can be surface-mounted in any position. The unit is supplied with a resistivity sensor. An optional polycarbonate NEMA 4X enclosure is available for environmental protection.

The resistivity sensor is made of titanium and PFA. To ensure the best possible measurement accuracy, the transmitter and sensor have been factory calibrated.

- ✓ Epoxy Encapsulated
- ✓ Two-Wire System Simplifies Wiring
- ✓ Small Size for Convenient Mounting

$470

Supplied with Sensor Calibrated to the Transmitter

Replacement Sensor RSEX-202
$205

Specifications:

OPERATIONAL

Ambient Conditions: −30 to 70°C (−22 to 158°F), 0-100% RH

Sensor-to-Transmitter Distance: 100 ft (30 m) max

Transmission Distance: Limited only by wire resistance and power

Power Requirements: 16 to 40 Vdc, connections via terminals

Measuring Range: 0-20 megohm/cm

Temperature Compensation: Automatic, 0-100°C (32-212°F), or fixed at 2% per °C

Dimensions: 4.8"W x 4.7"H x 2.2"D

PERFORMANCE (electrical, 4-20 mA output)

Sensitivity: Less than 0.01% of span

Stability: 0.06% of span per 24 hr, non-cumulative

Repeatability: 0.06% of span

Temperature Drift: Zero, 0.013% of span/°C; Span, 0.013% of span/°C

Non-Linearity: 0.125% of span

Response Time: 10 sec (to 90% of value upon step change)

Insertion Loss at 20 mA: 14.6 Vdc (730 ohms). Insertion loss represents a maximum resistance (listed above) in the 4-20 mA loop

Sensor Dimensions: ½" dia, 7" overall length, 4.1" max insertion length

MECHANICAL

Enclosure (optional): NEMA 4X, polycarbonate, surface mount

Net Weight (less enclosure): 0.6 lb (0.27 kg)

To Order	(Specify Model Number)	
Model No.	**Price**	**Description**
RSTX-201-202	$470	Resistivity Transmitter with Sensor
CDC-201	19	NEMA 4X Polycarbonate Enclosure
RSEX-202	205	Replacement Sensor
U24Y100	110	Unregulated 24 Vdc, 1,000 mA power supply, 110 V input power

Ordering Example: RSTX-201-202 plus CDC-201, $489. Resistivity transmitter with sensor and NEMA 4X polycarbonate enclosure.

Two-Wire Conductivity and pH Transmitters

pH Transmitter with Integral Sensor

- **Isolated 4 to 20 mA Output**
- **Field Adjustable Output Expansion**
- **Replaceable Double Junction Electrode**
- **NEMA 4X Enclosure**
- **Automatic Temperature Compensation**
- **LCD Readout**

The Model PHTX-80 is a two wire, field mounted, insertion pH transmitter with an integral sensor designed for accuracy, reliability and ease of maintenance. The 4 to 20 mA output may be field calibrated to represent any 2 to 14 pH span. Direct electronic sensing by the combination pH sensor eliminates common noise and stability problems. For quick and easy field commissioning and installation, the PHTX-80 features compact modular design, two-wire compatibility and weatherproof construction.

Optional Accessories:
Replacement Electrode
PHTX-80-E $125

Specifications:
TRANSMITTER
Power Required: 10 to 30 Vdc
Load Impedance: 0 to 1000 ohms, 700 ohms at 24 Vdc
Output: Isolated 4 to 20 mA
Accuracy: ±1% full scale
SENSOR
Ranges: 0 to 14 pH
Pressure Rating: 150 PSIG at 25°C, 25 PSIG at 100°C
Temperature Compensation: automatic, 0 to 95°C
Junction Type: annular double junction
Insertion Size: 1¼″ NPT

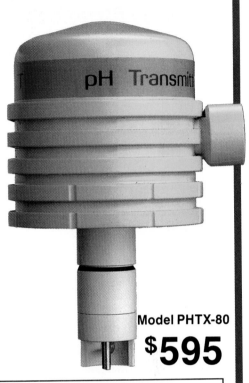

Model PHTX-80

$595

> **Flow Transmitter is also available, please see the OMEGA Complete Flow and Level Measurement Handbook and Encyclopedia™.**

CDTX-80 Series Conductivity Transmitters with Integral Sensor

- **Full Input/Output Isolation**
- **NEMA 4X Enclosure**

$595

The CDTX-80 Series are unique instruments that combine a conductivity sensor with a two wire transmitter in a NEMA 4X enclosure for insertion use in industrial processes. Full input/output isolation effectively eliminates ground loop problems.
To assure accurate conductivity measurements, automatic temperature compensation is provided. The CDTX-80 Series features square wave peak detection circuitry to reduce polarization effects and eliminates the need for troublesome platinized electrodes. Four models are available to cover the ranges of 0 to 20, 0 to 200, 0 to 2000 and 0 to 10,000 μS. An optional LCD readout is available for local indication (0 to 100%).

Specifications:
Power Required: external 10 to 30 Vdc
Current Loop Load Impedance: 0 to 1000 ohms

Output: Isolated 4 to 20 mA
Accuracy: (includes sensor) ±1% F.S.
Ranges: 0 to 20, 0 to 200, 0 to 2000 and 0 to 10,000 μS
Pressure Rating: 200 PSIG at 25°C
Temperature Compensation: automatic, 0 to 95°C
Materials of Construction: polypropylene
Electrodes: Titanium
Insertion Size: 1¼″ NPT

Optional Accessory:
Plug-in LCD Display. Add Suffix ''-D'' to part number. **$100**

To Order:

Model No.	Range μS	Price
CDTX-80	0 to 20	$595
CDTX-81	0 to 200	595
CDTX-82	0 to 2000	595
CDTX-83	0 to 10,000	595

F

INDUSTRIAL TRANSMITTERS

TYPICAL APPLICATION

A Reverse Osmosis System

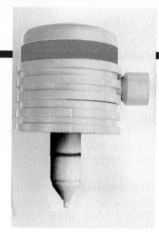

TEMPERATURE TRANSMITTER

Our temperature transmitter uses a solid state sensor that provides increased durability and a longer life than thermocouple type sensors.

- **Fast Response**
- **No Metallic Wetted Parts Ensure High Accuracy**
- **Range: −0° to 100°C**

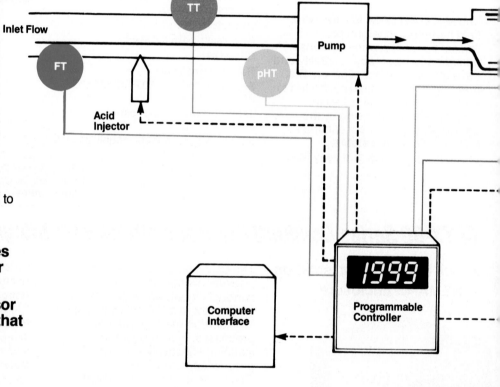

FLOW TRANSMITTER

The flow transmitter uses our insertion Flow Sensor—designed to give accurate and reliable measurements.

- **Easy Insertion into Pipes from ½″—36″ Diameter**
- **Uses Our Unique Paddlewheel Flow Sensor with Open-Cell Design that Eliminates Cavitation**
- **Linear and Accurate Output**
- **Wide Dynamic Range**
- **NEMA 4X Housing**

pH/ORP TRANSMITTERS

OMEGA pH/ORP sensor tranmitters have replaceable electrodes for easy in-the-field maintenance.

- **Adjustable Zero Span Over any 2 pH Units or Greater**
- **Accuracy ±1% of Span or .05 pH**
- **NEMA 4X Housing**

- **Automatically Temperature Compensated**
- **Convenient Calibration**
- **Double Reference Junction**
- **pH Unit Includes Display Board for Easy Calibration**

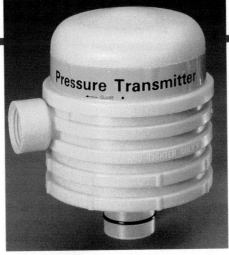

PRESSURE TRANSMITTER

OMEGA's pressure transmitter features unique ceramic construction that makes the transmitter resistant to the harsh chemicals found in process applications.

- **Capacitance Coupled Sensor**
- **No Metallic Wetted Parts for Corrosion Resistance**
- **Unique Solid State Circuit**
- **Exceptional Repeatability**
- **Accurate Over a Broad Temperature Range**
- **NEMA 4X Housing**

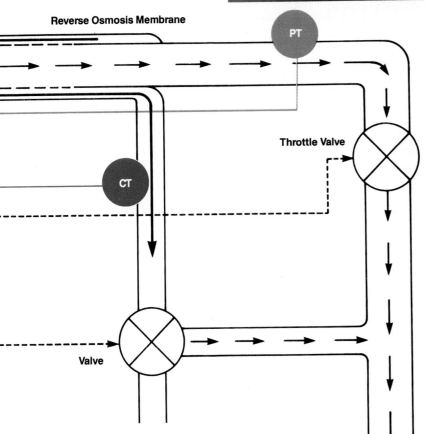

Reverse Osmosis Membrane

PT

Throttle Valve

CT

Valve

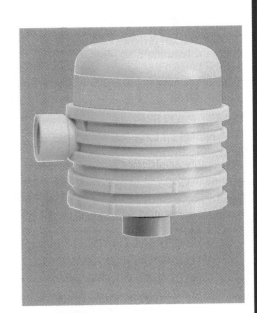

How to Order Analytical Transmitters (for ½" to 4" fittings)

Part No.	Description (Transmitters)	Material	Price
PHTX-80	pH 0-14	Polypro	$595
PHTX-80-E	Replacement pH Electrode	Polypro	125
ORTX-80	ORP −999 to +999 mV	Polypro	595
PRTX-80	Pressure 0-75 PSIG	Polypro	595
PRTX-81	Pressure 0-150 PSIG	Polypro	595
CDTX-80	Conductivity 0-20 μS	Polypro	595
CDTX-81	Conductivity 0-200 μS	Polypro	595
CDTX-82	Conductivity 0-2,000 μS	Polypro	595
CDTX-83	Conductivity 0-10,000 μS	Polypro	595
TMTX-80	Temperature −0 to +100°C	Polypro	495

CONDUCTIVITY TRANSMITTERS

Providing a full range of conductivity measurements, our sensors feature titanium electrodes that form either 2.00 or 0.05 cell constants.

- **Accurate to ±1% of Span**
- **Available Spans of 0-20, 0-200, 0-2,000, 0-10,000 μS/cm for Conductivity**
- **NEMA 4X Enclosure**

F

INDUSTRIAL TRANSMITTERS

TRANSMITTER SPECIFICATIONS

STANDARD TRANSMITTER

A transmitter consists of an electronics package and a sensor element designed to function in an externally powered, 2 wire closed loop system. A single 4-20 mA current signal is provided as information output for the sensed input parameter. The transmitter is designed to interface directly with existing OMEGA installation fittings.

Electrical Performance
Power: External 10-30 Vdc (24 Vdc Nom.)
Current Loop Load Impedance: 0 to 1000 OHMS
Outputs: Analog; 4-20 mA isolated, limited to 35 mA max. Frequency; 10-12 Hz per ft/sec min., 300 mV min. to 4V max. p-p amplitude
Accuracy of Electronics (Including Sensor): 1% of full scale nominal

Electrical Interface
½" NPT conduit connection

Environmental (External Enclosure)
Ambient Temperature: −30°C to 70°C (−22°F to 158°F)
Relative Humidity: 0 to 100% (Non Condensating)

TEMPERATURE TRANSMITTER

Operating Range
Minimum span any 20% of 0 to 100°C
Maximum span 0 to 100°C

Temperature Sensor
Accuracy: Better than ±1°C over temperature range
Range: 0°C to 100°C
Repeatability: ±0.1°C
Response Time: 5 second max. through 63% of change
Pressure Rating: 200 PSIG max. @ 0°C, 100 PSIG max @ 50°C, 50 PSIG max @ 100°C
Temp. Coefficient: 1 μA/1°C nominal

PRESSURE TRANSMITTER

Operating Range
0-75 PSIG, 0-150 PSIG

Pressure Sensor
Type: Strain gauge
Diaphragm Mat.: Alumina ceramic
Accuracy: ±0.5% of span
Repeatability: ±0.5% of span
Hysteresis: .05% of span
Burst Pressure: 150 PSI max. for PRTX-80; 300 PSI max for PRTX-81

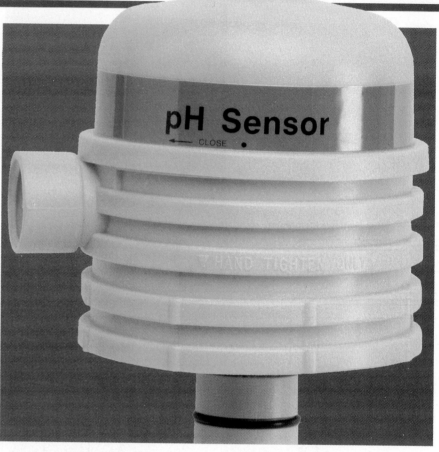

Temperature Compensation: −10 to 130°C automatic
Operating Temp.: −10 to 130°C
Response Time: 15 msec. max. @ 1 step change

pH TRANSMITTER

Operating Range
0 to 14 pH

pH Sensor
Input Range: 0 to 14 pH
Pressure Range: Up to 150 PSIG at 25°C; derated to 25 PSIG at 100°C
Response Time: 0-5 seconds for 99% of step change at constant temperature
Sensor/Electrode: High pH
Temp. Range: 0-100°C
Junction Type: Annular double junction of porous Teflon® materials
Configuration: Glass bulb featuring Ag/AgCl combination electrodes incorporated into a disposable sensor assembly
Temp. Sensor: Thermistor (3K Ohm, 1% @ 25°C)

ORP TRANSMITTER

Output Range
Maximum span −999 mV to +999 mV

ORP Sensor
Input Range: −999 mV to +999 mV ORP
Pressure Range: Up to 150 PSIG at 25°C; derated to 25 PSIG at 100°C
Sensor/Electrode: Platinum band with combination Ag/AgCl element with double reference junction
Junction Material: Porous Telfon®
Temp. Range: 0°C to 100°C

CONDUCTIVITY TRANSMITTER

Operating Range
0 to 20 μS, 0 to 200 μS, 0 to 2000 μS, 0 to 10,000 μS

Conductivity Sensor
Temp. Range: 95°C @ 50 PSIG
Pressure Rating: 200 PSIG max. @ 25°C
Cell Constant: .05 ±2%, 2.0 ±2%
Temperature Compensation: Automatic; 5-95°C with built-in 10K ohm thermistor

® *Teflon is a registered trademark of E.I. Dupont*

Dimensions:
Electronics head: 3.7" H, 3.25" O.D.
Weight of all transmitters: 2 lbs.

pH, ORP and Conductivity Two-Wire Transmitters and Probes

PHTX-20
pH Transmitter

PHTX-20-E1
pH Electrode Assembly

CDTX-20-E1
Conductivity Probe

pH Transmitter PHTX-20

- **Isolated Two-Wire 4 to 20 mA Signal Transmitters**
- **Automatic Signal Conditioning for Conductivity**
- **pH and ORP Available With or Without Signal Conditioning**
- **Mounting Hardware Included**

Common Specifications:
Power: 21 to 40 Vdc
Output Types: Isolated 4 to 20 mA into 600 ohm load max.
Display: 3½ digit LCD
Dimensions: 3.15″ H x 6.3″ W x 2.17″ D
Weight: 1.25 lb
Enclosure: NEMA 4X

Specifications for pH and ORP Transmitters:
Range: 0 to 14 pH, ±1999 mV
Span: Any 2 to 14 pH units, zero and span adjustable, 500 to 4000 mV
Resolution: 0.01 pH, 1 mV
Input Impedance: 10^{12} ohms
Temperature Compensation: Automatic, 0 to 100°C using 3 K ohm resistive temperature sensor or manual with fixed resistor (pH only)
Connector: BNC

Specifications for Conductivity Transmitter:
Range: Jumper Selectable
0 to 10, 100, 1000, 10,000, and 100,000 μmhos with CDTX-20-E1 probe. 0 to 1, 10, 100, 1000, 10,000 μmhos with CDTX-20-E2 probe
Accuracy: ±0.2% of full scale at 25°C
Compensated Temperature Range: 5 to 95°C

Specifications for pH and ORP Probes:
Range: 0 to 14 pH, ±1999 mV
Rating: 100 psig @ 100°C
Process Connection: ¾″ NPT 316SS reversible tube fitting
Electrical Connection: Polymer "J" box w/terminals
Length: 10″, Diameter: ¾″
Body: 316 SS
Seal Guard: Polypropylene
"O" Rings: Viton®

Specifications for Conductivity Probe:
Pressure Rating: 250 psig w/standard fitting
Length: 6″
Diameter: ¾″
Body: 316 SS
Insulator: KEL-F®
"O" Rings: Viton®

HIGHLIGHTED MODELS IN STOCK FOR FAST DELIVERY

To Order: *(Specify Model Number)*

Model No.	Description	Mating Component	Price
PHTX-20	pH Transmitter	PHTX-20-E1 electrode	$590
ORTX-20	ORP Transmitter	ORTX-20-E1 electrode	590
PHTX-20-SC	pH Transmitter with Signal Conditioner	Any electrode	715
ORTX-20-SC	ORP Transmitter with Signal Conditioner	Any electrode	715
PHTX-20-E1*	Signal conditioner pH electrode assembly with doublejunction, pH 0 to 12	PHTX-20 Transmitter	445
ORTX-20-E1*	ORP electrode assembly with signal conditioner, double junction Pt band	ORTX-20 Transmitter	460
PHTX-20-E1R	Replacement pH electrode for PHTX-20-E1 electrode assembly	—	110
ORTX-20-E1R	Replacement ORP electrode for ORTX-20-E1 electrode assembly	—	125
CDTX-20	Two-wire conductivity transmitter	CDTX-20-E-1, or CDTX-20-E2	590
CDTX-20-E1*	Conductivity probe constant 1.0	—	345
CDTX-20-E2*	Conductivity probe constant 0.1	—	345

* Probes include 10 feet of cable. ¾″ NPT compression fitting allows probe to be used in either insertion or submersion applications.

F-12

INDUSTRIAL TRANSMITTERS

F

Conductivity Transmitters and Sensors

Two Wire Conductivity Transmitters CDTX-101, CDTX-102

- Model CDTX-101 for Contacting Conductivity Sensors and Model CDTX-102 for Electrodeless Conductivity Sensor

- Epoxy Encapsulated
- NEMA 4X Enclosure Surface Mounting

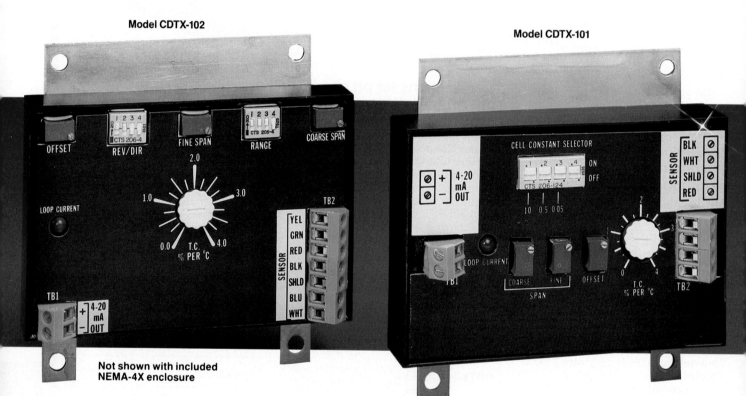

Model CDTX-102

Model CDTX-101

Not shown with included NEMA-4X enclosure

The CDTX-101 and 102 conductivity transmitters are designed to accept the signal from the model CDCN-100 Series conductivity sensors and provide a standard 4 to 20 mA current output which is proportional to the conductivity being measured. The CDTX-101 will accept the CDCN-102, 104 and 106 contacting conductivity sensors and the CDTX-102 accepts the input from the CDCN-108 electrodeless conductivity sensor. The transmitter electronics are fully encapsulated. Terminal strips are provided for field connections. For convenient and safe mounting, the CDTX-101 and 102 are provided with NEMA 4X enclosures that may be surface mounted in any position. These transmitters and sensors are a perfect match for a conductivity control system using the PHCN-105 conductivity controller.

To Order

Model No.	Price	Compatible Sensor	Measuring Range, μS
CDTX-101	$230	CDCN-102 CDCN-104 CDCN-106	0-10, 0-50, 0-100, 0-200 0-500, 0-1000, 0-2000, 0-5000 0-10,000, 0-20,000, 0-50,000
CDTX-102	$260	CDCN-108	0-1,000,000

Specifications

Sensor to Transmitter Distance: 100 feet maximum

Power Requirement: 16 to 40 Vdc

Connections: Stripped leads

Temperature Compensation: Automatic 0 to 100°C

Enclosure: NEMA 4X, polycarbonate, surface mount

Dimensions: 4.8″ x 4.7″ x 2.2″

Weight: 0.6 lb

Contacting Conductivity Sensors

- **Convertible For Submersion Or Flow Through Applications**
- **Used with CDCN-100 Series Controllers and CDTX-101 Transmitter**

Designed for convertible mounting in either submersion or flow-through applications, the CDCN-102, 104 and 106 conductivity sensors are the perfect match for the CDCN-100 Series conductivity controllers and the CDTX-101 conductivity transmitter. They are threaded on both ends for easy mounting.

Specifications

Cable Length: 10 feet (all models)
Maximum Cable Length: 100 feet
Maximum Pressure: 100 PSI
Maximum Temperature: 80°C
Mounting: 1 Inch NPT, threaded on both ends

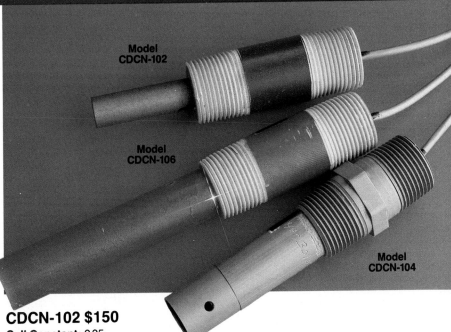

Model CDCN-102
Model CDCN-106
Model CDCN-104

CDCN-102 $150
Cell Constant: 0.05
Electrode Material: Titanium palladium alloy
Body Material: CPVC

CDCN-104 $130
Cell Constant: 0.5
Electrode Material: Graphite
Body Material: Vinyl Ester

CDCN-106 $170
Cell Constant: 10.0
Electrode Material: Graphite
Body Material: Vinyl Ester

All Cells Come With 10 Feet Cable, Additional Cable Available Up To 100 Feet Total. Add $0.50 Per Additional Foot.

CDCN-108

$**345**

Non-Contact Conductivity Sensor CDCN-108

- **No Polarization, Electrode Coating or Ground Loop Problems**
- **Anti-clogging, Large Bore Design**
- **Used With the CDTX-102 Conductivity Transmitter**

Designed for use in difficult environments, the CDCN-108 electrodeless conductivity sensor is a non-contacting design that prevents clogging. Since conventional electrodes are not used, polarization and electrode coating problems are eliminated. The large bore design greatly reduces fouling, so sensor maintenance is significantly reduced. The CDCN-108 is constructed so that only one material is wetted by the process to simplify chemical resistance problems. Because the wetted material (vinyl ester) is non-conductive, the sensor is electrically isolated from the process fluid, eliminating ground loops which can affect accuracy. The sensor has an integral temperature compensator to automatically adjust the conductivity reading to a 25°C reference. This sensor must be used with the CDTX-102 conductivity transmitter.

Specifications

Wetted Materials: Vinyl Ester
Measuring Range: 0 to 1,000,000 μS/cm
Temperature Range: 0 to 95°C
Maximum Pressure: 100 PSI
Temperature Compensation: Automatic, 0 to 95°C
Mounting Connection: 1″ NPT female mates to 1″ mounting pipe
Cable Length: 4½ feet
Maximum Cable Length: 100 feet

The CDCN-108 comes with 4½ feet of cable. Additional cable available up to 100 feet total. Add $0.50 per additional foot.

G INDUSTRIAL CONDUCTIVITY CONTROLLERS

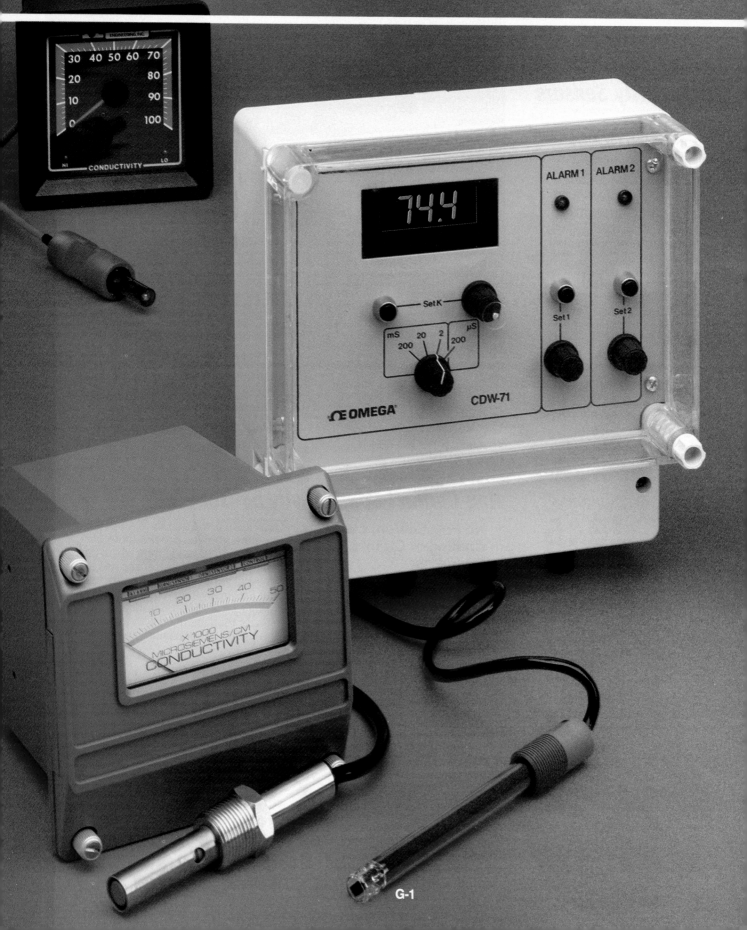

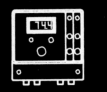

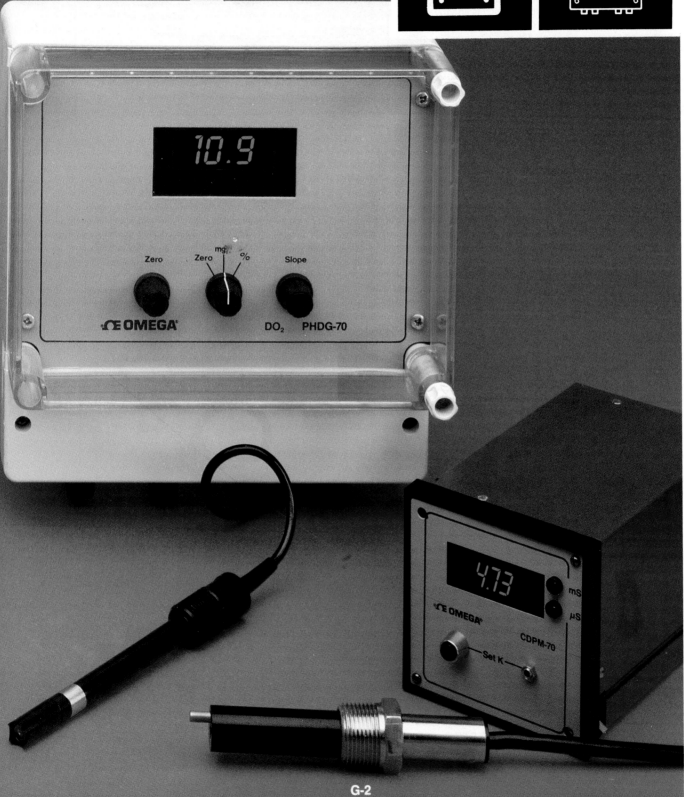

G

About Conductivity

All aqueous solutions conduct electricity to some degree. The measure of a solution's ability to conduct electricity is called "conductance" and is the reciprocal of resistivity (resistance). Adding electrolytes such as salts, acids or bases to pure water increases conductance (decreases resistivity).

A conductivity system measures conductance with electronics connected to a sensor immersed in a solution. The analyzer circuitry impresses an alternating voltage on the sensor and measures the size of the resulting signal which is linearly related to the conductivity. Because conductivity has a large temperature coefficient (as much as 4% per °C—see Fig. 1) an integral temperature sensor along with its circuitry adjusts the reading to a standard temperature, usually 25°C.

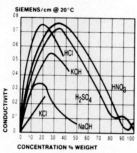

Figure 1.
Conductivity vs. Concentration

Historically, the standard unit of conductivity measurement has been "mhos/cm" (mho is the reciprocal of ohm). A resistivity of 100 ohms•cm is equivalent to a conductivity of 1/100 mhos/cm. The mhos/cm unit of measurement is now being replaced throughout industry by an equal and interchangeable international unit of measurement called the "Siemen/cm." Conductivity usually is expressed in millionths of a Siemen, that is, microSiemens/cm. Resistivity is still expressed as Megohm•cm for high purity water—usually from 0.1 to 20 Megohm•cm.

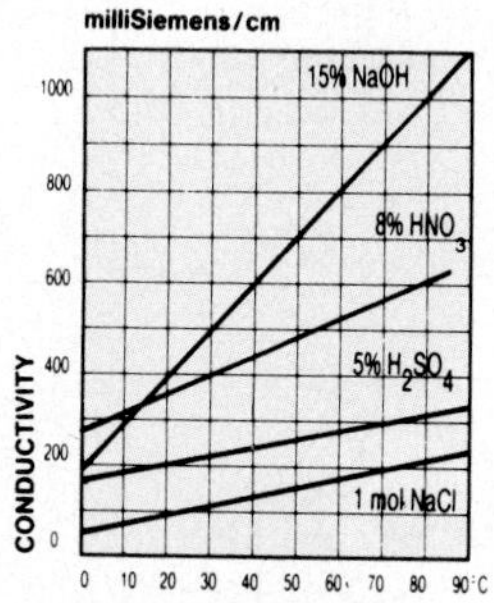

RESISTIVITY
In high purity water, typically less than 1 microSiemen/cm, the measurement is referred to as resistivity with units of Megohm•cm. Pure water has a resistivity of about 18.3 Megohm•cm at 25°C. One consideration that must be made when measuring solutions is the temperature coefficient of the conductivity of the water itself. To compensate accurately, a second temperature sensor and compensation network is used. Specific sensors and analyzers are recommended for measurement in high purity water.

Figure 2.
Conductivity vs. Temperature

About Conductivity Sensors . . .

The Contacting-Type Sensor usually consists of two electrodes, insulated from each other. The electrodes . . . typically 316 stainless-steel, titanium-palladium alloy or graphite . . . are specifically sized and spaced to provide a known "cell constant." Theoretically, a cell constant of 1.0 implies two electrodes, each one square centimeter in area, spaced one centimeter apart (Fig. 3).

Cell constants must be matched to the analyzer for a given range of operation. For instance, if a sensor with a cell constant of 1.0 were used in pure water with a conductivity of 1 microSiemen/cm, the cell would have a resistance of 1,000,000 ohms. Conversely, the same cell in seawater may have a resistance of 30 ohms. Since the resistances are so different, it is difficult for ordinary instruments to measure these extremes accurately with only one cell constant.

In measuring the 1 microSiemen/cm solution, the cell would be configured with large electrodes spaced a small distance apart. This results in a cell resistance of approximately 10,000 ohms which can be measured quite accurately. By using cells of different constants, the measuring instrument can operate over the same range of cell resistance for both ultra-pure water and high conductivity seawater.

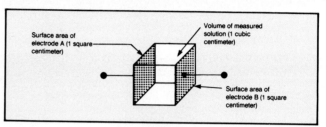

Figure 3.
Theoretical Cell Constant of 1.0

The Electrodeless-Type Sensor operates by inducing an alternating current in a closed loop of solution and measuring its magnitude to determine the conductivity (Fig. 4). The conductivity analyzer drives Torroid A which induces the **alternating** current into the solution. This AC signal flows in a closed loop through the sensor bore and surrounding solution. Torroid B senses the magnitude of the induced current which is proportional to the conductance of the solution. This signal is processed in the analyzer to display the corresponding reading.

Since the electrodeless sensor has no electrodes, common problems facing contacting-type sensors are eliminated. Polarization, oily fouling, process coating or non-conducting electrochemical plating do not affect the performance of electrodeless sensors until gross fouling occurs.

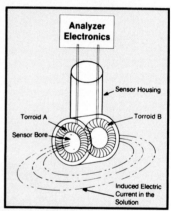

Figure 4.
Electrodeless Sensor

THE TEMPERATURE COMPENSATION
Conductivity measuring system accuracy can only be as good as its temperature compensation. Since common solution temperature coefficients vary on the order of 1-3% per °C, measuring instruments with adjustable temperature compensation should be utilized. Solution temperature coefficients are somewhat non-linear and usually vary with actual conductivity as well (Fig. 5). Thus, calibration at the actual measuring temperature will yield the best accuracy.

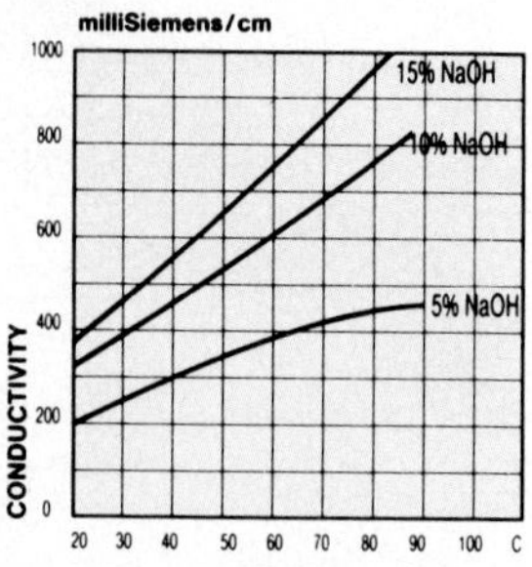

OMEGA ENGINEERING, INC. gratefully acknowledges Great Lakes Instruments, Inc. for permission to reprint the bulletin "About Conductivity"

Figure 5.
Conductivity vs. Temperature for Different Concentrations

CDCN-100 Series Conductivity Controllers

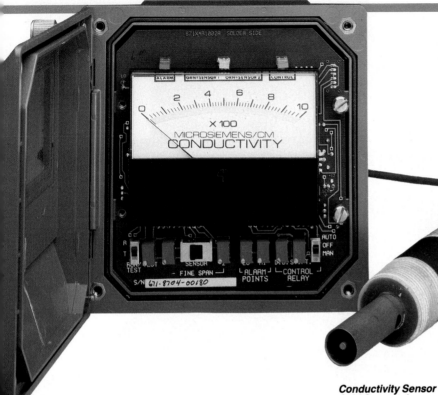

✔ **Accepts Two Conductivity Sensor Inputs**

✔ **Includes Control and Alarm Relays**

✔ **½ DIN NEMA 4X Enclosure**

✔ **Universal Mounting**

✔ **4 to 20 mA Output with Range Expand**

$545

Conductivity Sensor Sold Separately, See Chart Below.

Specifications:

Display: 3½" analog

Measuring Ranges: CDCN-101: 0 to 10, 0 to 50, 0 to 100 and 0 to 200 μS/cm (using CDCN-102 Sensor) CDCN-103: 0 to 500, 0 to 1000, 0 to 2000, and 0 to 5000 μS/cm (using CDCN-104 Sensor) CDCN-105: 0 to 10,000, 0 to 20,000 and 0 to 50,000 μS/cm (using CDCN-106 Sensor)

Relay Functions

Control/Alarm Setpoints: Continuously adjustable, 0 to 100% of full scale

Control Deadband: Continuously adjustable, 0 to 15% of full scale

Alarm Deadband: Fixed at 2% of measuring scale span

Indicators: LED lights when respective relay turns on

Contact Rating: SPDT, 5A 115/250 Vac, 5A at 30 Vdc resistive

Note: Control relay turns on in response to increasing or decreasing reading, switch selectable

Analog Outputs: Non-expandable and non-isolated (isolated from ground and line power, but not from input or each other) 0 to 1 mA, 100 ohms max load or 0 to 5 Vdc, 50 K ohms min. load. 4 to 20 mA, 825 ohms max, range expandable and non-isolated

Range Expand: The 4 to 20 mA output can be made to represent a selected segment of the display scale. This segment cannot be smaller than 10% of the measuring scale span, but may be positioned anywhere within that span.

Sensitivity: 0.1% of span

Repeatability: 0.1% of span

Temperature Compensation: Automatic, 0 to 100°C

Sensor to Analyzer Distance: 100 ft max

Connections: Stripped leads

Designed to provide conductivity measurement and control versatility in minimal space, the CDCN-100 Series conductivity controller will accept two sensor inputs of the same cell constant and has a front panel switch to select the desired signal for measurement and control. A bi-color LED above the meter display indicates which sensor has been selected. Readings are displayed on a 3½ inch analog meter, scaled in microSiemens/cm or milliSiemens/cm. For versatility, a range expand feature allows the 4 to 20 mA instrument output to represent a segment as small as 10% of the measuring span. The segment may be located anywhere within the measuring scale. The control relay can be selected to operate in response to increasing or decreasing conductivity and for added control flexibility, an AUTO/OFF/MANUAL mode switch is provided. The "dual alarm" relay has two individually adjustable controls to establish high and low alarm points so that the alarm relay is energized whenever the conductivity value is outside of these points. The instrument may be panel, surface or pipe mounted with the two stainless steel brackets provided. Must be used with the CDCN-102, 104 or 106 conductivity sensors depending on range required.

To Order

Controller Part No.	Price	Compatible Sensor Part No.	Price	Measuring Range, μS/cm
CDCN-101	$545	CDCN-102	$150	0-10, 0-50, 0-100, 0-200
CDCN-103	545	CDCN-104	130	0-500, 0-1000, 0-2000, 0-5000
CDCN-105	545	CDCN-106	170	0-10,000, 0-20,000, 0-50,000

Microprocessor Based Conductivity/ Resistivity Controllers

From

$625

RSCN-400
Resistivity Controller

Ultrapure Water Analyzers

- ✔ ±1% System Accuracy
- ✔ Measures Water Resistivity or Conductivity
- ✔ Available in 6 Measuring Ranges
- ✔ Two Cell Inputs
- ✔ Choice of Isolated 4-20 mAdc Output or RS232C/ 0-5 V Non-isolated Output
- ✔ 11 Self Diagnostic Functions
- ✔ CSA Approved

The OMEGA family of ultrapure water analyzers features two cell inputs, two types of conductivity cell calibrations, automatic temperature compensation from 0 to 100°C, self diagnostics, and communications capabilities. Four tactile membrane keypads provide selection and input of all set-up parameters.

Each unit has two (5 A 230 Vac) high/low alarm relays, a 3-1/2 digit 1/2″ LCD display and compact NEMA-4X polycarbonate enclosure. Each accepts two cell inputs. The alarms and output are derived from cell 1, while cell 2 provides monitoring only.

The controllers have two types of calibration. The first is based on the cell constant factor; the second automatically corrects for reading errors due to a dirty or fouled cell. When the correctable error exceeds 5%, an error message flashes to alert the user. This allows for longer cell use between routine maintenance schedules.

These units provide a system accuracy of better than ±1% (of reading) by employing an interactive dual matrix temperature compensation. This takes into account the temperature coefficient of the neutral salt component and that of the pure H_2O component. It separately calculates the conductive contribution of the solvent and solute.

The RSCN-400, CDCN-001, CDCN-002 and CDCN-003 are offered with a choice of an isolated 4-20 or 0-20 mAdc output (field selectable) or an RS232C interface with a non-isolated 0-5 V analog output for proportional control or recorder output. Self diagnostics alert the user to such conditions as open electrode, fouled cell, shorted RTD or internal circuitry malfunction. Each unit also employs a "watch-dog" timer to prevent a memory loss in the event of a power surge.

Conductivity cells for each resistivity or conductivity controller are available in submersible or in-line styles. Cell constants range from 0.01 to 10.0 cm; each cell has an integral 1000 ohm RTD for automatic temperature compensation.

For ordering convenience the controllers are listed with their corresponding cells (see page G-7).

Specifications

Conductivity Ranges: 0 to 9.99 μS/cm
0 to 99.9 μS/cm
0 to 999 μS/cm
0 to 9.99 mS/cm
0 to 99.9 mS/cm

Resistivity Range: 0 to 18.3 megohm-cm

Temp Compensation: 0 to 100°C interactive, dual matrix for high purity water

Temp Compensation Element: 1000 ohm RTD

Cell Constants: 0.01 cm, 0.10 cm, 1.0 cm, 10.0 cm

Display Accuracy: All displayed variables ±1 least significant digit

Conductivity Accuracy: ±0.002 microSiemens/cm or 1% of reading, whichever is greater temperature corrected to 25°C

Resistivity Accuracy: ±0.2 megohms-cm temperature corrected resistivity to 25°C

Temp Accuracy: ±0.1°C (0-100°C)

Stability: 0.02%/°C, 0-50°C ambient 0.1%, 105-135 V

Power Input: 120 V 50/60 Hz 8 Watts, 240 V 50/60 Hz 8 Watts, jumper selectable (requires fuse change)

Outputs: Choice of 0/4-20 mAdc isolated, RS232C with 0-5 V non-isolated

Alarm Relays: 2 SPST electromechanical relays rated 5 A 230 Vac, resistive load; supplied as normally open; high/low

Housing: NEMA-4X polycarbonate case with built-in front operated panel mounting clamps

Dimensions: 4.45″ H x 5.75″ W x 6.95″ D (43 × 146 × 177 mm)

Weight: 3 lbs (1.35 kg)(approx)

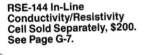

Conductivity Calibrated Instrument

CELL 1
CELL 2
μS/CM
°C
CONST.
CAL

Resistivity Calibrated Instrument

CELL 1
CELL 2
MΩ-CM
°C
CONST.
CAL

RSE-144 In-Line Conductivity/Resistivity Cell Sold Separately, $200. See Page G-7.

CDCN-003 Conductivity Controller

To Order *(Specify Model Number)*

Model No. Price	Input & Range	Output	Mating Cell
RSCN-400 $625	Resistivity 0-18.3 Mohm/cm	4-20 mA, isolated	RSE-144 RSE-154
RSCN-400-D* $730	Resistivity 0-18.3 Mohm/cm	RS-232C, 0-5V non-isolated	RSE-144 RSE-154
CDCN-001 $625	Conductivity 0.055-9.99 μS/cm	4-20 mA, isolated	RSE-144 RSE-154
CDCN-001-D* $730	Conductivity 0.055-9.99 μS/cm	RS-232C, 0-5V non-isolated	RSE-144 RSE-154
CDCN-002 $625	Conductivity 0-99.9 μS/cm, 0.01 cell constant	4-20 mA, isolated	RSE-144 RSE-154
	0-999 μS/cm 0.1 cell constant		CDE-244 CDE-254
CDCN-002-D* $730	Conductivity 0-99.9 μS/cm, 0.01 cell constant	RS-232C, 0-5 V non-isolated	RSE-144 RSE-154
	0-999 μS/cm 0.1 cell constant		CDE-244 CDE-254
CDCN-003 $625	Conductivity 0-9.99 mS/cm, 1.0 cell constant	4-20 mA, isolated	CDE-344 CDE-354
	0-99.9 mS/cm 10.0 cell constant		CDE-444 CDE-454
CDCN-003-D* $730	Conductivity 0-9.99 mS/cm, 1.0 cell constant	RS-232C, 0-5 V non-isolated	CDE-344 CDE-354
	0-99.9 mS/cm 10.0 cell constant		CDE-444 CDE-454

Software available. Consult Engineering for details.

G

INDUSTRIAL CONDUCTIVITY CONTROLLERS

Conductivity/Resistivity Cells

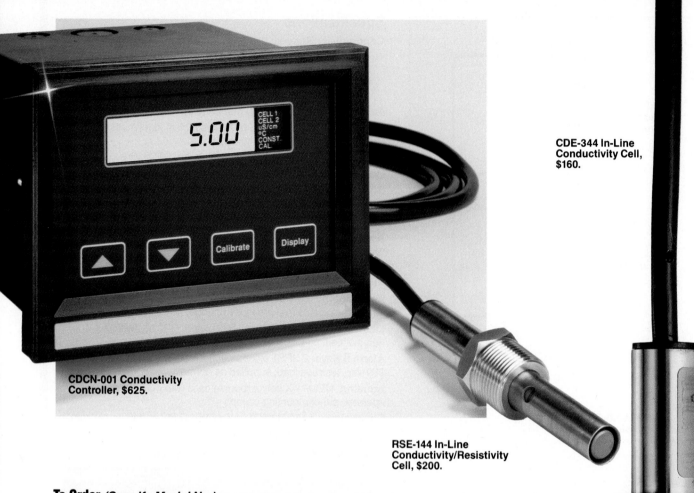

CDE-344 In-Line
Conductivity Cell,
$160.

CDCN-001 Conductivity
Controller, $625.

RSE-144 In-Line
Conductivity/Resistivity
Cell, $200.

To Order *(Specify Model No.)*

Model No. Price Cell Constant	Description	Dimensions (Dia. X Length)
RSE-144 $200 0.01 cm	In-line conductivity/resistivity probe. Stainless steel construction. Titanium-palladium electrodes with chloro-trifluoroethylene insulation. ¾" NPT 316 SS threaded connection. Rated 200 PSI at 105°C.	0.625" x 4.69" (2.06" insertion length)
RSE-154 $150 0.01 cm	Submersible conductivity/resistivity probe. Stainless steel construction. Titanium-palladium electrodes with chloro-trifluoroethylene insulation. Rated 200 PSI at 105°C	0.625" x 5.06"
CDE-244 $200 0.1 cm	In-line conductivity probe. Stainless steel construction. Titanium-palladium electrodes with chlorotrifluoroethylene insulation ¾" NPT 316 SS threaded connection. Rated 200 PSI at 105°C	0.625" x 3.81" (1.12" insertion length)
CDE-254 $150 0.1 cm	Submersible conductivity probe. Stainless Steel construction. Titanium-palladium electrodes with chlorotrifluoroethylene insulation.Rated 200 PSI at 105°C	0.625" x 5.06"
CDE-344 $160 1.0 cm	In-line conductivity probe. Graphite electrodes. Epoxy body. ¾" NPT 316 SS threaded connection. Rated 250 PSI at 105°C	0.75" x 5.00" (2.38" insertion length)
CDE-354 $122 1.0 cm	Submersible conductivity probe. Graphite electrodes. Epoxy body. Rated 250 PSI at 105°C	0.75" x 5.06"
CDE-444 $160 10.0 cm	In-line conductivity probe. Graphite electrodes. Epoxy body. ¾" NPT 316 SS threaded connection. Rated 250 PSI at 105°C	0.75" x 5.00" (2.38" insertion length)
CDE-454 $122 10.0 cm	Submersible conductivity probe. Graphite electrodes. Epoxy body. Rated 250 PSI at 105°C	0.75" x 5.06"

* All probes supplied with 10 ft of cable sealed at the cell.

Conductivity Controller
With In-Line, and Flow Through Electrodes

Model CDCN-36

$249

- ✔ High and Low Setpoints
- ✔ Compact 1/8 DIN Panel Meter
- ✔ Four Conductivity Ranges Internally Selectable
- ✔ 5 Amp Mechanical Relay
- ✔ In-Line, Submersible or Flow-thru Electrodes; Graphite or Platinum Band

Shown Smaller Than Acutal Size

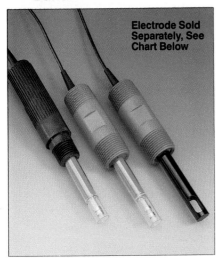

Electrode Sold Separately, See Chart Below

The CDCN-36 is a compact 1/8 DIN panel mounted on/off conductivity controller with two outputs for high and low setpoints. A one millivolt per count recorder output is included as standard. An internal switch allows the selection of four conductivity ranges which make the controller useful in diverse applications from potable water to brine solutions.

Four types of electrodes are available: one flow-thru and three different in-line/submersible electrodes. Each has a cell constant of one (K=1). Platinum band electrodes are recommended for greater stability. Graphite electrodes feature a parallel plate rather than a band design which can be more accurate in applications above 20,000 μS; they are also more rugged and easier to clean. The flow-thru cells allow continuous measurement of conductivity at flowrates up to seven GPM. Their tapered, serrated ends permit quick in-line tube connections.

Specifications:

Ranges (Selectable): 0 to 200 mS/cm (200,000 μS/cm), resolution 1 mS; 0 to 99.9 mS/cm (99,900 μS/cm), resolution 0.1 mS; 0 to 9.99 mS/cm (9990 μS/cm), resolution 0.01 mS; 0 to 999 μS/cm (999 uS/cm), resolution 1 μS

Accuracy: 1% FS ±1 digit, repeatable to 0.5% FS

Display: LED 3 digits

Recorder Output: 1 mV/count

ATC: 0 to 50 C; 10 K thermistor

Connections: Terminals on rear

Control Outputs: Dual point on/off for high and low setpoints

Deadband: ±5 LSD (counts) for each output

Relay Capacity: 2 ea 5 A @ 117 Vac, 2.5 A @ 230 Vac, SPDT

Power: 115/230 Vac, 50/60 Hz

Size: 2″ H x 3.9″ W x 7″ D (51 × 99 × 178 mm)

Weight: 1.5 lbs (.68 kg)

Panel Cutout: 1/8 DIN (1.772″ H x 3.622″ W)

To Order   (Specify Model No.)

Controller

Model No.	Price	Description
CDCN-36	$249	On/off conductivity controller

Electrodes*

Model No.	Price	Type	Construction	Body	Tube	Temp Rating @ 150 PSI
CDCN-36-EP	$110	In-line & Submersible	Platinum 2 bands	CPVC	Glass	0 to 80°C
CDCN-36-EP-K	135	In-line & Submersible	Platinum 2 bands	Kynar	Glass	0 to 120°C
CDCN-36-EG	100	In-line & Submersible	Graphite	CPVC	Epoxy	0 to 80°C
CDCN-36-EF	175	Flow-thru	Platinum 3 bands	CPVC	Glass	0 to 80°C

Electrode Installation Accessories

Model No.	Price	Description
CDEH-1TP	$40	1″ CPVC tee and CPVC reducing bushing 1″ MNPT ¾″ FNPT
CDEH-1TK	100	1″ Kynar tee and Kynar reducing bushing 1″ MNPT ¾″ FNPT

* See Section D for conductivity standardizing solutions for calibration.

Conductivity Controller

MADE IN USA

Conductivity Controller

Model CDCN-80 **$750**

- **Selectable Scale Range**
- **Receives, Computes and Displays Two Sensor Inputs on Large LCD Readouts**
- **Automatic Temperature Compensation**
- **Adjustable High & Low Alarm Settings**
- **4 to 20 mA Isolated Output**
- **Microprocessor Based**
- **Reject Ratios Displayed**
- **Panel Mountable**

Where fast and accurate conductivity control is required, OMEGA's Model CDCN-80 Conductivity Controller will simplify process measurements and control. The CDCN-80 combines the capabilities of two single channel conductivity controllers into one instrument. It can monitor two sensors and control two independent relay outputs to solenoid valves and pumps simultaneously. An acknowledge button disables each relay separately. When monitoring both inlet and product effluent quality, it has the added feature of displaying reject ratio (the input/output ratio of the process) and temperature. Operator selected high and low alarm thresholds provide double ended process control and can alert the operator when they have been exceeded. If line power goes out, a lithium battery back up for memory assures that alarm setpoints are retained. In addition, a membrane switch allows selection of three different ranges of conductivity which are shown on the large LCD readout. For ease of operation, the internal microprocessor computes the scale ranges from a single cell constant. Typical applications include de-ionization, reverse osmosis, demineralization, cooling tower control and PC board washing.

Specifications:

Input range: 0 to 37.5 mS/cm (high range); 0. to 3.75 mS/cm (med range); 0 to 370 µS/cm (low range)

Input temperature range: 0 to 100°C

Accuracy: ±0.8% of full scale

Repeatability: ±04% of full scale

Temperature Accuracy and Repeatability: ±1°C

Automatic Temperature Compensation: 0 to 100°C

Rejection Ratio Display: 0 to 100%

Alarm Ranges (high and low): 0 to 250 mS/cm

Alarm Relays: 1 per channel, SPDT, 3 A at 250 Vac or at 30 V dc; ACK (acknowledge) switch resets relays separately

Display: 3 digit LCD, 0.7″ plus eight display mode annunciators

Operating Temperature Range: 0 to 50°C

Recorder output: 4 to 20 mA isolated

Memory back-up Battery: 2 year 3 Vdc lithium battery

Power: 120 Vac

Weight: 2.2 lb

Dimensions: 5.5″ x 5.5″ x 5.1″, panel cut-out 5.1″.

For Conductivity Controller CDCN-80 use Sensor Models CDCN-81 and CDCN-82, each $200. (See opposite page).

For placing orders, call
1-800-TC-OMEGA
1-800-82-66342

Conductivity Monitor & Sensors

Conductivity Sensors

- **Versatile, Adapts to Many Applications**
- **In-Line or Submersible**
- **Automatic Temperature Compensation**

OMEGA's CDCN-81 and CDCN-82 conductivity sensors allow your process liquids to flow freely—resulting in highly accurate measurements. For versatility, they provide conductivity measurements ranging from 2 μS/cm to 25,000 μS/cm with an accuracy of $\pm$3% and 2.0 cell constant. 25 ft. cable.

*Model In-line Sensor, poly- **$200**
CDCN-81 propylene housing,
CDCN-81A stainless steel electrodes.
1¼" NPT

*Model Submersion **$200**
CDCN-82 Sensor, polypropy-
CDCN-82A lene housing, stainless steel electrodes
¾" NPT

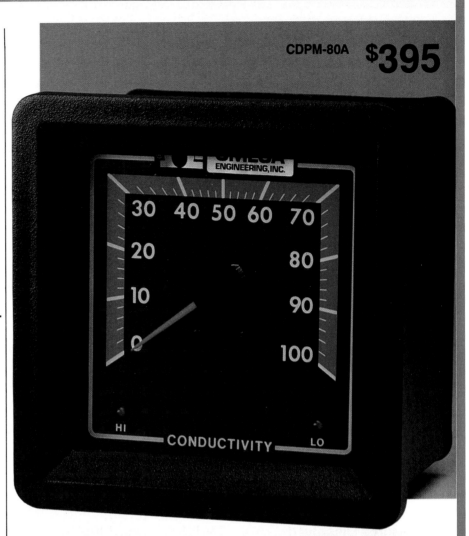

CDPM-80A **$395**

In-Line Sensor, Model CDCN-81, $200.

- **Field Selectable Measurement Ranges from 0-100 to 0-200,000 μS**
- **Automatic Temperature Compensation**
- **4 to 20 mA, 0 to 5 V Outputs**
- **Dual Alarms**

OMEGA's Model CDPM-80A Conductivity Monitor offers all of the features needed for accurate conductivity measurement in one economical unit.

Designed for processes requiring only conductivity measurement, the unit's dual alarm outputs quickly signal any abnormal conditions. With measurement ranges from 0 to 100 μS/cm to 0 to 200,000 μS/cm, the CDPM-80A is accurate to $\pm$1% of full scale.

A 4 to 20 mA output is included for interfacing with a recorder or other external equipment.

Specifications:

Range: 0 to 200 μS-CDPM-80A; 0 to 2000 μS-CDPM-80B; 0 to 20,000 μS-CDPM-80C (Requires CDCN-81 or CDCN-82 Sensor)

Accuracy: $\pm$2% of Full Scale

Repeatability: $\pm$0.5% of Full Scale

Automatic Temp. Comp.: 0 to 100ºC

Alarm Range: Full Scale of Dial (front adjustable)

Alarm Relay: SPDT, 3A at 250 Vac or 3A at 30 Vdc; 0 to 5 Vdc non-isolated

Temp Coefficient: 2%/ºC

* For conductivity monitor CDPM-80A use sensor models CDCN-81A and CDCN-82A, each $200.

G

INDUSTRIAL CONDUCTIVITY CONTROLLERS

Waterproof Dissolved Oxygen Meters
PHDG-70 and PHDG-71

Model PHDG-70
$741

Model PHDG-71
$936
with alarms

- **Measures Dissolved Oxygen in % and mg/L**
- **Automatic Temperature Compensation**
- **Includes Probe with Removable Membrane and 10 Ft Cable**
- **Available with Optional Alarms**
- **4-20 mA Recorded Output**

The PHDG-70 and PHDG-71 waterproof dissolved oxygen meters have been designed for use in damp environments and are waterproofed to IP54 standard. Perfect for monitoring oxygen levels in processes, fish farms or for BOD measurements, the PHDG-70 and 71 come complete with a membrane type oxygen sensor that is temperature compensated over the range of 0 to 40°C. The units will measure in percent or mg/L. The sensor features screw on pre-tensioned membranes to ensure repeatability of results. To record gas uptake, the 4 to 20 mA output may be used to drive a recorder. The PHDG-71 has a built in alarm system consisting of two totally independent alarm points each having its own relay and front panel indicator. To provide a fail safe backup in the event of power failure, the relays are energized below setpoint.

Specifications

Ranges: 0 to 200%, 0 to 19.9 mg/L
Resolution: 1%, 0.1 mg/L
Accuracy: for % and mg/L ±2% F.S. within ±10°C of calibration temperature
Automatic Temperature Compensation: 0 to 40°C
Alarm Relays: Two each, rated at 240V/2A
Recorder Output: 4 to 20 mA
Voltage: 110/240 Vac (user switchable)
Connections: stripped leads
Oxygen Sensor: In line, ½″ NPT, 6.1″ length, 10 ft cable
Dimensions: 8.9″ x 8.7″ x 4.9″
Weight: 4.4 lb

Options

Extra Cable: $1.50/ft
Replacement Membranes and Electrolyte: PHAC-71A $70

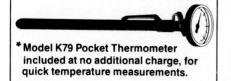

* Model K79 Pocket Thermometer included at no additional charge, for quick temperature measurements.

Waterproof and Panel Mount Conductivity Meters

Waterproof Conductivity Meters

The CDW-70 and CDW-71 Waterproof Conductivity Meters have been developed for use in damp and dirty environments and are housed in chemically resistant polycarbonate cases waterproofed to IP54 standard. All inputs and outputs from the units are through waterproof compression glands and access to the instrument controls is via a hinged clear front panel. Both units have the unique feature of a direct readout and setting of cell constant. In addition, the Model CDW-71 which has two independent alarm points each having its own relay and front panel LED indicator. The relay contacts are rated at 240V/2A. Requires CDCN-83 conductivity sensor.

Specifications

Ranges: 0 to 20 mS, 0 to 200 mS, 0 to 200 μS, 0 to 2000 μS
Accuracy: $\pm$0.5%, $\pm$2 digits
Resolution: 0.1 mS, 0.01 mS, 1 μS, 0.1 μS
Automatic Temperature Compensation: 0 to 50°C
Reference Temperature: 25°C
Recorder Output: 4 to 20 mA
Power: 110/240 V ac user switchable
Dimensions: 8.9″ × 8.7″ × 4.9″
Weight: 4.4 lb

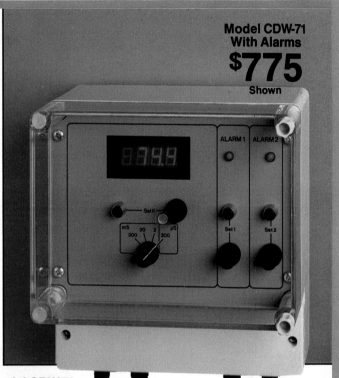

Model CDW-71 With Alarms
$775
Shown

Model CDW-70
$600
Not Shown

Model CDPM-70
$500
Not Shown

CDCN-83 In-Line Conductivity Sensor K = 1, 10 ft cable, ½″ NPT
$125
extra cable add $1/ft.

Panel Mounted Conductivity Meters

The CDPM Series of panel mounted conductivity meters measure conductivity from 0.1 μS to 200 mS in four switchable ranges. To ensure accurate readings, automatic temperture compensation is provided over the range 0 to 50°C. The meters have the unique feature of a digital readout and setting of cell constant to a resolution of 0.01 to overcome the normal problems of cell calibration. The meters are housed in a rugged steel panel mounting DIN case, allowing installation from the front to fit in limited access situations. The CDPM-71 has the additional feature of a Hi/Lo alarm system that consists of two independent alarm points with their own relay indicator. Requires CDCN-83 conductivity sensor.

Specifications

Ranges: 0 to 200 mS, 0 to 2000 μS, 0 to 200 μS
Accuracy: $\pm$0.5%, $\pm$2 digits
Resolution: 0.1 mS, 0.01 mS, 1 μS, 0.1 μS
Automatic Temperature Compensation: 0 to 50°C
Reference Temperature: 25°C
Cell Constant Range: 0.5 to 2.0
Recorder Output: 4 to 20 mA
Power: 110/240 V ac user switchable
Dimensions: 3.78″ × 3.78″ × 5.9″
Weight: CDPM-70 2.4 lb, CDPM-71 3.0 lb

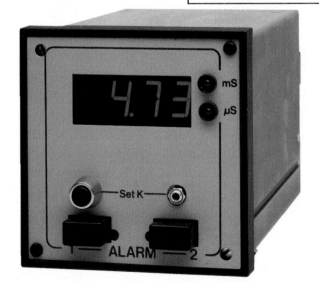

Model CDPM-71 With Alarms
$675
Shown

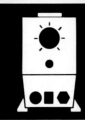

H-3 thru H-16

PUMPS AND TUBING

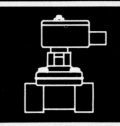

H-17 thru H-20

VALVES

H-21 thru H-28

MIXERS

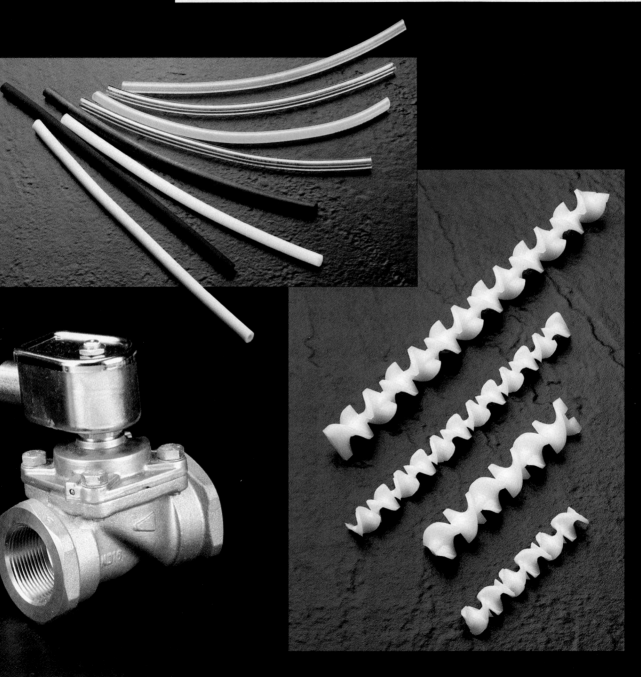

Chemical Metering Pumps
Microprocessor Based High Performance

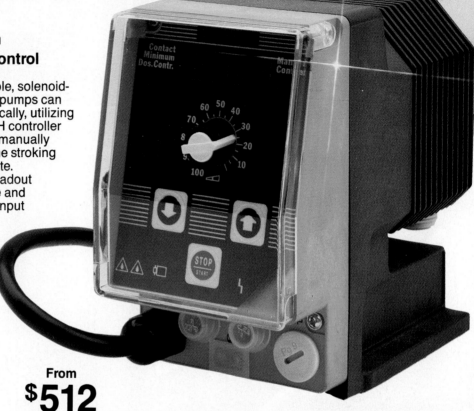

- ✔ **High Performance**
- ✔ **Easy Keypad Operation**
- ✔ **Manual or Automatic Control**

The PHP-200 Series programmable, solenoid-driven diaphragm liquid metering pumps can be operated manually or automatically, utilizing a pulse frequency signal from a pH controller or water meter. The flow output is manually adjustable from 10 to 100% and the stroking rate from 1 to 120 pulses per minute. All units feature a 3½ digit LCD readout and two LED's for operating mode and fault indication. Each unit has an input for a level switch.

The suction and discharge ports are equipped with double ball valves to ensure maximum repeatability at lower pump flow rates. The NEMA-4 glass fiber-reinforced Noryl plastic pump housing provides protection from corrosive chemicals, dust and water. The polypropylene liquid ends are equipped with air bleed valves for easy priming and continuous automatic bleeding if liquid tends to emit vapors and fumes.

From
$512

Model Number	Capacity at Maximum Back Pressure			Capacity at Average Back Pressure			Suction Line O.D. x I.D.	Discharge Line O.D. x I.D.	Material*
	PSI	USG PH (L/h)	cm³/ stroke	PSI	USG PH (L/h)	cm³/ stroke			
PHP-201/ PHP-211	145	0.05 (0.189)	0.028	72.5	0.06 (0.227)	0.036	6 x 4 mm 12 x 9 mm ¼"	6 x 4mm 12 x 9 mm ¼"	P T S
PHP-202/ PHP-212	290	0.18 (0.681)	0.096	145	0.25 (0.946)	0.132	6 x 4 mm 12 x 9 mm ¼"	6 x 4 mm 12 x 9 mm ¼"	P T S
PHP-203/ PHP-213	174	0.42 (1.59)	0.22	87	0.47 (1.78)	0.248	6 x 4 mm 12 x 9 mm ¼"	6 x 4 mm 12 x 9 mm ¼"	P T S
PHP-204/ PHP-214	116	0.81 (3.07)	0.43	58	0.94 (3.56)	0.493	6 x 4 mm 12 x 9 mm ¼"	6 x 4 mm 12 x 9 mm ¼"	P T S
PHP-205/ PHP-215	145	0.57 (2.16)	0.30	72.5	0.69 (2.61)	0.362	12 x 9 mm 12 x 9 mm ¼"	12 x 9 mm 12 x 9 mm ¼"	P T S
PHP-206/ PHP-216	50.8	2.04 (7.72)	1.08	29	2.27 (8.59)	1.195	12 x 9 mm 12 x 9 mm ¼"	12 x 9 mm 12 x 9 mm ¼"	P T S
PHP-207/ PHP-217	29	4.22 (15.97)	2.22	14.5	5.28 (20.46)	2.775	12 x 9 mm 12 x 9 mm ¼"	12 x 9 mm 12 x 9 mm ¼"	P T S

*"P" indicates Polypropylene; "T" indicates PFTE Teflon; and "S" indicates 316 Stainless Steel.

Each unit is supplied with foot and injection valves, 6 feet of contact cable for pulse input and level connector. Polypropylene models are supplied with 15 feet of PVC tubing.

1 YEAR WARRANTY

LCD readout of implemental and current functions

Monitoring functions

Input pulse indication

Lack-of-chemical annunciation

Metering monitor

Buffer memory

Predetermining counter

Signal step-up ratio*

Signal step-down ratio*
* Adaptation of stroking rate to external pulse signal sources

Down key
for entering the desired functions and data. These will be displayed by the LCD readout

Enter key
Functions to be selected by user

Yellow LED
Stroke indication

Control facilities

Manual stroking rate adjustment

Stroke control by external pulse signals (from water meter, pH controller, etc.)

Stroke control by external analog signals

Remote stroking rate adjustment by analog input signals

Infinitely variable stroke-length/stroke-volume control from 10 to 100%

Up key
for entering the desired functions and data. These will be displayed by the LCD readout

Start-stop key
for starting and stoppng pump operation

Red LED
Additional fault indication

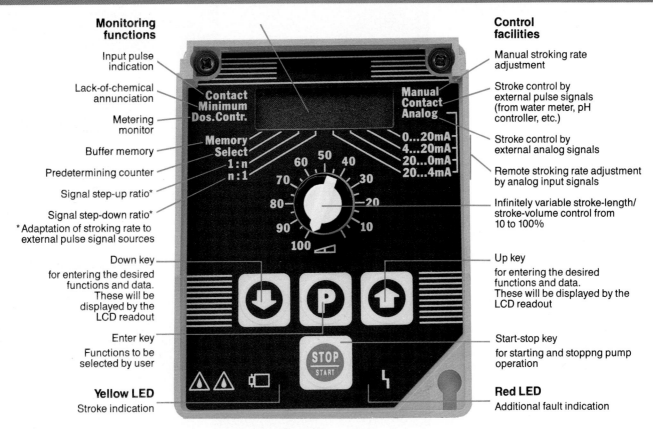

The PHP-210 Series incorporates all the features of the PHP-200 and also accepts a current input signal. This allows the stroking rate to be controlled by standard process signals. Multiple functions can be programmed through the front keypad, including step-up or step-down ratios and the predetermining counter mode which allows a pre-set number of strokes to be counted.

Specifications:

Power: 115 Vac, 60 Hz
Liquid End: Polypropylene on "P" models, PTFE on "T" models, 316 stainless steel on "S" models
Valve Balls: Ceramic on "P" and "T" models except Duran on PHP-205/6/7 and PHP-215/16/17, stainless steel on "S" models
Seals: Viton on "P" models, PTFE on "T" and "S" models
Diaphragm: PTFE-EDPM

Metering Range: 10 to 100% of capacity, overall turndown 1200:1
Maximum Frequency: 120 strokes/min., 7200 strokes/hr
Nominal Power: 12 Watts
Peak Power Consumption: 200 Watts
Dimensions: 6.75″ H x 3.40″ W x 9.25″ D (171 x 86 x 234 mm)
Weight: 5.38 lbs (2.44 kg)

To Order *(Specify Model Number)*

Pulse Frequency Input Models				Frequency/Current Input Models			
Model Number	**Price**			**Model Number**	**Price**		
	Polypropylene	**PTFE**	**316 SS**		**Polypropylene**	**PTFE**	**316 SS**
PHP-201-[*]	$705	$940	$1133	**PHP-211-[*]**	$805	$1040	$1233
PHP-202-[*]	512	838	1018	**PHP-212-[*]**	612	938	1118
PHP-203-[*]	512	838	1018	**PHP-213-[*]**	612	938	1118
PHP-204-[*]	515	840	1035	**PHP-214-[*]**	615	940	1135
PHP-205-[*]	567	814	1261	**PHP-215-[*]**	667	914	1361
PHP-206-[*]	585	818	1263	**PHP-216-[*]**	685	913	1363
PHP-207-[*]	643	882	1322	**PHP-217-[*]**	743	982	1422

*Insert "P" for Polypropylene, "T" for PTFE Teflon, or "S" for 316 Stainless Steel
Ordering Example: *PHP-214-T indicates a PHP-214 model pump with specifications shown on the chart (opposite page) and PTFE Teflon end.* **Price: $940.**

H

Chemical Metering Pumps
Heavy Duty Construction   PHP-80 Series

- ✓ **Viton Wetted Parts**
- ✓ **Flowrates from 4 to 100 Liters/Hour**
- ✓ **Resistant to Chemical and Atmospheric Corrosion**
- ✓ **Suppled with Injection and Foot Valves, Liquid Filter and Tubing**

From
$270

Tubing, Filter, Valves and Other Accessories Supplied, See Page H-9 for Additional Information.

Floating Level Probe, LEV-2, Sold Separately, $30, See Page H-9.

The OMEGA PHP-80 series metering pumps employ open and closed loop chemical dosing. The pump ensures a constant flowrate which can be set by manual control from 0 to 100% with an accuracy of ±5%. This setting varies the number of strokes. The enclosure is built from aluminum and Rilsan, a special coating which affords resistance to chemical and atmospheric corrosion, abrasion and impact. This coating also provides electrical insulation. The PHP-80 diaphragm, valves and seal gaskets are made from Viton. These rugged pumps, offered in a wide range of flowrates, are chemically compatible with a variety of liquids. They also offer an input for a level switch. Supplied with injection and foot valves, liquid filter and tubing for immediate operation.

Specifications:
Dimensions: 6.69"H x 9.61"W x 4.92"D (to 6.46"D), (170 × 244 × 125 mm to (164 mm D)
Weight: 10 lbs (4.5 kg)
Power: 110 Vac, 50/60 Hz

To Order *(Specify Model Number)*

Model No.	Price	Maximum Flowrate		Max. Back Pressure	mL/ stroke	Tubing id x od
		L/hr	GPD			
PHP-81	$373	4	24	290 PSI	.48	4x6 mm
PHP-82	329	15	96	72.5 PSI	1.25	4x6 mm
PHP-83	270	2	12	145 PSI	.34	4x6 mm
PHP-84	287	5	32	145 PSI	.58	4x6 mm
PHP-85	329	10	64	145 PSI	1	4x6 mm
PHP-86	414	30	190	58 PSI	3	8x12 mm
PHP-87	505	50	317	14.5 PSI	5	8x12 mm
PHP-88	415	18	114	87 PSI	–	4x6 mm
PHP-89	471	100	634	4.4 PSI	7.5	8x12 mm

Compact, Modular pH Controller and Chemical Dosing Pumps

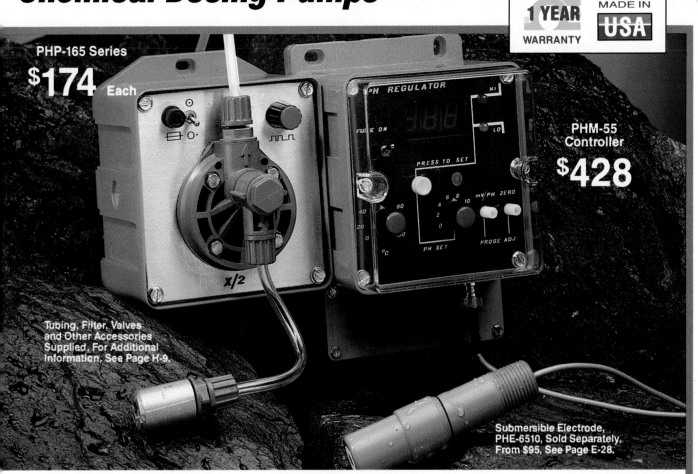

PHP-165 Series

$174 Each

x/2

PHM-55 Controller

$428

Tubing, Filter, Valves and Other Accessories Supplied. For Additional Information. See Page H-9.

Submersible Electrode, PHE-6510, Sold Separately. From $95, See Page E-28.

✔ **EDPM PTFE Diaphragm Valves and Seal Gaskets**

✔ **Polypropylene Suction and Outlet Valves**

The PHP-165 series chemical dosing pumps are compact, modular wall-mounted units. They can regulate from 0-100% via external knob and have a stainless steel front. Units are supplied with injection and foot valves, filter, tubing and mounting screws.

Specifications
Dimensions: 5.67″ H x 5.67″ W x 4.40″ D (144 × 144 × 112 mm)
Weight: 3.75 lbs (1.70 kg)
Power: 110 Vac, 50/60 Hz

Model PHM-55 Controller

✔ **Adjustable Setpoint**

✔ **5 Amp Control Relay, 3 Digit Display**

✔ **Automatic and Manual Temperature Compensation**

The PHM-55 is a modular wall-mounted controller designed for applications as wide-ranging as water

purification and industrial waste-water control. It has an adjustable setpoint, 5 Amp control relay and 3-digit pH display. The PHM-55 is contained in a rugged plastic enclosure with IP512 protection and extended bottom section for terminal board connections. Modular design allows for coupling with PHP-165 series pumps.

Specifications
Range: 0 to 14.0 pH
Resolution: 0.1 pH
Accuracy: ±0.1 pH
Input Impedance: > 10^{12} ohms
Temperature Compensation: Manual or automatic 100 ohm Pt RTD
Connections: pH-BNC, ATC-stripped leads
Relay: High or low setpoint 5 Amp
Setpoint Hysteresis: ±0.1 pH
Recorder Output: 4-20 mA
Power: 110 Vac, 50/60 Hz
Dimensions: 7.49″ H x 5.67″ W x 3.94″ D (190 × 144 × 100 mm)
Weight: 1.54 lbs (0.7 kg)

To Order *(Specify Model Number)*

Model No.	Price	Maximum Flowrate		Max. Back Pressure	mL/ stroke	Tubing id x od
		L/hr	GPD			
PHP-165	$174	3	19	42 PSI	.3	4x6 mm
PHP-166	174	1.5	9.5	84 PSI	–	4x6 mm
PHP-167	174	6	38	0	.35	4x6 mm

H

Chemical Metering Pumps for On/Off or Proportional Control

Tubing, Filter, Valves and Other Accessories Supplied. Floating Level Probe, LEV-2, Sold Separately, $30, See Bottom of Page H-9 for Additional Information.

PHP-70 Series

From

$179

- ✓ Wall Mounted ABS Enclosure
- ✓ Capacities From 1.5 to 6 Liters Per Hour
- ✓ Manually Adjustable From 0 to 100%

The PHP-70 series chemical metering pumps include models PHP-74/75 which can be used in conjunction with a pH controller for on/off control. Models PHP-75-MA/76-MA/77-MA, which accept a 4-20 mA signal from a pH controller, are designed for applications requiring proportional control. The pumps are manually adjustable from 0 to 100% of maximum capacity with an external regulating knob. The wall mounted enclosure is made from ABS. Model PHP-74 is supplied with lip valves and Viton seal gaskets. All other models are equipped with ball valves and silicone seal gaskets. Pumps which accept a milliamp input can operate in manual or automatic mode simply by changing the position of the electrical switch; they also include an input for a level switch.

Specifications
Power: 110 Vac 50/60 Hz
Dimensions: 6.50″ H x 7.36″ W x 5.91″ D (165 × 187 × 150 mm)
Weight: 7.62 lbs. (3.34 kg)

To Order (Specify Model Number)

Model No.	Price	Maximum Flowrate		Max. Back Pressure	mL/ stroke	Tubing id x od
		L/hr	GPD			
PHP-74	$195	4	25	98 PSI	.64	4x6 mm
PHP-75	179	1.5	9.5	112 PSI	.16	4x6 mm
PHP-75MA	302	3	19	42 PSI	.3	4x6 mm
PHP-76MA	302	6	38	-	.35	4x6 mm
PHP-77MA	302	1.5	9.5	84 PSI	-	4x6 mm

Large Capacity Chemical Metering Pumps

 NEW!

✔ **Rugged, Heavy Duty Pumps**

✔ **Accept 4-20 mA Input Signal for Proportional Control**

✔ **Applications From Water Chlorination to Control of Nickel Plating Baths**

The PHP-50 series large capacity chemical metering pumps have PTFE diaphragms. The PHP-51 has suction/outlet valves and Viton seal gaskets, while the PHP-52/53 employ Viton ogival valves with hastelloy springs and Viton seal gaskets. The pumps are wall mounted and have an aluminum cast enclosure coated with a special polymer resin. They also feature manual control with an external knob for 0 to 100% adjustment of pump capacity. Automatic control is accomplished through the mA input signal. There is also an input for a level switch.

Specifications
Power: 110 Vac, 50/60 Hz

Dimensions: 6.69″ H x 9.61″ W x 4.92″ (to 6.46″) D (170 × 244 × 125 (to 164) mm)

Weight: 10 lbs (4.54 kg)

PHP-50 Series

From **$365**

Tubing, Filter, Valves and Other Accessories Supplied. Floating Level Probe, LEV-2, Sold Separately, $30, See Bottom of Page H-9 for Additional Information.

PHP-120 Series

✔ **Accepts Pulse Frequency Input for Proportional Control**

✔ **Selector Switch for Changing Frequency, Up to 1200 Pulses/Min**

✔ **Viton Wetted Parts**

The PHP-120 series of large capacity, heavy duty pumps can accept pulse signals from pH controllers or watermeters. These pumps can take a maximum of 166 pulses per minute with a ratio of 1:1, one stroke per pulse. This ratio can be modified by an external thumbwheel switch so that the pump can accept a faster frequency of up to 1200 pulses per minute. The enclosure is aluminum coated with Rilsan for protection from atmospheric and chemical corrosion. The unit has an input for a level switch and comes complete with an injection valve, foot valve, filter and tubing.

Specifications
Dimensions: 6.69″ H x 9.61″ W x 4.92″ D (to 6.46″D)(170 x 244 x 125 (to 164) mm)

Weight: 10 lbs (4.54 kg)

Power: 110 Vac, 50/60 Hz

To Order (Specify Model Number)

Model No.	Price	Maximum Flowrate		Max. Back Pressure	mL/ stroke	Tubing id x od
		L/hr	GPD			
PHP-121	$307	10	64	145 PSI	1	4x6 mm
PHP-122	486	50	317	14.5 PSI	5	8x12 mm
PHP-51	365	10	64	140 PSI	1	4x6 mm
PHP-52	524	50	317	14 PSI	5	8x12 mm
PHP-53	524	100	634	42 PSI	7.5	8x12 mm

H

Chemical Metering Pumps for Continuous or Automatic Operation

PHP-180 Series
From
$405

✔ **Manual or Proportional Control**
✔ **Accept Pulse Frequency Input Signal**
✔ **Rugged and Heavy Duty**

PHP-180 series chemical metering pumps can be operated continuously or automatically by means of a pulse frequency signal. The operator simply changes the switch position from C to H. The pump is designed for applications involving the chemical dosing of a solution in relation to the volume of liquid being treated (i.e. the chlorination of water). By setting the second switch for x1 the pump responds with one dose for every four input pulses received. In the x10 position the pump will respond with one dose for every 40 input pulses received. By adjusting the regulating knob from 0 to 100% in the x10 position the dosing ratio can be varied. These pumps are available in three capacities. Model PHP-181 features Viton wetted parts. Models PHP-182/183 have polyethylene Ogival valves with hastelloy springs and Viton gaskets. Pump housing is aluminum coated with a polymer resin for corrosion protection.

Tubing, Filter, Valves and Other Accessories Supplied. Floating Level Probe, LEV-2, Sold Separately, $30.

Specifications
Power: 110 Vac, 50/60 Hz
Dimensions: 6.69" H x 9.61" W x 4.92" (to 6.46") D (164 x 244 x 125 (to 164) mm)
Weight: 10 lbs (4.54 kg)

To Order (Specify Model Number)

Model No.	Price	Maximum Flowrate		Maximum Back Pressure	mL/ stroke	Tubing id x od
		L/hr	GPD			
PHP-181	$405	10	64	142 PSI	1	4x6 mm
PHP-182	520	50	317	14.2 PSI	5	8x12 mm
PHP-183	520	30	190	57 PSI	3	8x12 mm

Accessories and Options for Pumps Shown on Pages H-5 Thru H-9

Supplied:
Each pump comes with foot and injection valves, 6½ ft. of PVC suction tubing, 6½ ft. of polyethylene delivery tubing, filter, mounting hardware, connector for pumps with mA or frequency input, and a bracket for pumps with a level input to hold level switch and filter.

Optional:
Floating level probe with reversible magnetic actuation, PVC float, 6½ ft. of cable and connector. Model number: **LEV-2, $30.**

For additional tubing see pages H-15 and H-16.

OMEGAFLEX™ Peristaltic Pumps
PHP-1S and PHP-SX Series

PHP-1S Series

✔ **Silicone Membrane Tube**
✔ **Sliding Compression Action**
✔ **1.5 to 65 Liters Per Hour Flowrate**

From **$123**

Specifications:
Power: 110 Vac, 50/60 Hz

The OMEGAFLEX PHP-1S series peristaltic pumps are designed for quiet continuous operation. The pumps work by a sliding compression action which is powered by an induction motor. The membrane tube which contains the liquid is compressed by applying rotary movement through a series of rollers, in a triangular form, which pushes the liquid through the tube. The main feature of these pumps is a minimum number of parts in contact with the liquid. This is limited to the membrane tube and PVC connectors. The standard membrane tube is made from silicone; for greater chemical compatibility, membrane tubes in dutral, viton and natural rubber can be substituted (consult pH Engineering). The membrane tube should provide at least 1800 hours of operation. The pumps are housed in a modular ABS enclosure designed for wall or panel mounting. The modular design allows for pumps to be adjoined to one another. An additional option for this line is a regulating knob with adjustment from 0 to 100% of the pump capacity. This allows the user to fine tune the pump's output. The regulating knob controls an internal electronic circuit which helps maintain a constant flowrate. For example, if the viscosity of the liquid should change, the pump will adjust accordingly to maintain the same flowrate. (For this option add "-R" to the part number and $75.00 to the price). External tubing dimensions are 4 × 6mm or 6 × 8 mm (id × od).

To Order (Specify Model Number)

Model No.	Price	Maximum Flowrate		Maximum Back Pressure
		L/hr	GPD	
PHP-1S-(*)	$123	1.5	9.5	14.2 PSI
PHP-2S-(*)	123	3	19	14.2 PSI
PHP-3S-(*)	140	1	6.3	57 PSI
PHP-4S-(*)	140	6	38	14.2 PSI
PHP-5S-(*)	169	10	63	14.2 PSI
PHP-6SX	162	15	95	14.2 PSI
PHP-7SX	172	30	190	14.2 PSI
PHP-8SX	212	65	412	14.2 PSI

*Add "-R" for optional regulating knob and $75 to price.
Ordering Example: PHP-2S-R, $123 + $75 = $198.

Accessories

Model No.	Price	Description
PHP-1S-RED	$2	Output reducer, nylon construction, restricts outlet flow, for capacities to 10 L/hr (PHP-1S series)
PHP-SX-RED	3	Output reducer, nylon construction, restricts outlet flow, for capacities from 15 L/hr to 65 L/hr (PHP-SX series)

For OEM applications the OMEGAFLEX series PHP-SX peristaltic pumps are large capacity pumps without enclosures. These pumps also operate by a sliding compression action and feature silicone membrane tubes as standard. Membrane tubes in dutral, viton and natural rubber can also be substituted (consult pH Engineering).

The pumps are available in capacities of 15 L/hr, 30 L/hr and 65 L/hr and have a duty cycle of 30%. The pumps have PVC tubing connections of 8 mm id. × 12 mm od. Note: the maximum working time of the PHP-SX pumps is 10 minutes with a 30 minute pause.

H

OMEGAFLEX™ OEM STYLE PERISTALTIC PUMPS

The FPU100 series peristaltic pumps offer exceptional simplicity and a very low cost. The UL listed AC or DC motor turns the rollers, which squeeze fluid through the precision-bore, high tolerance tubing in a wave-like motion, acting like a positive displacement pump. The fluid doesn't contact the pump, only the tubing. This makes the pump suitable for fluids carrying small particles. The FPU100 pumps continuously overocclude the tubing, which makes the pump self-priming and non-siphoning. They are easy to maintain, with few moving parts, and no seals or valves to clog, clean, or replace. As one section of tube fatigues, just move the tubing to a section which hasn't been under the rollers, and continue pumping. Or simply replace the supplied tubing. The replacement 9″ lengths of precision-bore tubing insure repeatable pumping rates time after time. The pumps are supplied with tubing that has polyethylene union connectors for hooking up your system tubing (see page L-15 for extension tubing). The replacement 9″ lengths of precision-bore tubing are supplied without connectors. The pumps are supplied standard with a mounting panel. The AC powered pumps are also available in a rugged, polycarbonate enclosure for bench mounting. See page L-13. Maximum backpressure is 15 psi without derating (up to 20 psi @ 98% of maximum flow). Maximum suction head is 28 feet. Flow rate repeatability from one pump to the next or when replacing tubing is within 8% of maximum flowrate listed. Shipping weight is 3.5 lbs. for all sizes. These pumps are ideal for metering/dosing, repetitive dispensing, and general liquid/gas transfer, and they have a 100% duty cycle for continuous operation.

Dimensions
Mounting Plate: 3.74″H × 5.12″W × 4.28″ depth. The .218″ diameter holes are centered 3.0″ × 4.34″ on the plate. For units with rear fan: 5.11″H × 5.12″W × 5.28″D overall.
Case: 6″H × 6″W × 4″D.
Shipping Weight: 3.5 lbs.

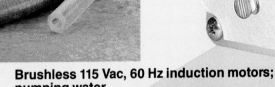

Brushless 115 Vac, 60 Hz induction motors; flow rates based on pumping water

To Order *(Specify Model Number)* Norprene Tube Standard

| Model No. | Price | Approx. Flow Rate | | Tube ID | Average Tube Life | | RPM | Amper-age*** |
		@ 60 Hz. Ml/Min	GPM		Silicone Hours†	Norprene Hours†		
FPU101	$60	3	.0008	¹⁄₁₆″	2600	5200	14	.35
FPU102	60	5	.0013	¹⁄₁₆″	1600	3200	23	.35
FPU103	60	6	.0016	¹⁄₁₆″	1300	2600	28	.35
FPU104	60	12	.0032	⅛″	2600	5200	14	.35
FPU105	60	20	.0052	⅛″	1600	3200	23	.35
FPU106	60	25	.0065	⅛″	1300	2600	28	.35
FPU107	60	30	.008	³⁄₁₆″	2600	5200	14	.35
FPU108	75	45	.012	³⁄₁₆″	1600	3200	23	.35
FPU109	75	50	.013	¼″	2600	5200	14	.35
FPU110	75	55	.015	³⁄₁₆″	1300	2600	28	.35
FPU111	75	70	.018	³⁄₁₆″	1000	2000	36	.35
FPU112	75	80	.022	¼″	1600	3200	23	.35
FPU113	83	100	.026	³⁄₁₆″	750	1500	49	.48
FPU114	75	100	.026	¼″	1300	2600	28	.35
FPU115	83	115	.030	³⁄₁₆″	600	1200	58	.63
FPU116	75	130	.034	¼″	1000	2000	36	.35
FPU117	96	150	.040	³⁄₁₆″	500	1000	75	.85
FPU118	96	165	.044	¼″	750	1500	49	.48
FPU119	96	195	.052	¼″	600	1200	58	.63
FPU120	96	250	.066	¼″	500	1000	75	.85
FPU121	96	360	.095	¼″	350	700	108	1.2
FPU122	96	425	.110	¼″	300	600	129	1.2
FPU123	99	635	.168	¼″	200	400	172	1.8
FPU124	99	750	.200	¼″	180	360	203	1.8
FPU125	99	1000	.265	¼″	130	260	282	2.2

* For units powered by 24 Vdc, add suffix ''-24 Vdc'' to part number, and add $19 to price. For units powered by 240 Vac @ 50 Hz, add suffix ''-240 Vac'' to part number, and add $5 to price. 50 Hz units have approximately 5/6 of the capacity of standard 60 Hz units. For dual head units with two separate outputs, add suffix ''-DUAL'' to part number, and add $25 to list price. Example: FPU119-240VAC-DUAL calls out a 240 Vac, 50 Hz powered, dual head unit with a total flow of 5/6 x 2,000 ml/min.= 1,666 ml/min. Price = $99 + $5 + $25 = $129
*** 240 Vac amperage is ½ that for 115 Vac; 24 Vdc amperage, .8 amps nominal max. For dual head units, consult flow department.

REPLACEMENT 9″ TUBING LENGTHS

To Order *(Specify Model Number)*

Model No.	Price	Description (ID x OD)
FPU16-N	$4	¹⁄₁₆″ × ⅛″ Norprene tubing *
FPU16-S	4	¹⁄₁₆″ × ⅛″ silicone tubing *
FPU18-N	2	⅛″ × ⅜″ Norprene tubing
FPU18-S	2	⅛″ × ⅜″ silicone tubing
FPU316-N	2	³⁄₁₆″ × ⅜″ Norprene tubing
FPU316-S	2	³⁄₁₆″ × ⅜″ silicone tubing
FPU14-N	2	¼″ × ⁷⁄₁₆″ Norprene tubing
FPU14-S	2	¼″ × ⁷⁄₁₆″ silicone tubing

*These tubes are supplied inserted into ³⁄₁₆″ x ⅜″ tubes. Connection is made to the ¹⁄₁₆″ x ⅛″ internal tubing.

1 YEAR WARRANTY

MADE IN USA

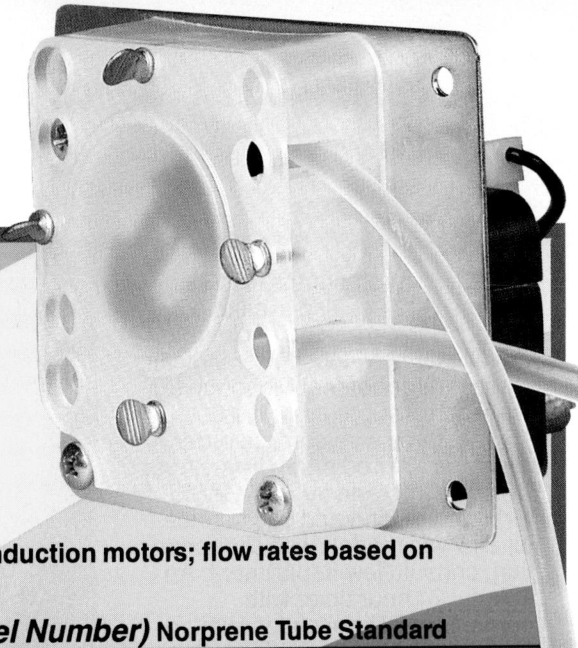

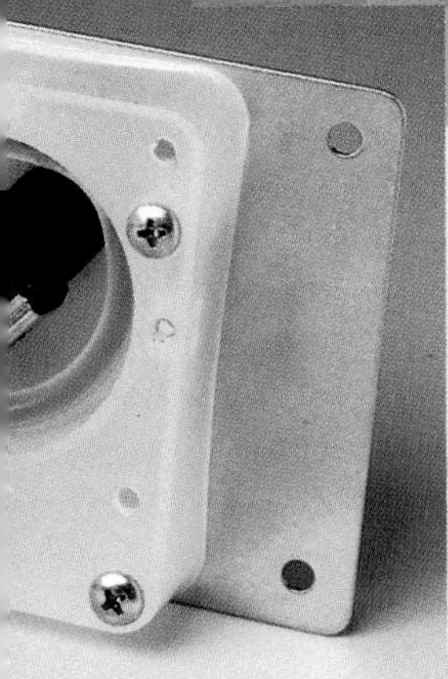

Shown Smaller Than Actual Size

DISCOUNT SCHEDULE

1-5= NET
6-12= 10%
13-24= 15%
25-49= 20%
50-UP= CONSULT SALES

† Pumps are supplied with Norprene Tubes standard. For Silicone Tubing add suffix ''-SL'' to Model Number. No additional charge. Example: FPU119-SL calls for a 195 ml/min. pump with silicone tube. Price $96.

H

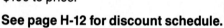

OMEGAFLEX™ Bench Top Peristaltic Pump Assemblies

NEW!

The AC powered pumps from pages H-11 and H-12 are also available in a rugged, polycarbonate enclosure with ON/OFF switch, power indicator lamp, and rubber feet for bench top use. Each is supplied with a 6', 115 Vac, three wire cord. To order, select the desired pump from pages H-11 and H-12. Add suffix ''-CASE'' to part number, and add $63 to price. For 240 Vac models with European plug, consult flow department. An optional 24 hour timer with momentary ON switch for priming the pump is also available for the case unit. The timer is settable up to 24 hours in increments of 15 minutes by internal dip switches. To order case unit with timer for 115 Vac, add suffix ''-CT'' to part number, and add $100 to price.

See page H-12 for discount schedule.

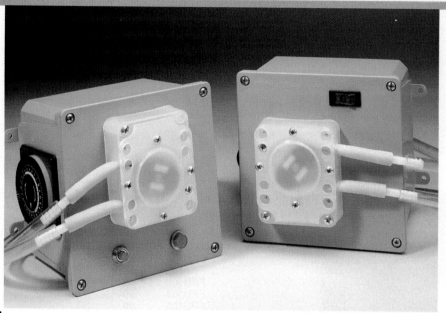

Complete pH Control System

Shown is a pH control system, with one FPU100-CASE pump adding base, and the other FPU100-CASE-CT pump adding acid. The PHE-2123 electrode, mounted on the PHA-33 third arm, is displayed on the PHB-51, and the pumps are turned on and off to vary the pH level. An LV820 level switch is used for high level alarm. See the complete pH Handbook for further details on pH control systems.

FPU-104-CASE Pump in bench top case, Price $123
FPU-104-CASE-CT Pump in case with timer, Price $160
PHE-2123 Electrode, Price $79
PHA-33 Third Arm, Price $69
PHB-51 pH Meter, Price $300
LV820 Level Switch, Price $259

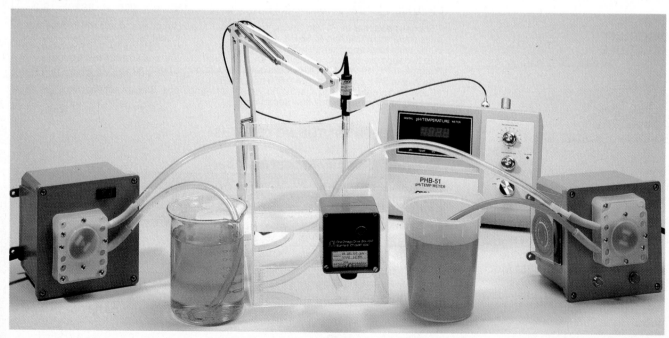

PHP-190 Series Chemical Metering Systems

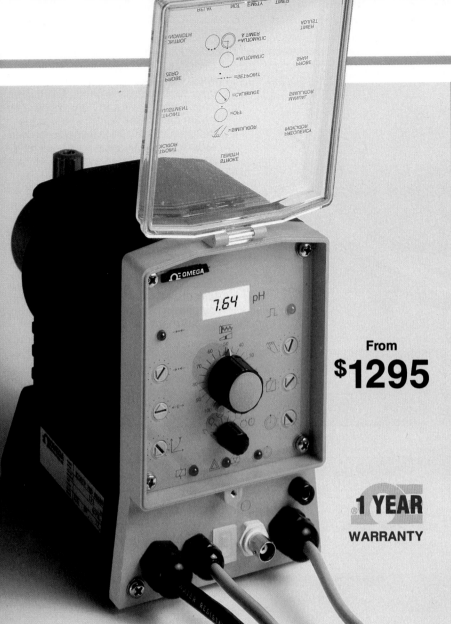

- **Combines Controller and Pump in One Unit**
- **Proportional Control**
- **LCD Readout of Process pH or Set Point**
- **Reverse Direction Control**
- **Control Bandwidth Manually Adjustable, 1 to 3 pH Units**
- **NEMA 4X Enclosure**
- **Choice of PVC, PTFE or 316 SS Liquid Ends**

From
$1295

1 YEAR WARRANTY

The PHP-190 Series of chemical metering systems are unique instruments that combine a pulse frequency controller with a diaphragm type pump in one compact unit.
In the control mode, deviations from set point are converted to pulses which vary the stroke rate of the metering pump. As the set point is approached, the pump feed slows down to minimize chemical loss and overshoot of the endpoint. Variation of the stroke rate is controlled by a front panel potentiometer or through process controlled operation by external electric or mechanical pacing or by closed loop control. The units are supplied with foot valve, injection valve, power cord, level switch connector and PVC models include 15 feet of PVC tubing.

Specifications:
Range: pH control 0 to 14 pH
Electrode Connector: BNC
Input Impedance: $> 10^{12}$ ohms
Analog Output (optional): 0 to 20 mA or 4 to 20 mA into 350 ohms max.
Zero Point Adjustment: ± 3 pH
Slope Adjustment: 85 to 102%
Set Point Adjustment: 0 to 100%
Display: 3 digit LCD
Control Bandwidth: 1 to 3 pH units, adjustable
Control Direction: Reversible
Linearity: Better than $\pm 1\%$ range
Reproducibility: Better than $\pm 0.5\%$ range
Operating Temperature: -10 to 45°C
Power: 115 V ac

Option Accessories:
Available on all models:
Signal output 0 to 20 mA, 4 to 20 mA.
PHP-01 $74

One additional option may be chosen from the following:
Relay output "tank level"
PHP-02 $38
Relay output "pump stops"
PHP-03 $55
Relay output "pacing relay" for pump stroke **PHP-04 $38**
Control timer with output relay for pump cut-off **PHP-07 $207**

To Order: *(Specify Model Number)*

Model No.	Price		
	PVC	PTFE	316 SS
PHP-191-[*]	$1295	$1500	$1717
PHP-192-[*]	1543	1919	2154
PHP-193-[*]	1543	1919	2159
PHP-194-[*]	1548	1922	2174
PHP-195-[*]	1630	1866	2496
PHP-196-[*]	1703	1955	2578

*** To order, specify P for PVC, T for PTFE Teflon®, or S for 316 stainless steel.**

OMEGAFLEX™ Tubing and Accessories

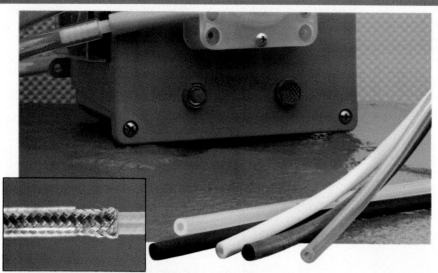

OMEGAFLEX™ tubing is offered in a wide variety of materials to meet all your tubing requirements. From low cost Tygon, Vinyl and Polyethylene, to chemically inert Teflon, spool sizes include 5, 50 or 100 foot spools for your ordering convenience. A wide variety of diameters are also available to suit your most demanding applications.

To improve durability, tubing up to ¾ inch diameter can be overbraided with 304 Stainless Steel on special order. As an additional option, OMEGA can supply overbraided tubing with an additional PVC coating to protect the 304SS overbraiding from chemical attach or to permit sealing the tubing with standard compression fittings. For details on overbraiding, consult sales department.

To Order (Specify Model Number)

I.D. in.	I.D. mm	O.D. in.	O.D. mm	Wall in.	Wall mm	Silicone 50' PKG Model Number	$ Per 50' pkg	Norprene 50' PKG Model Number	$ Per 50' pkg	Tygon 50' PKF Model Number	$ Per 50' pkg	Vinyl 100' PKG Model Number	$ Per 100' pkg
1/50	0.5	1/12	2.1	1/32	0.8	TYSC-112150-50	32.00	—	—	—	—	—	—
1/32	0.8	1/16	1.6	1/64	0.4	—	—	—	—	—	—	—	—
1/32	0.8	3/32	2.4	1/32	0.8	TYSC-332132-50	24.00	—	—	TYTY-332132-50	4.50	—	—
1/16	1.6	1/8	3.2	1/32	0.8	TYSC-18116-50	17.00	—	—	TYTY-18116-50	6.00	TYVV-18116-100	8.00
1/16	1.6	3/16	4.8	1/16	1.6	—	—	TYNP-316116-50	13.00	TYTY-316116-50	16.00	—	—
3/32	2.4	1/8	3.2	1/64	0.4	—	—	—	—	—	—	—	—
3/32	2.4	5/32	4.0	1/32	0.8	TYSC-532332-50	26.00	—	—	TYTY-532332-50	8.00	—	—
1/8	3.2	3/16	4.8	1/32	0.8	TYSC-31618-50	34.00	—	—	TYTY-31618-50	9.60	—	—
1/8	3.2	1/4	6.4	1/16	1.6	TYSC-1418-50	52.00	TYNP-1418-50	17.00	TYTY-1418-50	20.00	TYVY-1418-100	10.00
1/8	3.2	3/8	9.6	1/8	3.2	TYSC-3818-50	76.00	TYNP-3818-50	31.00	TYTY-3818-50	50.00	—	—
9/64	3.6	3/16	4.8	1/40	0.6	—	—	—	—	—	—	—	—
5/32	4.0	7/32	5.6	1/32	0.8	TYSC-732532-50	36.00	—	—	TYTY-732532-50	12.00	—	—
5/32	4.0	1/4	6.4	3/64	1.2	—	—	—	—	—	—	—	—
3/16	4.8	1/4	6.4	1/32	0.8	TYSC-14316-50	38.00	—	—	TYTY-14316-50	14.00	—	—
3/16	4.8	5/16	8.0	1/16	1.6	TYSC-516316-50	40.00	TYNP-516316-50	16.00	TYTY-516316-50	29.00	TYVV-516316-100	10.00
3/16	4.8	7/16	11.2	1/8	3.2	TYSC-716316-50	86.00	—	—	TYTY-716316-50	77.00	TYVV-716316-100	24.00
7/32	5.6	5/16	8.0	3/64	1.2	—	—	—	—	—	—	—	—
1/4	6.4	5/16	8.0	1/32	0.8	TYSC-51614-50	50.00	—	—	TYTY-51614-50	18.00	—	—
1/4	6.4	3/8	9.6	1/16	1.6	TYSC-3814-50	48.00	TYNP-3814-50	20.00	TYTY-3814-50	35.00	TYVV-3814-100	12.00
1/4	6.4	7/16	11.2	3/32	2.4	TYSC-71614-50	68.00	TYNP-71614-50	33.00	TYTY-71614-50	60.00	TYVV-71614-100	18.00
1/4	6.4	1/2	12.8	1/8	3.2	TYSC-1214-50	102.00	TYNP-1214-50	48.00	TYTY-1214-50	81.00	TYVV-1214-100	26.00
19/64	7.6	3/8	9.6	1/25	1.0	—	—	—	—	—	—	—	—
5/16	8.0	3/8	9.6	1/32	0.8	—	—	—	—	—	—	—	—
5/16	8.0	7/16	11.2	1/16	1.6	TYSC-716516-50	68.00	TYNP-716516-50	24.00	TYTY-716516-50	47.00	TYVV-716516-100	14.00
5/16	8.0	1/2	12.8	3/32	2.4	TYSC-12516-50	82.00	TYNP-12516-50	39.00	TYTY-12516-50	76.00	TYVV-12516-100	26.00
5/16	8.0	9/16	14.4	1/8	3.2	TYSC-916516-50	114.00	—	—	TYTY-916516-50	92.00	TYVV-916516-100	54.00
3/8	9.6	7/16	11.2	1/32	0.8	—	—	—	—	—	—	—	—
3/8	9.6	1/2	12.8	1/16	1.6	TYSC-1238-50	60.00	TYNP-1238-50	28.00	TYTY-1238-50	49.00	TYVV-1238-100	17.00
3/8	9.6	9/16	14.4	3/32	2.4	TYSC-91638-50	98.00	TYNP-91638-50	45.00	TYTY-91638-50	79.00	TYVV-91638-100	26.00
3/8	9.6	5/8	16.0	1/8	3.2	TYSC-5838-50	112.00	TYNP-5838-50	64.00	TYTY-5838-50	102.00	TYVV-5838-100	35.00
2/5	10.2	1/2	12.8	1/20	1.4	—	—	—	—	—	—	—	—
7/16	11.2	1/2	12.8	1/32	0.8	—	—	—	—	—	—	—	—
7/16	11.2	9/16	14.4	1/16	1.6	—	—	TYNP-916716-50	38.00	TYTY-916716-50	72.00	TYVV-916716-100	23.00
1/2	12.8	9/16	14.4	1/32	0.8	—	—	—	—	—	—	—	—
1/2	12.8	5/8	16.0	1/16	1.6	TYSC-5812-50	104.00	TYNP-5812-50	36.00	TYTY-5812-50	74.00	TYVV-5812-100	24.00
1/2	12.8	3/4	19.2	1/8	3.2	TYSC-3412-50	140.00	—	—	TYTY-3412-50	125.00	TYVV-3412-100	44.00
9/16	14.4	5/8	16.0	1/32	0.8	—	—	—	—	—	—	—	—
5/8	16.0	3/4	19.2	1/16	1.6	—	—	—	—	—	—	—	—
5/8	16.0	13/16	20.8	3/32	2.4	TYSC-131658-50	158.00	TYNP-131658-50	68.00	TYTY-131658-50	122.00	TYVV-131658-100	36.00
5/8	16.0	7/8	22.4	1/8	3.2	TYSC-7858-50	166.00	TYNP-7858-50	95.00	TYTY-7858-50	158.00	TYVV-7858-100	50.00
5/8	16.0	29/32	23.2	9/64	3.6	—	—	—	—	—	—	—	—
3/4	19.2	1	25.4	1/32	0.8	TYSC-134-50	230.00	TYNP-134-50	110.00	TYTY-134-50	178.00	TYVV-134-100	60.00
3/4	19.2	1 1/42	26.0	23/168	3.4	—	—	—	—	—	—	—	—
3/4	19.2	13/16	21.2	1/25	1.0	—	—	—	—	—	—	—	—
3/4	19.2	7 1/8	28.6	3/16	4.8	—	—	—	—	—	—	—	—
3/4	19.2	1 5/16	33.3	1/25	1.0	—	—	—	—	—	—	—	—

OMEGA tubing union connectors are offered in polyethylene, standard nylon, or rugged glass-filled nylon. They are one piece connectors, barbed at both ends. (Not suitable for use with teflon tubing.)

STRAIGHT TUBING UNION CONNECTORS

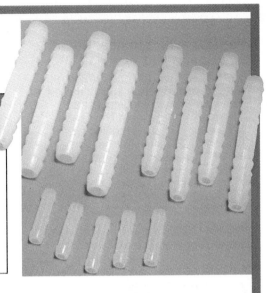

Model No. Polyethylene	Price PKG of 10	Model No. Nylon	Price PKG of 10	Tubing I.D.
TYPP-UN-116	$1.45	TYNY-UN-116	$1.90	1/16"
TYPP-UN-332	1.45	TYNY-UN-332	1.90	3/32"
TYPP-UN-18	1.45	TYNY-UN-18	1.90	1/8"
TYPP-UN-316	1.45	TYNY-UN-316	2.00	3/16"
TYPP-UN-14	1.55	TYNY-UN-14	2.10	1/4"
TYPP-UN-516	1.55	TYNY-UN-516	2.10	5/16"
TYPP-UN-38	1.65	TYNY-UN-38	2.15	3/8"
TYPP-UN-12	1.65	TYNY-UN-12	2.25	1/2"
TYPP-UN-58	1.80	TYNY-UN-58	2.45	5/8"
TYPP-UN-34	4.25	TYNY-UN-34	5.30	3/4"

Polypropylene 100' PKG		Viton 5' or 50' PKG		Teflon TFE 50' PKG		Teflon FEP 50' PKG		Teflon PFA 5' or 50' PKGS		Reinforced PVC 50' PKG	
Model Number	$ Per 100' pkg	Model Number	$ Per 5' or 50' pkg	Model Number	$ Per 50' pkg	Model Number	$ Per 50' pkg	Model Number	$ Per 5' or 50' pkg	Model Number	$ Per 50' Pkg
—	—	—	—	—	—	TYTF-116132-50	15.00	—	—	—	—
—	—	—	—	—	—	—	—	—	—	—	—
TYPP-18332-100	11.00	TYVT-18116-50	34.00	TYVT-18116-50	35.00	TYTF-18116-50	21.00	TYTP-18116-50	50.00	—	—
—	—	—	—	—	—	TYTF-532332-50	32.00	—	—	—	—
TYPP-1418-100	15.00	TYVT-31618-50	46.00	—	—	TYTF-31618-50	36.00	—	—	—	—
TYPP-316964-100	17.00	—	—	—	—	—	—	—	—	—	—
TYPP-14316-100	18.00	TYVT-14316-50	68.00	TYTT-14316-50	82.00	TYTF-14316-50	48.00	TYTP-14532-50	124.00	—	—
TYPP-516316-100	19.00	—	—	—	—	—	—	—	—	—	—
TYPP-51614-100	23.00	TYVT-51614-50	76.00	—	—	TYTF-51614-50	57.00	TYTP-516732-50	202.00	—	—
TYPP-3814-100	24.00	—	—	—	—	—	—	TYTP-3814-50	252.00	TYRP-1214-50	20.00
TYPP-381964-100	28.00	—	—	TYTT-381964-50	184.00	TYTF-38516-50	73.00	—	—	—	—
TYPP-716516-100	29.00	TYVT-716516-50	180.00	—	—	—	—	—	—	—	—
—	—	—	—	—	—	TYTF-71638-50	84.00	—	—	—	—
TYPP-1238-100	34.00	TYVT-1238-50	210.00	—	—	—	—	TYTP-1238-50	35.00/5'	—	—
—	—	—	—	TYTT-1225-50	227.00	—	—	—	—	TYRP-5838-50	26.00
—	—	—	—	—	—	TYTF-12716-50	111.00	—	—	—	—
TYPP-5812-100	44.00	TYVT-5812-50	234.00	—	—	TYTF-91612-50	124.00	—	—	TYRP-3412-50	32.00
—	—	—	—	—	—	TYTF-58916-50	142.00	TYTP-3458-5	50.00/5'	—	—
—	—	TYVT-7858-5	57.00/5'	—	—	—	—	—	—	TYRP-293258-50	42.00
—	—	TYVT-134-5	66.00/5'	—	—	—	—	—	—	TYRP-114234-50	48.00
—	—	—	—	—	—	—	—	TYTP-131634-5	35.00/5'	—	—

Solenoid Valves
For Process Applications

1 YEAR WARRANTY

For Use With Liquids, Steam, Gases and Hot Water

The OMEGA SV-100 and SV-200 series solenoid valves for liquids and gases cover most industrial and laboratory applications. The valves are available in sizes ranging from ¼″ to 2″ NPT, with CV's as high as 38. OMEGA also offers general-purpose 2, 3, and 4- way valves made of brass or stainless steel, and specialty valves for hot water and steam applications.

The SV-100/200 valves are modularly constructed from three basic parts: the valve body, the electrical coil, and the coil enclosure. The valve bodies are normally stainless steel or brass for greatest media compatibility, while the wetted parts consist of just the shading ring, valve material, and O-ring. The standard electric coils are all rated as "continuous duty" to eliminate overheating. Each coil is encased in a protective encapsulated material that resists moisture, fungus, and extreme environmental conditions. The standard electrical enclosures meet NEMA 4 ratings and have a ½″ conduit port.

OMEGA's SV-100/200 Series valves are of poppet, piston or diaphragm design.

DIRECT LIFT
Direct lift valves combine the features of a direct acting valve with those of a pilot-operated valve. Due to a flexible link between the solenoid plunger and the diaphragm, the valve functions as a direct acting valve at low pressures and as a pilot-operated valve at higher pressures. It is sometimes referred to as a Zero Delta P (Pressure) valve or a hung diaphragm valve.

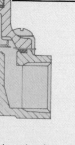

IN   OUT

PILOT-OPERATED
A pilot-operated solenoid valve utilizes the energy stored in the pressurized fluid to actuate the valving mechanism. A direct acting solenoid valve is an integral part of the pilot-operated valve and is used to affect the balance of pressure above and below a diaphragm or piston.

DIRECT ACTING
In this construction, the magnetic force of the solenoid acts directly on the valve's sealing mechanism. The pressure and flow capabilities of these valves are limited by the power of the solenoid.

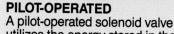

Selecting A Solenoid Valve
To Your System Specifications

SELECTION GUIDELINES

General purpose solenoid valves are used with a wide variety of liquids and gases in a broad spectrum of applications. Rating of the valve capacity in terms which relate to all operating conditions is accomplished by determining the "flow factor" (Cv) of the valve. The Cv value is the number of U.S. gallons of 60°F water per minute that, when flowing through the valve, causes a pressure drop of 1 PSI. This measure of capacity is stated for each model in this catalog.

There are five main parameters to consider when selecting a valve: Cv, media compatibility, pressure, temperature, and process fitting. For each of these parameters, maximum values are listed for each valve. To choose the correct valve, compare each parameter and check that it is less than the maximum value listed.

LIQUID APPLICATIONS

For most applications, liquids are considered incompressible and only the following factors need be considered in sizing a valve:

Cv = Flow Factor of valve.
Q = Flow expressed in U.S. gallons per minute (GPM)
ΔP = Pressure Drop across the valve
$\quad = P_1 - P_2$
P_1 = Inlet Pressure PSIG
P_2 = Outlet Pressure PSIG
G = Specific Gravity of the fluid

(G = 1.0 for water at 60°F)

These factors relate per the following equation:

$$Cv = Q \sqrt{\frac{G}{\Delta P}}$$

Sample Problem: A 2-way normally closed valve is needed to control the transfer of a liquid (G = 1.1) at a rate of 2 GPM. The pressure available is 10 PSI; downstream pressure is 0 PSI.

Solution:
$\Delta P = P_1 - P_2 = 10 - 0 = 10$ PSI

$$Cv = Q \sqrt{\frac{G}{\Delta P}} = 2 \sqrt{\frac{1.1}{10}} = 0.67$$

Therefore a valve is needed with a Cv of at least 0.67, and a max operating pressure differential of at least 10 PSID. Referring to the general purpose valves on C-28, the SV105 with a Cv = .75 is O.K. Check temperature, media compatibility and end fittings, to insure a correct valve choice.

Note: The Cv values given in this catalog are applicable to liquids with viscosities to 100 SSU (22 Centistokes)

GAS APPLICATIONS

When compressible media such as air or gases are used the sizing of the valve must include additional factors which affect performance.

Cv = Flow factor
Q = Flow expressed in Standard Cubic Feet per Hour (SCFH).

ΔP = Pressure drop across the valve (inlet to outlet) in PSID.
P_1 and P_2 = Inlet and outlet absolute pressures respectively (PSIA)
PSIA = Gage Pressure + (14.7 PSIA)
t = Gas temperature (°F)
G = Specific gravity of gas
(G = 1 for air at 55°F)

These factors relate as shown in the following equations:
If $(.53) P_1 < P_2$

$$Cv = \frac{Q}{1349} \sqrt{\frac{(460 + t) \times G}{\Delta P \times P_2}}$$

If $(.53) P_1 \geq P_2$

$$Cv = \frac{Q \sqrt{(460 + t) \times G}}{704 \times P_1}$$

Sample Problem: A normally closed 2-way valve is needed to control gas entering a furnace. Also known are:
Q = 500 SCFH   G = .7   t = 60°F.
P_1 = 35 PSIA or (20 PSIG + 14.7)
P_2 = 30 PSIA or (15 PSIG + 14.7)
Solution:
$\Delta P = 35 - 30 = 5$ PSID
$P_1(.53) = 35 (.53) = 18.55 < P_2$

therefore, use the formula:

$$Cv = \frac{Q}{1349} \sqrt{\frac{(460 + t) \times G}{\Delta P \times P_2}} =$$

CV = 0.58

Therefore, a valve is needed with a $C_V \geq .58$ and a max. operating pressure differential $\geq$ 5 PSID.

Again, the general purpose stainless steel SV105 with a C_V = .75 is sufficient, and temperature and media compatiblity are good.

Sample Problem: A 3-way normally closed valve is needed to control a single acting spring return cylinder. Also known are:
Q_A = 28.3 cubic inches/sec at 56 PSIG to obtain 2" stroke of a 6" diameter cylinder in 2 sec.
P_1 = 115 PSIA or (100 PSIG + 14.7)
P_2 = 71 PSIA or (56 PSIG + 14.7) (for a 1600 lb. force)
G = 1 for Air, t = 90°F
ΔP = 115 − 71 = 44 PSID

Since the flow was determined at a pressure of 56 PSIG; it must be converted to its equivalent volume at standard pressure. Boyles law for converting to standard conditions.

$$Qs = Q_A \left(\frac{P_A}{P_S} \right) \left(\frac{515}{t+460} \right)$$

= 127 Standard Cubic Inches per second
Where Q is Flow
P is Pressure in PSIA
A is for Actual Conditions
S is for Standard Conditions
Converting this to SCFH

$$Q = 127 \frac{in.^3}{sec.} \times \left[2.08 \frac{sec. - ft^3}{in.^3 - hr.} \right]$$

= 265 SCFH

Select the Cv formula using:
$P_1 (.53) = 115 (.53) = 60.95 < P_2$

$$Cv = \frac{265}{1349} \sqrt{\frac{550 \times 1}{44 \times (56 + 14.7)}} = 0.083$$

Therefore, valve SV241, which has a C_V = .18, max. MODP = 150 PSID, and max. temp. = 165°F will work.

General Purpose NEMA 4 Stainless Steel and Brass Solenoid Valves

✔ **NEMA 4 Standard**
✔ **Mounts in Any Position**
✔ **Continuous Duty**

Two-way solenoid valves cover most industrial laboratory applications. A two-way valve controls the flow of fluid through a single passage. It has two ports, an inlet (1) and an outlet (2). A normally closed valve does not pass fluid unless it is energized. A normally open valve operates just the opposite.

SPECIFICATIONS:

Wetted Parts: SV-100 Series: stainless steel, silver, and seal (SV-106 polysulfone additional); SV-200 Series: brass, stainless steel, copper and seal (SV-201, 202 Viton additional, SV-211, 212 Ruby additional)

Medium: Liquid or gases (SV-101-105, 107-113, Filter 40 microns)

Max. Static Pressure: 5 times max. differential pressure

Ambient Temp.: 15-122°F (−9 to 50°C)

Mounting: Pipe mounting, any direction

Power: 10 Watts, 120 Vac coils, Class F (SV-101-105 and SV-107, 22 Watts, 120 Vac coils, Class H)

Normally Closed

Normally Open

From **$80**

To Order *(Specify Model number)* GENERAL-PURPOSE VALVES

MODEL	PRICE	FITTING NPT	ORIFICE	CV	SEAL	DIFF. PRESS (PSID) MIN	DIFF. PRESS (PSID) MAX	TEMP (°F)	RESPONSE TIME OPEN	RESPONSE TIME CLOSE
Direct Acting (*Pilot Operated), 2-Way Normally Closed Stainless Steel										
SV101	$ 80	1/4	3/32	0.18	Kel-F	0	650	165	4-8 ms	4-8 ms
SV102	80	1/4	1/8	0.28	Kel-F	0	520	165	4-8 ms	4-8 ms
SV103	80	1/4	5/32	0.4	Viton	0	115	210	4-8 ms	4-8 ms
SV104	80	1/4	3/16	0.5	Viton	0	100	210	4-8 ms	4-8 ms
SV105	80	1/4	1/4	0.75	Viton	0	50	210	4-8 ms	4-8 ms
SV106	135	1/4	1/4	0.76	Teflon	5	1500	210	35-40 ms	35-40 ms*
SV107	80	1/4	5/16	0.95	Viton	0	35	210	4-8 ms	4-8 ms
Direct Acting (*Pilot Operated), 2-Way Normally Open Stainless Steel										
SV111	140	1/4	3/64	0.054	Kel-F	0	750	165	4-8 ms	4-8 ms
SV112	140	1/4	1/16	0.107	Kel-F	0	400	165	4-8 ms	4-8 ms
SV113	140	1/4	3/32	0.15	Kel-F	0	170	165	4-8 ms	4-8 ms
SV114	165	1/4	1/4	0.76	Buna N	5	200	185	70-90 ms	70-90 ms*
Pilot Operated (*Direct Lift), 2-Way Normally Closed Brass										
SV201	95	3/8	5/8	4.4	Buna N	0	230	180	30-100 ms	350-900 ms*
SV202	95	1/2	9/16	4.6	Buna N	0	230	180	30-100 ms	350-900 ms*
SV203	130	3/4	3/4	9.5	Buna N	5	230	185	50-80 ms	1.8-3 s
SV204	155	1	1	13.0	Buna N	5	230	185	50-80 ms	1.8-3 s
SV205	245	1 1/4	1 1/4	19.0	Buna N	5	230	185	50-80 ms	1.8-3 s
SV206	330	1 1/2	1 9/16	30.0	Buna N	5	170	185	50-80 ms	1.8-3 s
SV207	385	2	1 9/16	38.0	Buna N	5	170	185	50-80 ms	1.8-3 s
Pilot Operated, 2-Way Normally Open Brass Valves										
SV211	185	3/8	7/16	3.5	Buna N	5	600	185	120 ms	200 ms
SV212	255	1/2	9/16	4.2	Buna N	5	600	185	120 ms	200 ms
SV213	190	3/4	3/4	9.5	Buna N	5	230	185	50-80 ms	1.8-3 s
SV214	220	1	1	13.0	Buna N	5	230	185	50-80 ms	1.8-3 s
SV215	250	1 1/4	1 1/8	19.0	Buna N	5	230	185	50-80 ms	1.8-3 s
SV216	350	1 1/2	1 9/16	30.0	Buna N	5	170	185	50-80 ms	1.8-3 s
SV217	465	2	1 9/16	38.0	Buna N	5	170	185	50-80 ms	1.8-3 s

*Non-Adjustable response time

Special Purpose Solenoid Valves

For Steam, Hot Water, Anti-Water Hammer, 3-Way 4-Way and Selectable Service

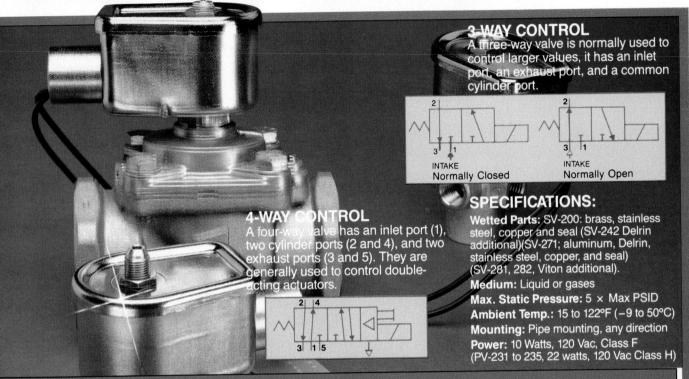

3-WAY CONTROL
A three-way valve is normally used to control larger values, it has an inlet port, an exhaust port, and a common cylinder port.

INTAKE Normally Closed

INTAKE Normally Open

4-WAY CONTROL
A four-way valve has an inlet port (1), two cylinder ports (2 and 4), and two exhaust ports (3 and 5). They are generally used to control double-acting actuators.

SPECIFICATIONS:
Wetted Parts: SV-200: brass, stainless steel, copper and seal (SV-242 Delrin additional)(SV-271; aluminum, Delrin, stainless steel, copper, and seal) (SV-281, 282, Viton additional).

Medium: Liquid or gases

Max. Static Pressure: 5 × Max PSID

Ambient Temp.: 15 to 122°F (−9 to 50°C)

Mounting: Pipe mounting, any direction

Power: 10 Watts, 120 Vac, Class F (PV-231 to 235, 22 watts, 120 Vac Class H)

To Order (Specify Model Number) SPECIAL PURPOSE VALVES

MODEL	PRICE	FITTING NPT	ORIFICE	CV	SEAL	DIFF. PRESS (PSID) MIN	MAX	TEMP (°F)	RESPONSE TIME OPEN	CLOSE
Hot Water (Direct Lift), 2-Way Normally Closed Brass										
SV221	$ 95	1/4	13/64	0.77	EPDM	0	60	210	4-8 ms	4-8 ms
SV222	95	3/8	9/16	4.4	EPDM	0	150	210	30-100 ms	30-100 ms
SV223	95	1/2	9/16	4.6	EPDM	0	150	210	30-100 ms	30-100 ms
SV224	130	3/4	9/16	5.6	EPDM	0	150	210	30-100 ms	30-100 ms
SV225	225	1	1	11.2	EPDM	0	150	210	30-100 ms	30-100 ms
Steam (Direct Lift), 2-Way Normally Closed Brass										
SV231	95	1/4	13/64	0.77	EPDM	0	40	285	4-8 ms	4-8 ms
SV232	95	3/8	9/16	4.6	EPDM	0	45	293	30-100 ms	350-900 ms
SV233	95	1/2	9/16	4.6	EPDM	0	45	293	30-100 ms	350-900 ms
SV234	130	3/4	9/16	5.6	EPDM	0	45	293	30-100 ms	350-900 ms
SV235	220	1	1	11.2	EPDM	0	45	293	30-100 ms	350-900 ms
General Purpose (Direct Acting), 3-Way Normally Closed, Exhaust Brass										
SV241	75	1/4	1 to 2/2 to 3 5/64, 1/8	.18 .32	Viton	0	150	165	10 ms	10 ms
SV242	85	1/4	3/32, 9/64	.25 .38	Viton	0	150	165	10 ms	10 ms
Selectable Service (Direct Acting), 3-Way Customer Switchable Normally Closed or Normally Open Brass										
SV251	80	1/4	5/64 5/64	.18 .18	Viton	0	100	165	10 ms	10 ms
Quick Exhaust (Pilot-Operated), 3-Way Normally Closed Brass										
SV261	185	1/4	3/32 1/4	.20 1.12	Buna N	2	100	165	15 ms	45 ms
General Purpose (Pilot-Operated), 4-Way Normally Closed Aluminum, Air only (filtered 40 microns)										
SV271	120	1/8	5/32	.35	Buna N	15	150	165	10-30 ms	10-30 ms
Anti-Water Hammer (Pilot-Operated), 2-Way Normally Closed Brass										
SV281	135	3/8	7/16	2.5	Buna N	3	150	185	0.015 s	0.85 s*
SV282	135	1/2	7/16	2.5	Buna N	3	150	185	0.015 s	0.85 s*
SV283	140	3/4	3/4	9.5	Buna N	3	230	185	0.1-0.25 s	0.6-4.5 s
SV284	280	1	1	13.0	Buna N	3	230	185	0.1-0.25 s	0.5-4.5 s
SV285	330	1 1/4	1 1/8	19.0	Buna N	3	230	185	0.2-0.5 s	0.8-5.8 s
SV286	475	1 1/2	1 9/16	30.0	Buna N	3	170	185	0.2-0.4 s	1.5-9.0 s
SV287	575	2	1 9/16	38.0	Buna N	3	170	185	0.25-0.45 s	1.5-9.5 s
Anti-Water Hammer (Pilot-Operated), 2-Way Normally Open Brass										
SV291	165	3/4	3/4	9.5	Buna N	5	230	185	0.1-0.25 s	0.6-4.5 s
SV292	295	1	1	13.0	Buna N	5	230	185	0.1-0.25 s	0.5-4.5 s
SV293	350	1 1/8	1 1/8	19.0	Buna N	5	230	185	0.2-0.5 s	0.8-5.8 s
SV294	495	1 9/16	1 9/16	30.0	Buna N	5	170	185	0.2-0.4 s	1.5-9.0 s
SV295	595	1 9/16	1 9/16	38.0	Buna N	5	170	185	0.25-0.45 s	1.5-9.5 s

*Non-Adjustable response time

Static Mixers
Reference Section

For Complete Ordering Information and Specifications, refer to pages H-23 through H-28.

Static mixers are an economical and virtually maintenance-free alternative to motorized propeller mixers. Instead of mixing materials a batch at a time in a holding tank, static mixers conveniently mix liquids or liquids and gases continuously as they flow through a pipeline. When properly sized, they prevent under or overmixing. As your process changes, multiple static mixing sections can easily be added to or removed from your pipe.

Static mixers consist of fixed, in-line baffles which cause the mixing fluids to shear and swirl, clockwise and counterclockwise, separating and combining, to provide a homogeneous output. They are available in stainless steel, Kynar , PVC, CPVC, polypropylene, and polyacetal components. Polyacetal plastic has the toughness and chemical resistance required by the Adhesive and Insulation industries, being completely inert to most common solvents, such as MEK, acetone, and methylene chloride. Its maximum service temperature is 250°F. Polyacetal is not recommended for service with bases or acids. Polypropylene is a polyolefin plastic with excellent chemical resistance and a maximum service temperature to 200°F.

The following describes what parameters must be taken into account to properly select a static mixer.

SELECTION GUIDE

For each application, the designer must first determine the number of mixing sections required to achieve a complete mix. Below are given guidelines based upon the Reynolds number of your system. Also included are tables with some general application guidelines.

Next, the designer should select a diameter and/or a construction that will give the desired mixing performance without exceeding your system's maximum allowable pressure drop (See item 3 below). And that's all there is!

1. Calculate the Reynolds Number. Use the diameter given in the charts. If inside and outside diameters are supplied, use inside diameter.

$$RE = \frac{3157 \times Q \times S}{D \times MU}$$

2. Select a model based on the Reynolds Number

FMX7000 Series Mixers

Reynolds No.	No. of Stages
800-1000	14
>1000	7

Typical Applications	No. of Stages
Ozone Absorption	7
pH Control	7
Gas/Gas Blending	7
Dilution of chemicals	7
Polyelectrolyte Dilution	14

FMX8000 Mixers

Reynolds No.	No. of Elements
<10	24-32
10-5000	16-24
500-2000	8-16
>2000	4-8

Typical Application	No. of Elements
1-1 Epoxies	24
Urethanes Elastomers	32
Urethane Foam	16
In-line Aeration	8
Admixing of additives	8

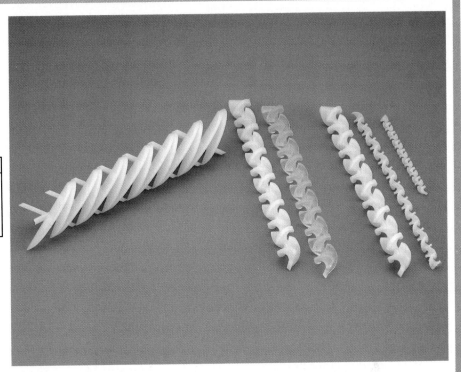

FMX7100 and FMX8100 Series Mixers shown. See page H-23 for complete details.

3. Determine Pressure Drop

Laminar Flow: Reynolds Number < 500

$$DP = Q \times MU \times L$$

Turbulent Flow: Reynolds Number > 500

$$DP = Q^2 \times S \times T$$

NOTE: If the pressure drop across the mixer exceeds its maximum rating, a modular mixer is required. For example, if a 24 element FMX8300 mixer is required and the pressure drop exceeds the 250 psi rating, we recommend coupling two 12 element mixers in series.

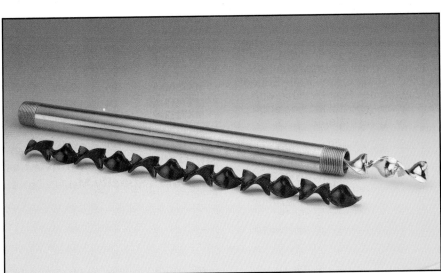

FMX8400 Series Mixers shown. See page H-26 fof details.

Symbols

RE =	Reynolds Number - Dimensionless
Q =	Flow Rate - Gallons per Minute
S =	Specific Gravity - Dimensionless
MU =	Viscosity - Centipoise
D =	Diameter - Inches
DP =	Pressure Drop - P.S.I.
L =	Laminar Factor See Mixer Tables
T =	Turbulent Factor See Mixer Tables

MIXERS

Static Mixing Elements Without Housing

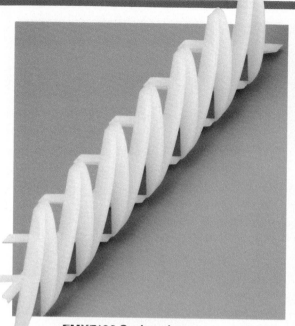

FMX7100 Series shown

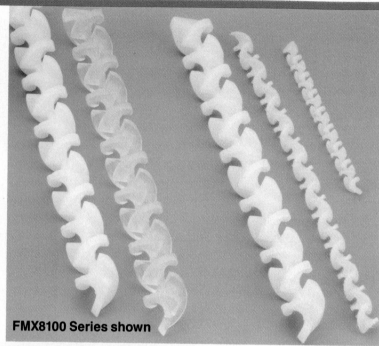

FMX8100 Series shown

The FMX7100 and FMX8100 series mixing elements are injection molded in one operation to ensure low cost with excellent quality. The FMX7100 series are specifically designed for low viscosity applications. The FMX8100 plastic spiral elements were developed for adhesive and sealant and other high viscosity mixing applications. The leading and trailing edges of the FMX8000 mixers are "Knife Edged" so that the unit flushes clean with less solvent - no flat leading edges to accumulate material.

Polyacetal is completely inert to most common solvents, such as MEK, acetone, and methylene chloride for use in the Adhesive and Insulation industries. Its maximum service temperature is 250°F. Polyacetal is not recommended for service with bases or acids. Polypropylene has excellent chemical resistance and a maximum service temperature to 200°F.

Metal or plastic tubing may be used to house the mixing sections. However, to achieve maximum performance, the sections must fit snugly inside the tube. Accepted tolerance is no more than 2% greater than the mixer diameter.

LOW VISCOSITY MIXING ELEMENTS
To Order (Specify Model Number)

Model No.	Price (10/pkg)	Diam.	No. of Elements	Length	Factors L	Factors T	Material
FMX7103-AC	$ 14	.300″	7	1.4″	.18	8.74	Polyacetal
FMX7103-P	37	.300″	7	1.4″	.18	8.74	Polypropylene
FMX7104-AC	18	.432″	7	2.5″	.06	2.18	Polyacetal
FMX7104-P	37	.432″	7	2.5″	.06	2.18	Polypropylene
FMX7106-AC	28	.685″	7	4.2″	.015	.276	Polyacetal
FMX7106-P	45	.687″	7	4.2″	.015	.276	Polypropylene
FMX7109-AC	39	.903″	7	5.3″	.0066	.092	Polyacetal
FMX7109-P	69	.906″	7	5.3″	.0066	.092	Polypropylene
FMX7113-AC	54	1.375″	7	8.0″	.0018	.0172	Polyacetal
FMX7113-P	91	1.380″	7	8.0″	.0018	.0172	Polypropylene
FMX7120-AC	86	2.040″	5	9.0″	.0003	.0018	Polyacetal
FMX7120-P	121	2.050″	5	9.0″	.0003	.0018	Polypropylene

HIGH VISCOSITY MIXING ELEMENTS
To Order (Specify Model No.)

Model No.	Price (10/pkg)	Diam.	No. of Elements	Length	Factors L	Factors T	Material
FMX8112-AC	$ 13	.125″	12	1.3″	1.29	328.7	Polyacetal
FMX8112-P	30	.125″	12	1.3″	1.29	328.7	Polypropylene
FMX8118-AC	14	.187″	16	2.5″	.5152	104.7	Polyacetal
FMX8118-P	32	.187″	16	2.5″	.5152	104.7	Polypropylene
FMX8118-P2	42	.187″	24	2.5″	*	*	Polypropylene
FMX8124-AC	14	.250″	16	4.0″	.216	35.7	Polyacetal
FMX8125-P	34	.251″	16	4.0″	.216	35.7	Polypropylene
FMX8125-P2	44	.251″	24	4.0″	*	*	Polypropylene
FMX8137-AC	17	.370″	12	3.9″	.048	4.27	Polyacetal
FMX8137-P	38	.373″	12	3.9″	.048	4.27	Polypropylene
FMX8137-P2	49	.373″	24	3.9″	*	*	Polypropylene
FMX8149-AC	31	.498″	12	5.1″	.0192	1.23	Polyacetal
FMX8150-P	42	.500″	12	5.1″	.0192	1.23	Polypropylene
FMX8150-P2	67	.500″	24	5.1″	*	*	Polypropylene

*Consult Flow Department for pressure drop data.

All Plastic Static Mixer Assemblies

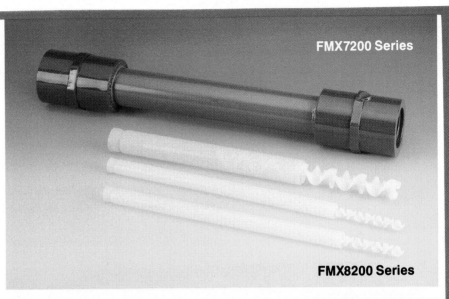

FMX7200 Series

FMX8200 Series

The FMX7200 series mixers are specially designed for waste water treatment, mixing of additives, pH control, and polyelectrolyte dilution. These all-plastic mixers combine PVC or CPVC pipe with polypropylene internals. Certain sizes feature clipped sections, which eliminates sharp crevices where material can accumulate and plug up the mixer. Polypropylene has excellent chemical resistance to most acids and bases. The maximum service temperature of a standard FMX7200 series mixer is 140°F with PVC housing, 180°F with CPVC housings.

SPECIFICATIONS

Section: Polypropylene Non-Removable
Housing: PVC or CPVC; schedule 80 up to and including 1"; sched. 40 for 1¼" and 2"

PRESSURE LIMITATION

Pipe Size	PSIG @ 75°F
⅜"	850
¾"	690
1"	630
1¼"	370
2"	280

The Series FMX8200 Disposable Spiral Mixers are ideal for adhesives or other high viscosity applications. The leading and trailing edges of the mixers are "Knife Edged" to flush clean with less solvent - no flat leading edges to accumulate material. For polyacetal or polypropylene selection, See FMX8100 information on page H-23.

Maximum Pressure Drop: 250 PSI (See pg. H-21 for pressure drop calculation)

SPECIFICATIONS

Element: Polyacetal; polypropylene opt.
Housing: Nylon Plain Ends

PRESSURE LIMITATION

OD	PSIG @ 75°F
.187	580
.250	430
.375	600
.500	460
.625	350

To Order (Specify Model Number) *HIGHLIGHTED MODELS STOCKED*

Model Number (PVC)	Price	Model Number (CPVC)	Price	Diam.	No. of Elements	Ends FNPT	Length	Factors L	Factors T
FMX7211	$98	FMX7211-CP	$142	.432"	7	⅜"	5.7"	.18	7.6
FMX7212	105	FMX7212-CP	152	.432"	14	⅜"	7.0"	.36	15.2
FMX7221	111	FMX7221-CP	161	.687"	7 clipped	¾"	7.0"	.015	.24
FMX7222	122	FMX7222-CP	177	.687"	14 clipped	¾"	10.5"	.03	.48
FMX7231	120	FMX7231-CP	174	.906"	7 clipped	1"	8.2"	.0066	.08
FMX7232	135	FMX7232-CP	196	.906"	14 clipped	1"	12.6"	.013	.16
FMX7241	145	FMX7241-CP	210	1.38"	7 clipped	1¼"	10.3"	.0018	.015
FMX7242	172	FMX7242-CP	250	1.38"	14 clipped	1¼"	17.5"	.0036	.03
FMX7251	162	FMX7251-CP	235	2.05"	5	2"	11.3"	.0003	.0016
FMX7252	190	FMX7252-CP	275	2.05"	10	2"	19.3"	.0006	.0032

To Order (Specify Model Number)

Model No. Polyacetal	Price (pkg of 10)	Diam.	No. of Elements	O.D.	Tube Length	Factors L	Factors T
FMX8211	$27	.125"	12	.187"	1.5"	1.29	328.7
FMX8212	29	.125"	18	.187"	2.2"	1.94	493.0
FMX8213	32	.125"	24	.187"	2.8"	2.58	657.4
FMX8214	37	.125"	30	.187"	3.5"	3.23	821.7
FMX8221	28	.187"	8	.250"	1.5"	.2576	52.4
FMX8222	30	.187"	16	.250"	2.8"	.5152	104.7
FMX8223	33	.187"	24	.250"	4.1"	.7728	157.1
FMX8224	38	.187"	32	.250"	5.4"	.9660	209.4
FMX8231	29	.250"	8	.375"	2.1"	.1080	17.9
FMX8232	31	.250"	16	.375"	4.1"	.2160	35.7
FMX8233	34	.250"	24	.375"	6.1"	.3240	53.6
FMX8234	39	.250"	32	.375"	8.1"	.4320	71.4
FMX8251	32	.370"	12	.500"	4.1"	.0480	4.27
FMX8252	34	.370"	18	.500"	6.1"	.0720	6.40
FMX8253	45	.370"	24	.500"	8.1"	.0960	8.54
FMX8254	59	.370"	30	.500"	10.1"	.1200	10.7
FMX8261	55	.498"	12	.625"	5.6"	.0192	1.23
FMX8262	60	.498"	18	.625"	8.3"	.0288	1.85
FMX8263	78	.498"	24	.625"	10.8"	.0384	2.46
FMX8264	95	.498"	30	.625"	13.3"	.0480	3.07

* For polypropylene elements, add suffix ''-PP'' to part number, and add $4 to price.
Example: FMX8231-PP. Price = $29 + 4 = $33.

H

MIXERS

Rugged 304SS Static Mixer Assemblies
With Removable Plastic Internals

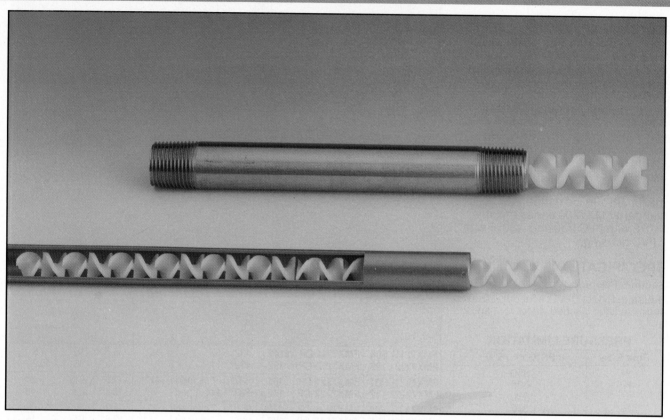

The Series FMX7300 Mixers can be used for chemical mixing, absorption, and pH Control applications.

The Series FMX7300 Mixer is available with removable polypropylene mixing sections inside 304SS pipe for up to 200°F. Certain sizes feature clipped sections, which eliminate sharp crevices where material can accumulate and plug up the mixer.

SPECIFICATIONS

Section: Polypropylene Removable
Housing: 304 Stainless Steel Male NPT Ends

PRESSURE LIMITATION

Pipe Size	PSIG @ 75°F
⅜″	2540
¾″	3140
1.0″	3150
1¼″	1520
2.0″	1340

The Series FMX8300 Spiral Mixers feature 304SS housing with removable plastic mixing elements for high pressure adhesive, sealant, or other high-viscosity mixing applications.

The leading and trailing edges of the mixers are "Knife Edged" to flush clean with less solvent - no flat leading edges to accumulate material.

Polyacetal is completely inert to most common solvents, such as MEK, acetone, and methylene chloride for use in the Adhesive and Insulation industries. Its maximum service temperature is 250°F. Polyacetal is not recommended for service with bases or acids. Polypropylene has excellent chemical resistance and a maximum service temperature to 200°F. Maximum Pressure Drop: 250 PSI (See pg. H-21 for pressure drop calculation)

To Order (Specify Model No.)

Model No.	Price	Diam.	No. of Elements	Factors L	Factors T	Ends MNPT	Length
FMX7301	$108	.432″	7	.18	7.6	⅜″	3.0″
FMX7302	137	.432″	14	.36	15.2	⅜″	5.5″
FMX7311	114	.687″	7 clipped	.015	.24	¾″	4.7″
FMX7312	146	.687″	14 clipped	.030	.48	¾″	8.5″
FMX7313	126	.906″	7 clipped	.0066	.080	1″	6.0″
FMX7314	165	.906″	14 clipped	.013	.160	1″	10.5″
FMX7315	135	1.38″	7 clipped	.0018	.015	1¼″	9.0″
FMX7316	181	1.38″	14 clipped	.0036	.030	1¼″	16.0″
FMX7321	153	2.05″	5	.0003	.0016	2″	10.0″
FMX7322	203	2.05″	10	.0006	.0032	2″	18.0″

SPECIFICATIONS

Element: Polyacetal, removable. Polypropylene Optional
Housing: 304 SS

PRESSURE LIMITATION

OD	PSIG @ 75°F
.187	5800
.250	4300
.405	5300
.540	3400
.675	3025

FMX8300 Continued on Page H-26

To Order (Specify Model No.) FMX8300 Series

Model No. Polyacetal	Price	Inside Diam.	No. of Elements	Factors L	Factors T	OD	Ends	Length
FMX8311	$20	.125″	12	1.29	328.7	.187″	Plain	1.5″
FMX8312	24	.125″	18	1.94	493.0	.187″	Plain	2.2″
FMX8313	29	.125″	24	2.58	657.4	.187″	Plain	2.8″
FMX8314	34	.125″	30	3.23	821.7	.187″	Plain	3.5″
FMX8321	21	.187″	8	.2576	52.4	.250″	Plain	1.5″
FMX8322	24	.187″	16	.5152	104.7	.250″	Plain	2.7″
FMX8323	30	.187″	24	.7728	157.1	.250″	Plain	4.0″
FMX8324	35	.187″	32	.9660	209.4	.250″	Plain	5.3″
FMX8341	72	.250″	8	.1080	17.9	.405″	⅛″ MNPT	2.4″
FMX8342	77	.250″	16	.2160	35.7	.405″	⅛″ MNPT	4.4″
FMX8343	82	.250″	24	.3240	53.6	.405″	⅛″ MNPT	6.4″
FMX8344	86	.250″	32	.4320	71.4	.405″	⅛″ MNPT	8.4″
FMX8351	86	.370″	12	.0480	4.27	.540″	¼″ MNPT	4.2″
FMX8352	91	.370″	18	.0720	6.40	.540″	¼″ MNPT	6.1″
FMX8353	94	.370″	24	.0960	8.54	.540″	¼″ MNPT	8.1″
FMX8354	100	.370″	30	.1200	10.7	.540″	¼″ MNPT	10.0″
FMX8361	108	.498″	12	.0192	1.23	.675″	⅜″ MNPT	5.5″
FMX8362	115	.498″	18	.0288	1.85	.675″	⅜″ MNPT	8.0″
FMX8363	122	.498″	24	.0384	2.46	.675″	⅜″ MNPT	10.7″
FMX8364	127	.498″	30	.0480	3.07	.675″	⅜″ MNPT	13.1″

* For polypropylene elements, add suffix ''-PP'' to part number, and add $5 to price.
Example: FMX8354-PP. Price = $100 + 5 = $105.

The Series FMX8400 Pipe Mixers feature 304SS piping (schedule 40 nominal) with 316SS elements. This series is available with Teflon coated or non-coated stainless elements. Teflon coating DOES NOT impart chemical resistance better than stainless steel. The coating enhances the cleanability of the mixing elements. For routine maintenance, the elements can be pushed out and cleaned.

The leading and trailing edges of the mixers are ''Knife Edged'' to flush clean with less solvent - no flat leading edges to accumulate material. See page H-21 for selection guide and pressure drop data.

To Order (Specify Model Number) *HIGHLIGHTED MODELS STOCKED*

Model No. 316SS Elements	Price	Model No. Teflon Coated Elements	Price	I.D.	No. of Elements	Ends MNPT	Length	Factors L	Factors T
FMX8441S	$106	FMX8441T	$127	.28″	6	⅛″	2.7″	.0588	6.1
FMX8442S	141	FMX8442T	163	.28″	12	⅛″	5.4″	.1176	12.2
FMX8451S	114	FMX8451T	137	.37″	6	¼″	3.7″	.0237	1.9
FMX8452S	153	FMX8452T	176	.37″	12	¼″	7.0″	.0474	3.8
FMX8461S	122	FMX8461T	148	.51″	6	⅜″	5.0″	.0092	.55
FMX8462S	163	FMX8462T	190	.51″	12	⅜″	9.5″	.0184	1.1
FMX8481S	143	FMX8481T	166	.64″	6	½″	5.7″	.0049	.22
FMX8482S	192	FMX8482T	218	.64″	12	½″	11.0″	.0098	.44
FMX8411S	156	FMX8411T	189	.80″	6	¾″	7.7″	.0023	.04
FMX8412S	209	FMX8412T	260	.80″	12	¾″	14.7″	.0046	.08
FMX8413S	198	FMX8413T	243	1.06″	6	1″	9.5″	.001	.024
FMX8414S	264	FMX8414T	317	1.06″	12	1″	18.5″	.002	.048
FMX8415S	261	FMX8415T	305	1.61″	6	1½″	14.0″	.0002	.004
FMX8416S	347	FMX8416T	413	1.61″	12	1½″	27.2″	.0004	.008
FMX8421S	312	FMX8421T	378	2.07″	6	2″	17.5″	.0001	.0013
FMX8422S	417	FMX8422T	505	2.07″	12	2″	34.5″	.0002	.0026

H

MIXERS

ECONOMICAL STATIC MIXERS
Featuring Efficient Mixing With Low Pressure Drop

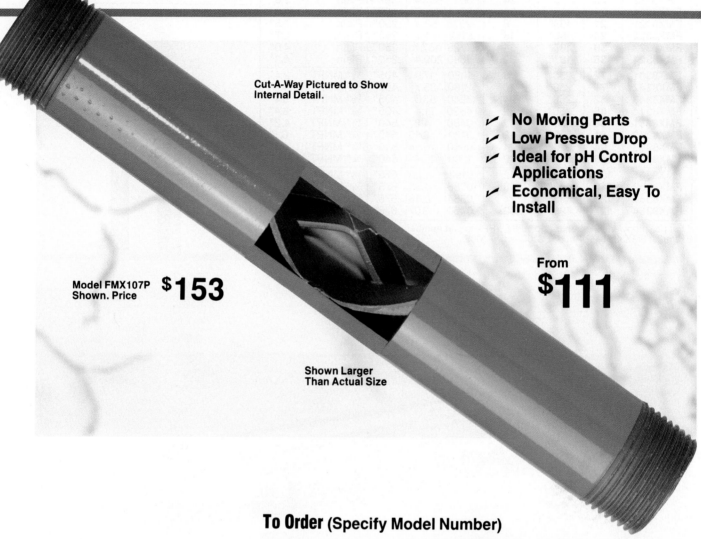

Cut-A-Way Pictured to Show Internal Detail.

✔ **No Moving Parts**
✔ **Low Pressure Drop**
✔ **Ideal for pH Control Applications**
✔ **Economical, Easy To Install**

Model FMX107P Shown. Price **$153**

From **$111**

Shown Larger Than Actual Size

The OMEGA FMX Series mixers deliver excellent results at an economical price. These fixed, in-line ''baffles'' cause component fluids to shear and swirl during their regular flow and travel through a pipe line. The results are 100% mixing effectiveness with almost zero maintenance cost. These mixers are constructed of various materials such as PVC, 316SS and PVDF. Since there are no moving parts, these mixers are ideal for applications in food and beverage processing. These mixers are also superb for pH control systems involving acid or base addition to a flowstream.

OMEGA mixers come in 2 Styles: pipe mixers, for food and chemical processing as well as wastewater treatment; and tube mixers, for low flowrate applications.

To Order (Specify Model Number)

Pipe Mixers

Model No.	Price	Nominal Pipe Size MNPT	Number of Elements	Pipe ID	Mixer Length	Weight lbs.
Schedule 40 PVC Pipe Mixers With Non-Removeable Elements						
FMX105-P	$143	½″	6	0.62″	5″	2
FMX205-P	239	½	12	0.62″	10″	2
FMX107-P	153	¾″	6	0.82″	7″	2
FMX207-P	255	¾″	12	0.82″	13″	2
FMX110-P	165	1″	6	1.05″	9″	2
FMX210-P	276	1″	12	1.05″	17″	2
Schedule 40, 304 SS Mixers With Non-Removeable Elements						
FMX105-S	$192	½″	6	0.62″	5″	2
FMX205-S	272	½	12	0.62″	10″	2
FMX107-S	198	¾″	6	0.82″	7″	2
FMX207-S	278	¾″	12	0.82″	13″	3
FMX110-S	209	1″	6	1.05″	9″	2
FMX210-S	348	1″	12	1.05″	17″	3
Schedule 80 Kynar® Pipe Mixers With Non-Removeable Elements						
FMX107-K	186	¾″	6	0.82″	7″	3
FMX207-K	326	¾″	12	0.82″	13″	5
FMX110-K	203	1″	6	1.05″	9″	4
FMX210-K	354	1″	12	1.05″	17″	7

For Reynolds number between 500-1000, use 12 elements; >1000, use 6.

Model FMX110-S Shown Price

$209

Cut-A-Way Pictured to Show Internal Detail.

Shown Smaller Than Actual Size

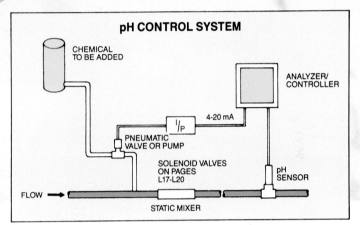

pH CONTROL SYSTEM

CHEMICAL TO BE ADDED

ANALYZER/ CONTROLLER

4-20 mA

I/P

PNEUMATIC VALVE OR PUMP

SOLENOID VALVES ON PAGES L17-L20

pH SENSOR

FLOW →

STATIC MIXER

To calculate the pressure drop of the FMX100, 200 series pipe mixers, determine laminar or turbulent flow conditions: Turbulent Flow occurs-if Re is greater than 1000. Laminar Flow occurs-if Re is less than 1000. Then solve one of the following equations:

$$P = \frac{Q^2 \times S \times M^{0.06}}{A} \quad \text{Turbulent Flow}$$

Laminar Flow

$$P = \frac{11.4 \times 10^{-4} \times Q \times M}{D^3}$$

Nominal Pipe Size	Actual I.D. Inches	A Value
½	.622	2.5
¾	.824	13
1	1.049	22

where
Re=Reynolds number-dimensionless
Q=Flow rate-gallons per minute
S=Specific gravity-dimensionless
M=Viscosity-centipoise
D=Inside pipe diameter-inches
P=Pressure drop per every
6 elements-P.S.I.D
A=See Table (A Value)

All 316SS Tube Mixers with Nickel Brazed, Non-Removeable Elements

Model No.	Price	Nominal Tube Size	Number of Elements	Tube ID	Mixer Length	Wt lbs.	Max. Press. (PSIG)
FMX316-S	$111	³⁄₁₆"	17	0.13"	4⅞"	1	
FMX416-S	113	³⁄₁₆"	21	0.13"	6"	1	4642
FMX516-S	120	³⁄₁₆"	27	0.13"	7½"	1	
FMX314-S	114	¼"	21	0.19"	7"	1	
FMX414-S	126	¼"	27	0.19"	9¼"	1	3391
FMX514-S	137	¼"	34	0.19"	11½"	1	
FMX338-S	117	⅜"	21	0.32"	11"	1	
FMX438-S	129	⅜"	27	0.32"	14"	1	2197
FMX538-S	137	⅜"	32	0.32"	17"	1	
FMX312-S	143	½"	15	0.44"	11⅞"	1	
FMX412-S	156	½"	21	0.44"	16⅜"	1	1625
FMX512-S	174	½"	32	0.44"	24¾"	1	
Tube Mixers with Glass* Tube and Removeable 316 SS Mixing Elements							
FMX314G-S	172	¼"	12	0.19"	5½"	2	50
FMX414G-S	207	¼"	24	0.19"	10"	2	
FMX338G-S	187	⅜"	12	0.32"	8"	2	50
FMX438G-S	227	⅜"	24	0.32"	15"	2	
FMX312G-S	216	½"	12	0.44"	11"	2	50
FMX412G-S	261	½"	24	0.44"	19"	2	

*Standard glass, not borosilicate
Selection: For 12 to 24 elements, fluid viscosities from 0-200 centipoise are acceptable; Use 27 elements for viscosities from 200-750 cp; Use 32-34 elements for viscosities from 750-30,000 cp.

H

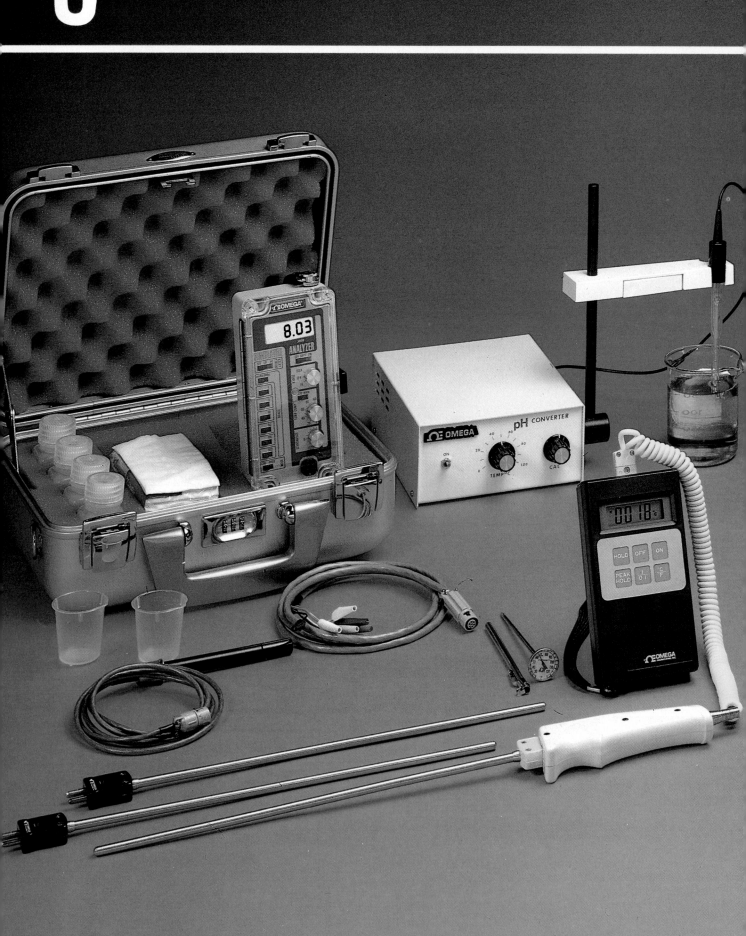

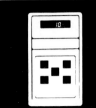

J-3 thru J-6

pH METER/ CALIBRATORS

J-9, J-10 J-27, J-28

RECORDERS

J-7, J-8, J-11 thru J-24, J-29 thru J-34

MULTIMETERS, ACCESSORIES

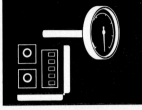

J-25, J-26

THERMOMETERS AND TEMPERATURE LABELS

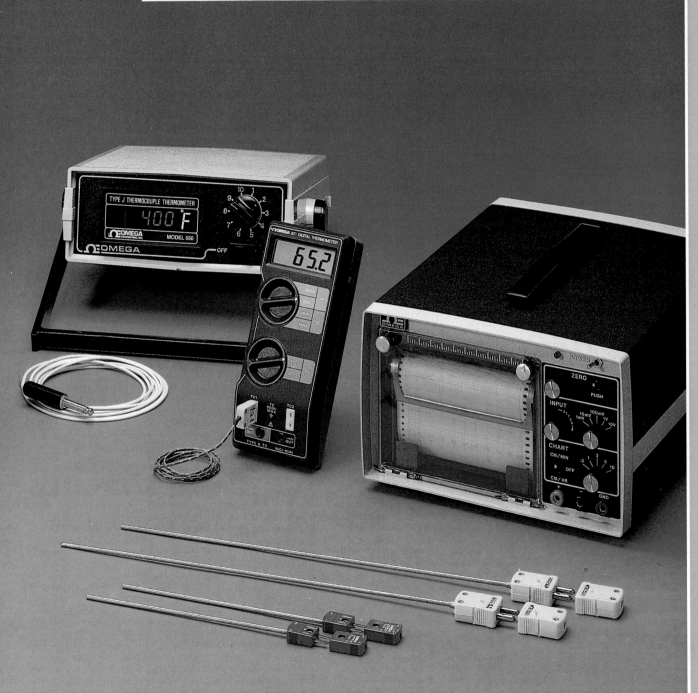

Conductivity and pH Meter/Calibration Kits

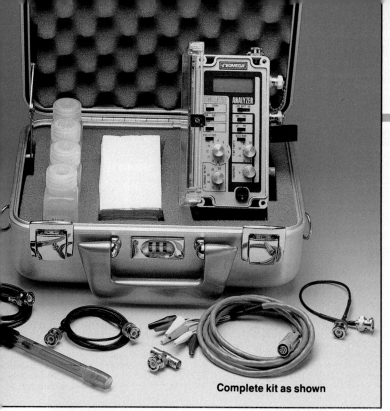

Complete kit as shown

Model PHCL-35

2 YEAR WARRANTY

MADE IN USA

✔ Simulates pH Electrode System or Measures pH
✔ Simulates or Measures ORP
✔ Recorder Output

The PHCL-35 pH Meter/Calibrator is a rugged portable unit for pH measurements or calibrating process pH systems. A high resolution LCD readout makes it perfect for on-site analyses or troubleshooting. The PHCL-35 accepts a BNC input. In the calibrator mode, millivolt and pH outputs are available. The pH outputs can simulate the inherent high impedance of glass electrodes. The PHCL-35 includes a PHE-1301 rugged combination electrode, pH 4,7,10 buffers, adaptors and BNC extensions and 5 ft output cable enclosed in an aluminum carrying case.

Specifications:

pH Meter
Accuracy: ±0.01 pH
Stability: ±0.05 pH over the life of the battery
Resolution: ±0.01 pH
Range: 0 to 14 pH or −1999 mV to +1999 mV
Temperature Compensation: Manual 0 to 100°C
Battery: 9 V (typical life 200 h)

Display: LCD 3½ digit
Input Impedance: > 10^{12} ohm
Recorder Output: 0 to 100 μA
Connector: BNC

pH Calibrator
Accuracy: ±1%
Resolution: 1 pH step in the pH mode, 100 mV steps in the mV mode variable position (settable to 0.05 pH or 5 mV)

$985

Range: 0 to 14 pH, or −1000 to +1000 mV

Weight: 1.25 lb
Housing: Polycarbonate NEMA-4X
Dimensions: 3.15″ × 2.17″ × 6.3″ meter only
Connectors: BNC for simulator output

Model CDCL-35   ### $985

The CDCL-35 Conductivity Calibration Kit can be used as an analyzer to measure conductivity or as a simulator to check and calibrate conductivity instruments exclusive of the electrode. In the analyzer mode, it can be used to measure ionic concentrations or perform trend analysis of effluents using the recorder output.

In the simulator mode, the CDCL-35 provides a conductivity signal referenced to 25°C that can be sent to a conductivity meter to allow precise calibration or detection of sensor malfunction.

The CDCL-35 includes an electrode with a 1.0 cell constant, three bottles of conductivity standardizing solution, distilled water, two disposable beakers, 5 ft output cable, aluminum carrying case, and 100, 1,000 and 10,000 μmho/cm calibration standards.

Specifications:

Analyzer Mode
Range: 0 to 1,000, 0 to 10,000, 0 to 100,000 μmhos
Accuracy: ±1.5%
Temperature Compensation: Manual and automatic 0 to 100°C
Power: 9 V dc battery

Recorder Output: 0 to 100 μA
Display: LCD 3½ digit
Dimensions (Calibrator): 3.15″ × 2.17″ × 6.3″
Weight: 1 lb meter only

Simulator Mode
Range: 1; 5; 50; 100; 1000; 5000; 10,000; 50,000; 100,000; 500,000 μmhos–switch selectable. Values are additive.
Calibration Standards: 100, 1,000, 10,000 μmho/cm
Replacement Conductivity Cell: CDE-35-1 $150

Complete kit as shown

pH Electrode Simulators

The PHCL-1 electrode simulator conveniently tests all types of pH meters, controllers, transmitters, recorders and alarms by simulating the characteristics of a pH electrode. With an accuracy of 1%, the simulator can also be used for routine calibration. Switch selectable 0 to 14 pH and millivolt ranges allow simulation of redox and specific ion probes as well as pH electrodes. Temperature values from 0 to 100°C can be selected to check pH meter temperatuure and slope compensators. A switch also provides 1000 megohm series resistance for checking meter input impedance.

Specifications

Output: 0 to 14 pH switch-selected in 2 pH increments (1 pH increments between pH 6 and 8 for checking meters with expanded scales). 0 to 700 mV switch selected in 100 mV increments.

Temperature/Slope Compensation: Switch selects temperature values of 0, 25, 50, and 100°C. Simulates changes in electrode output with temperature.

Impedance: Switchable 1000 megohm series resistance for checking pH meter input impedance.

Accuracy: Within 1%

Connector: BNC. Supplied with BNC to BNC cable

Size: 3½" wide x 5" high x 2" deep

Weight: 0.5 lb

Power: 1.35 V "AA" mercury battery with expected life in excess of one year.

Optional Accessories:

PHCL-1C:

Industrial interface cable— terminated with alligator clips for use with industrial pH equipment, recorders, etc. **$10**

PHCL-1K:

Field kit—leather carrying case with adjustable shoulder strap. Holds 2 oz. bottles of 4.00 and 7.00 buffers. Has space for test leads and spare electrode. Permits mini-test operation without removal from case. Only 7 oz. **$19**

PHCL-1S:

BNC to U.S. Standard Connector Adaptor Cable **$10**

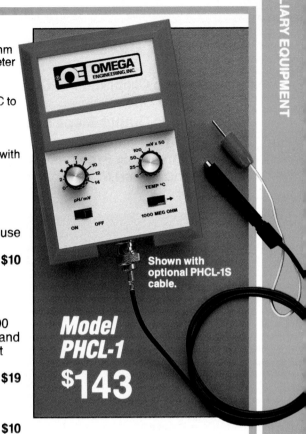

Shown with optional PHCL-1S cable.

Model PHCL-1 $143

Model PHCL-33

Model PHCL-33 $105

The PHCL-33 is a versatile instrument that can simulate the millivolt output of a pH electrode in 2 pH increments to test pH meters, recorders and other instruments with a millivolt input level. It can be used to determine which components in a pH measurement system are malfunctioning, and also check the accuracy of manual and automatic temperature compensation networks. To further enhance the PHCL-33's capabilities, a high/low impedance switch is incorporated to determine if an instrument's high impedance has been compromised and also allows calibration of lower impedance recorders and meters.

Specifications:

Outputs: pH 7   0 mV
pH 6 or 8   ±59 mV
pH 4 or 10 ±177 mV
pH 2 or 12 ±295 mV
pH 0 or 14 ±414 mV

Accuracy: ±1%

Impedance: Switch selectable from low to 1000 megohms

Connector: BNC

Power: 9 V battery

Size: 3⅝" x 5¾" x 1½"

Automatic Loop Calibrators

MADE IN **USA**

Automatic Digital Process Control (Loop) Calibrator

- **Automatic Calibration of Current and Voltage Loops**
- **Automatic Output Steps Every 25% for Linearity Check.**
- **Simultaneously Provides Input to Transmitter and Measures Transmitter Output**

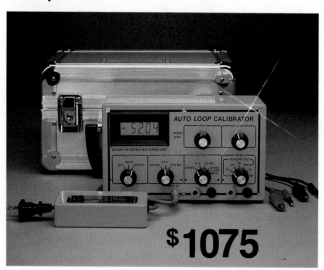

$1075

The PHCL-406 is an automatic control loop calibrator designed for the process control industry. The PHCL-406 eliminates the need for running between the transducer and control panel to set span, zero and perform linearity checks. The PHCL-406 can automatically switch between user preset zero and span or a constant output may be selected. In addition, the PHCL-406 can monitor an input signal while simultaneously supplying a preset calibrated output signal (such as with transmitters).

Specifications:

Accuracy: ±0.05% full range
Output Ranges: 0 to 20.00 mA (0 to 600 ohms load), 0 to 50.00 mA (0 to 200 ohms load), 0 to 11.00 V, 0 to 199.99 mV
Input Ranges: 0 to ±199.99 mA, 0 to ±11.000 V, 0 to ±199.99 mV
Two-Wire Transmitter Output (Loop Powered): Maximum Supply Voltage 100 Vdc—0 to 20.00 mA (any load 0 to 1000 ohms at 24 Vdc), 0 to 50.00 mA (any load 0 to 350 ohms at 24 Vdc)
Display: 4½ digit LCD
Automatic Switching: 7, 15, 30, 60 seconds
Automatic Ramp: 7, 15, 30, 60 seconds
Operating Temperature: 0 to 50°C
Battery Life: 100 h
AC Power Module: 24 V output
Size: 7.5″ x 4.3″ x 2.3″
Weight: 8 lb

1 YEAR WARRANTY

Automatic pH Loop Calibrator

Model PHCL-109 **$925**

- **Automatic or Manual Switching Between Two pH Levels**
- **Built-In High Impedance Check**
- **Provides Both Stepped and Variable pH Signal Output**
- **Output Short Circuit Proof**

Designed to calibrate pH loops in the process industry, the PHCL-109 provides both a stepped and variable pH output. To eliminate the need to run back and forth between the pH transducer, transmitter and control panel, the PHCL-109 automatically switches between two preset pH levels that are compliments of each other Comes complete with carrying case and test leads.

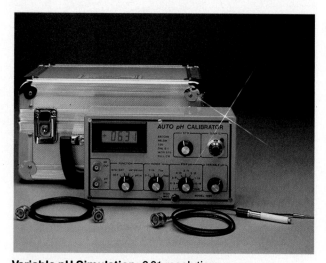

Specifications:

Accuracy: pH simulation ±0.01 pH, pH measurement ±0.01 pH
Input Impedance: 10^{15} ohms
pH Simulation: 0.00 to 14.00 in one pH steps

Variable pH Simulation: 0.01 resolution
Temperature Compensation: 0 to 100°C with 0.1°C resolution
Automatic Switching: 7 and 15 seconds
Operating Temperature: 0 to 50°C
Battery: two 9 V, 1 year battery life
Size: 7.5″ x 4.3″ x 2.3″
Weight: 4 lb

1 YEAR WARRANTY

Process Loop Indicator and Unregulated Power Supply

Model TX-81

The Model TX-81 Process Loop Indicator is a versatile meter that can be used in any transmitter loop. It has a large easy-to-read LCD readout for monitoring a signal from your 4 to 20 mA or 10 to 50 mA transmitter and is user scalable.

A JIC/NEMA enclosure provides environmental protection for use in most industrial applications. It can be used in any process variable measurement application where a two wire transmitter is required. No external power is needed.

The TX-81 works off your existing current loop power supply and has a voltage drop of only 2.30 volts. Independent adjustments for zero and span over the entire 4000 count range makes this meter usable for most process applications.

General Specifications:

Linearity: ±2 counts
Resolution: 500 PPM of full scale
Temperature Range: 0°C to 50°C
Range Span: 2000 counts (high reading minus low reading)

Model TX-81

$229

Model U24Y100

U24Y100
24 Volt dc, 1000 mA unregulated power supply
−10°C to +65°C operating range
110 V ac input power
3.71″ Sq. x 4.5″ W

Model U24Y100

$110

Series 880 Multimeters and Accessories

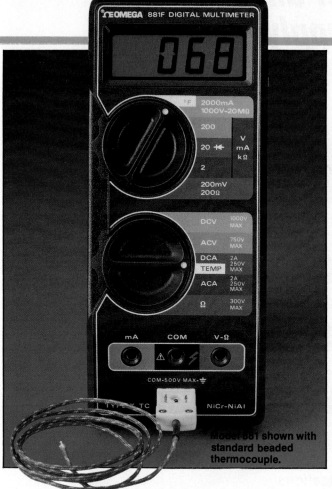

Model 881 shown with standard beaded thermocouple.

The 880 and 881 fully portable Digital Multimeters are designed with a rugged, high impact case to withstand daily field use. These precision DMM's measure dc voltage and current, ac voltage and current, and resistance. In addition, the Model 881 features TRMS ac voltage and current, and Temperature Measurement from a type K thermocouple. Both the Model 880 and 881 feature 0.25% accuracy, and the Model 881 is available with either °C or °F temperature readout. Included with both models is a set of general purpose test leads (Kit 880-A10). Model 881 also has a type K beaded wire thermocouple.

MULTIMETER ACCURACY

| | dc | dc | ac | ac | |
	Voltage	Current	Voltage*	Current*	Resistance
Sensitivity:	100 μV	1 μA	100 μV	1 μA	100 mΩ
Model 880:	± (.25% rdg ± 1 digit)	± (.75% rdg + 1 digit)	+(1% + 3 digits)	± (2% rdg + 2 digits)	± (0.5% rdg + 4 digits)
Model 881:	± (.25% rdg + 1 digit)	± (.75% rdg + 1 digit)	+(1% + 9 digits)	± (2% rdg +9 digit)	± (0.5% rdg + 4 digits)

TRMS with Model 881

TEMPERATURE—MODEL 881

Model	Range	Resolution	Accuracy
881F	0 to +2000°F	1°F	+(5°F + 1 digit) up to 225°F
881C	−20 to +1370°C	1°C	+(3°C + 1 digit) up to 150°C

Notes: ± 3% rdg over 225°F/150°C, chart correctable to 1.5% rdg over 350°C (600°F)

Model 880	Model 881
$139	**$229**

ACCESSORIES

Accessories For All Series 800 Meters:

	Model KS-871	Tilt stand-Models 871, 872, 880, 881 (not shown)	$10.00
	Model KS-860	Tilt stand, belt clip, probe holder—Models 865, 866, 868, 869, 873 (not shown)	10.00
A	Model SC-800	Soft carrying case	10.00
	MN-1604	9 V battery (not shown)	3.00
	OT-201-1	2 oz. jar of high thermal conductivity paste for fast surface measurements (not shown)	7.50
B	Model 880-A2	Deluxe carrying case	25.00

For Series 880 Multimeters:

	Model 880-A3	Spare parts kit (not shown)	42.00
C	Model 880-A4	High voltage probe	85.00
D	Model 880-A5	50 Ampere current shunt	55.00
E	Model 880-A6	Clip-on test lead set	15.00
F	Model 880-A7	RF probe (250 MHz)	79.00
G	Model 880-A8	Universal test lead kit	18.00
H	Model 880-A9	Clamp-on ac current probe (200A)	105.00
J	Model 880-A10	General purpose test lead set (one supplied)	10.00

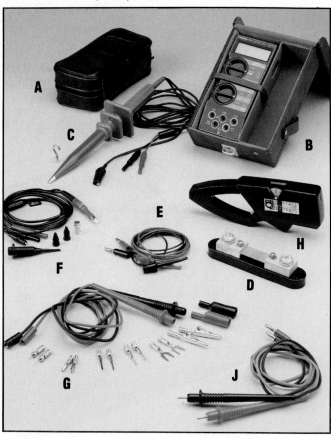

Alarm Module and Isolator

Model PHA-51
$185

Model PHA-52
$215
Not Shown

Dual Alarm Modules

- **Adds Alarm Relay Capability to Common Analog Outputs**
- **Ideal for Use with Two Wire Transmitters**
- **Independent Setpoint and Dead Band Controls for Each Relay**
- **Relays Energize on Increasing or Decreasing Input Value—Switch Selectable**
- **NEMA 4X Gasketed Enclosure Provides Watertight Protection**

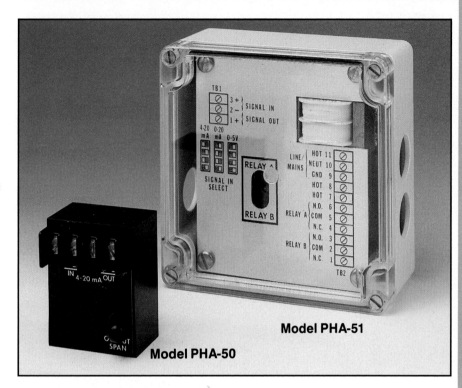

Model PHA-51

Model PHA-50

The Model PHA-51 and PHA-52 dual alarm modules provide an ideal way to add alarm capability to a control system loop. The module's two relays each have setpoint and deadband controls and a LED to indicate on/off relay status. Relay phasing switches individually select each relay to operate in response to increasing or decreasing input signal value. For compatibility with many systems, input levels are user selectable. The PHA-51 accepts 0 to 20 mA, 4 to 20 mA, or 0 to 5 Vdc inputs and the PHA-52 takes 0 to 50 mV, 0 to 100 mV, 0 to 5 Vdc.

Specifications

Inputs: PHA-51: 0 to 20 mA, 4 to 20 mA, 0 to 5 Vdc; PHA-52: 0 to 50 mV, 0 to 100 mV, 0 to 5 Vdc
Outputs: 0 to 5 Vdc, 100 K ohms min. load; 0 to 1 mA, 100 ohms max.
Power: 100-130 Vac
Relays: Setpoints: 0 to 100% of Input Signal Range; Deadbands: 0 to 50% of Signal Input Range; Contact Rating: SPDT, 3A resistive, 250 Vac max. 3A max. resistive, 30 Vdc max.
Dimensions: 4¾″ × 4¾″ × 2½″
Weight: 1.25 lb

Model PHA-50
$125

Loop Powered Isolator

- **Prevents Ground Loops**
- **Transformer Isolated**
- **Loop Powered**
- **Virtually Zero Temperature Drift**

The PHA-50 loop-powered isolator provides an isolated 4 to 20 mA output equal to the 4 to 20 mA non isolated input. This one to one current isolator is used in 4 to 20 mA two wire circuits to prevent ground loops. To eliminate moisture and humidity problems, the electronics are encapsulated in epoxy and the output is compensated for virtually zero temperature drift. The PHA-50 can be surface mounted in any position, and a trimpot control to adjust the output span is accessed by removing a protective cap.

Specifications:

Input: 4 to 20 mA non isolated
Output: 4 to 20 mA Isolated
Insertion loss at 20 mA: 4.5 Vdc (this represents a max. resistance of 225 ohms into the 4 to 20 mA loop)
Allowable Isolated Load: 20 to 500 ohms
Isolation: 1000 Vac or dc, transformer isolated
Sensitivity: 0.01 mA
Stability: 0.01 mA
Non-linearity: ±0.03% of span
Accuracy: ±0.01% of span
Temperature Range: −20 to 50°C
Dimensions: 2¼″ × 1¾″ × 1″

1 YEAR WARRANTY

For placing orders, call
1-800-TC-OMEGA
1-800-82-66342

Function Recorders with Interchangeable Modules *Series RD-2000*

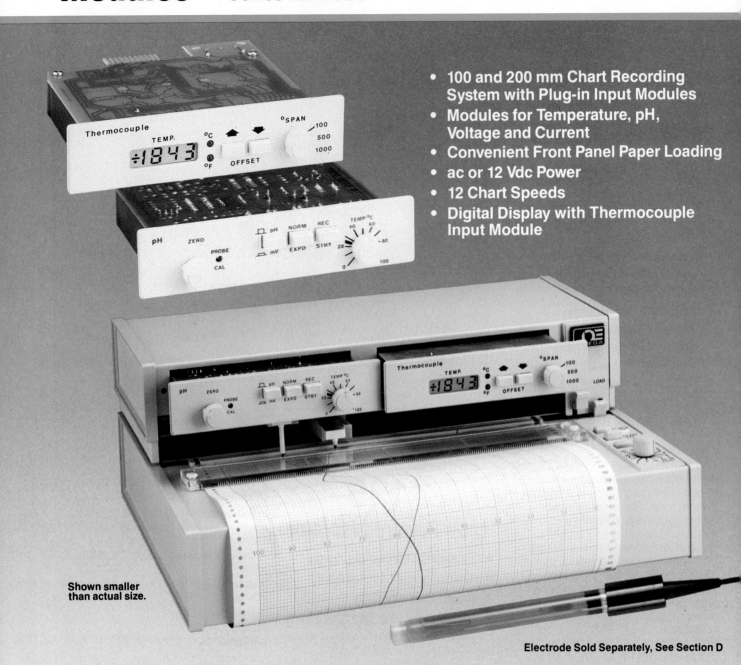

- 100 and 200 mm Chart Recording System with Plug-in Input Modules
- Modules for Temperature, pH, Voltage and Current
- Convenient Front Panel Paper Loading
- ac or 12 Vdc Power
- 12 Chart Speeds
- Digital Display with Thermocouple Input Module

Shown smaller than actual size.

Electrode Sold Separately, See Section D

The RD-2000 Function Recorder System introduces low cost to modular recorders. With a choice of input modules, the RD-2000 can measure temperature from thermocouples, pH, millivolts/volts, or milliamps. To select any input type, simply plug in the appropriate module. The mainframe recorder is available in three varieties; a one pen model with a 100 mm chart, and a 200 mm chart model with either one or two pens. With the two pen model, you can record two completely different input signals,

such as temperature and pH, or have two channels record the same type of input signal. Designed for ease of use, the RD-2000 system has all user controls on the main control panel. Select one of 12 chart speeds (from 1 cm/hr to 30 cm/min), chart feed, chart start/stop, power and pen lift. For easy paper loading, the control deck unlatches and swings away to reveal the paper feed spindle. A roll of chart paper is dropped into place, and the deck is then lowered and latched.

COMPLETE ONE CHANNEL RECORDER

From

$720

Model RD-2010
with RD-PH
input module

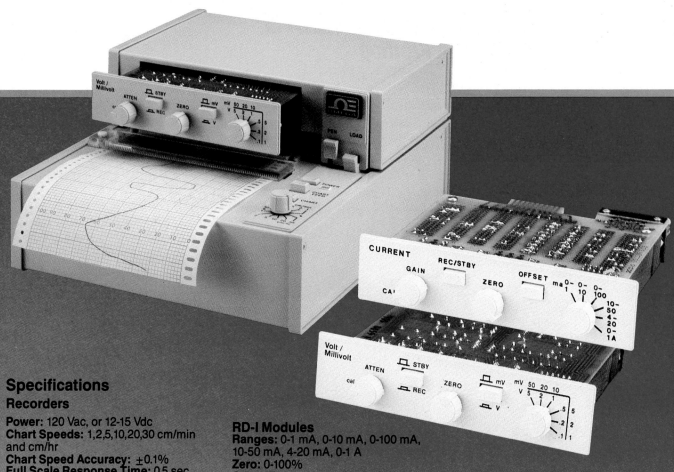

Specifications

Recorders

Power: 120 Vac, or 12-15 Vdc
Chart Speeds: 1,2,5,10,20,30 cm/min and cm/hr
Chart Speed Accuracy: ±0.1%
Full Scale Response Time: 0.5 sec
Overshoot: None, system critically damped
Override Event Marker: Standard, approx. 2% spike
Pen Lift: Manual external lever

RD-MV Module

Ranges: 1,2,5,10,20,50,100 mV and 0.2, 0.5, 1,2,5 V
Zero Adjust: ±100%
Attenuation: 2.5:1
Connection: 5-way binding post
Input Type: Single ended floating to ±50V
Input Impedance: 2.5M ohm fixed
Accuracy: ±0.1% full scale
Output Buffer: 0-5 Vdc (customer adjustable), 0-100 mV (factory set)

RD-PH Module

Range: 0-14, 0-1.4 (expanded scale) pH
Zero: −150 to 50%, −1500 to 500% (expanded scale)
Temperature Compensation: 0 to 100°C
Accuracy: ±0.1% full scale
mV Mode: ±700 mV range
Probe Calibration: ±20% from normal

RD-TC Module

Ranges: 0-100, 0-500, 0-1000°C or °F span within −250 to 1900°F range
Display: 3½-digit LCD
Thermocouple Types: J,K,T,E; jumper selectable
Analog Output: 1 mV per degree
Input Connector: Screw terminals
Indications: Open circuit, over- and underrange

RD-I Modules

Ranges: 0-1 mA, 0-10 mA, 0-100 mA, 10-50 mA, 4-20 mA, 0-1 A
Zero: 0-100%
Offset Zero: 25%, switch selectable
Gain: Boost low signal, up to 25% gain for full scale

How To Order

Recorders

Model Number	Price	Chart Width	No. of Channels
RD-2010	**$575**	100 mm	one
RD-2020	625	200 mm	one
RD-2030	795	200 mm	two

Modules

Model Number	Price	Input Type
RD-MV	**$275**	Millivolt/Volt
RD-I	275	Current
RD-TC	415	Thermocouple
RD-PH	240	pH

Accessories

Part Number	Price	Description
0100-0011	**$36**	100 mm chart paper, 0-100 scale*
0100-0026	36	200 mm chart paper, 0-100 scale*
0100-0041	57	100 mm chart paper, 0-14 scale*
0100-0042	57	200 mm chart paper, 0-14 scale*

* pkg of 6 rolls

Circular Chart Recorders
Standard and Thermal Printing

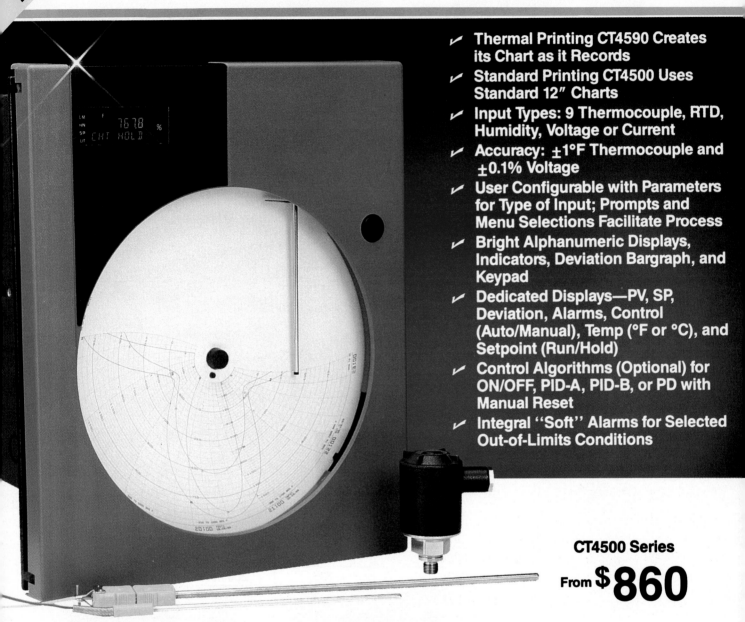

- ✔ **Thermal Printing CT4590 Creates its Chart as it Records**
- ✔ **Standard Printing CT4500 Uses Standard 12″ Charts**
- ✔ **Input Types: 9 Thermocouple, RTD, Humidity, Voltage or Current**
- ✔ **Accuracy: ±1°F Thermocouple and ±0.1% Voltage**
- ✔ **User Configurable with Parameters for Type of Input; Prompts and Menu Selections Facilitate Process**
- ✔ **Bright Alphanumeric Displays, Indicators, Deviation Bargraph, and Keypad**
- ✔ **Dedicated Displays—PV, SP, Deviation, Alarms, Control (Auto/Manual), Temp (°F or °C), and Setpoint (Run/Hold)**
- ✔ **Control Algorithms (Optional) for ON/OFF, PID-A, PID-B, or PD with Manual Reset**
- ✔ **Integral "Soft" Alarms for Selected Out-of-Limits Conditions**

CT4500 Series

From **$860**

Thermocouple probes, from $19. See Section A of the OMEGA Temperature Measurement Handbook.

PX441 Pressure Transducer, $629. See Section B of the OMEGA Pressure Measurement Handbook.

The OMEGA Series CT4500 and CT4590 Circular Chart Recorders are ideal for applications with food, pharmaceuticals, environmental testing, and metalworking—wherever measured variables must be documented on a single chart and retained to meet application requirements. Microprocessor-based and field configurable, these circular chart recorders are designed for heavy-duty industrial use as well as in the laboratory.

Standard printing CT4500 recorders use pre-printed 12″ charts to record process variables from a variety of sensors or transmitters with configurable range limits. The thermal printing CT4590 Series one to four channel recorder produces up to four analog traces and prints alphanumeric data on a blank heat-sensitive chart. This means that chart data such as range markings in engineering units, digital values for process variables, and precise trace identification are easily customized.

Also, models are available with one or two independent digital controllers to generate controlled output signals to operate valves, dampers, testing elements, etc., for process control.

Users need configure only those functions which are specific for a given application, by following prompts in the digital displays. The configuration data (type of input, chart speed, chart range, alarm settings, tuning constants, etc.) are stored in nonvolatile memory for safekeeping in the event of power failure.

Microprocessor Controlled Recording

Both chart and pen are driven by stepper motors which are controlled by the microprocessor for precise maintenance-free operation. Since the chart speed is configurable, users can easily alter it through the keypad. The microprocessor uses the configured chart range data as well as the input data to determine proper pen position.

Specifications

PERFORMANCE

Number of Inputs: 1-pen model (CT4501), 1 input; 2-pen model (CT4502), 2 inputs; CT4590 has 1-4 inputs

Thermocouples: B, E, J, K, N, R, S, T, C

RTD: 100Ω Pt, alpha = 0.00385

Linear: 4-20 mA, 0-10 mV, 10-50 mV, 1-5 V

DESIGN

Input Impedance: 4-20 mA dc, 250Ω; 0-10 Vdc, 200 kΩ; all others, 10 M Ω

Span Step Response Time: 6 s max with no filtering

Sampling Rate: Input sampled 3 times/s for 2 inputs; for 3 and 4 input models 1.5 samples/s

Input Filter: Software, single pole low pass section with selectable time constants (off to 120 s)

Deviation Bargraph: 21 segment, color coded

Transmitter Supply Voltage: 22 to 26 Vdc at input terminals (1.2 W)

Configurable Parameters: Set through keypad; include time, date, chart speed (8 hr, 24 hr, 168 hr, or selected hr/rev) and inputs (range value −999.0 to 9999)

Chart: CT4500: 12″ (304.8 mm) dia with standard preprinted markings and calibrated width of 4.62″ (117.5 mm); CT4590: blank thermal-sensitive paper

Alarms (Soft Indication Only): In engineering units; none, inputs 1, 2, 3, PV, deviation, output, rate of change; resolution 0.1

Alarm Output Option: 2 SPST relays, resistive load 1 A @ 120 Vac (or ½ A @ 240 Vac)

Panel Cutout: 12.7″ × 12.7″

Control Output Option: Modes: manual operation; Automatic with local and remote setpoints; Algorithm (PID); Control: on/off, PID-A, PID-B, PD+MR, 3 position step; Output: current proportional simplex or duplex, position proportional, time proportional, current-relay duplex (relay=heat or cool)

Dimensions: 16.5″ H x 14″ W x 5.6″ D

Weight: 13.2 lbs (6 kg)

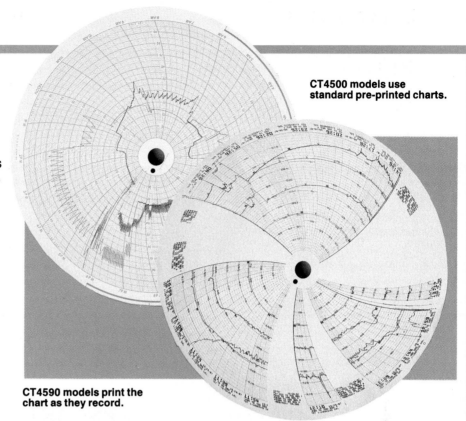

CT4500 models use standard pre-printed charts.

CT4590 models print the chart as they record.

Ordering Example: CT4501-AL, $860 + 130 = **$990**, one-channel standard printing recorder with optional alarm board and 2 relays.

To Order (Specify Model Number)

Model No.	Price	Description
CT4501	$860	1- channel standard recorder
CT4502	1145	2-channel standard recorder
CT4591	940	1-channel thermal printing recorder
CT4592	1225	2-channel thermal printing recorder
CT4593	1510	3-channel thermal printing recorder
CT4594	1795	4-channel thermal printing recorder
CT4500C	28	Add'l 100 thermal charts
CT4500-PUR	26	Add'l 6 purple pens
CT4500-RED	26	Add'l 6 red pens
CT4500C-0-100/7	11	Add'l 100 charts, 0-100 scale, 7 days
CT4500C-0-100/24	11	Add'l 100 charts, 0-1000 scale, 24 hrs
CT4500-0-2000/24	11	Add'l 100 charts, 0-2000 scale, 24 hrs
CT4500-0-500/24	11	Add'l charts, 0-500 scale, 24hrs.

Each recorder supplied with 100 charts; CT4501 and CT4502 also supplied with pens.

Options

Order Suffix	Price	Description
-AL	$130	Alarm board, 2 relays
-C1	315	Control output on channel 1
-AL-C1	445	Alarm board & control output option
-S1	515	Control with setpoint ramp, channel 1 (CT4590 only)
-AL-S1	645	Alarm board & control, setpoint ramp option (CT4590 only)
-T1	200	Totalization on channel 1
-AL-T1	330	Alarm board & totalization option

Environmental Monitoring Anemometer
Microprocessor-Based

Digital Monitoring of Air Velocity and Temperature.

- ✔ Velocity: 0-12,000 SFPM and 0-60.00 SMPS, autoranging.
- ✔ Temperature: −40.0 to 250.0°F and −40.0 to 125.0°C, autoranging.
- ✔ Direct Monitoring of air mass flow rate— no temperature or pressure corrections required.
- ✔ Accuracy of 2% of reading ±1% of Full Scale
- ✔ All in one instrument!

Microprocessor-Based Velocity Averaging. Instantly averages up to 5 sets of 200 points each.

Carrying Cord. Provides secure grasp of instrument case.

Power On-Off Switch and Velocity/ Temperature Measurement Selector.

Velocity Averaging or Individual Point Pushbutton.

Printer/Relative Reading Pushbutton. Commands instrument to transmit data to printer. Also computes readings relative to another reading.

Display Speed Selection. Fast, slow or hold.

Units Selector/Auxiliary Transducer Operation. Selects either English (FPM or °F) or metric units (MPS or °C). Also allows instrument to operate and read out another auxiliary transducer, such as OMEGA's FMA 5600 Flow Monitor.

Output Connector. Type DB-9. Has 0-5 Vdc and RS 232 output signals linearly proportional to velocity, temperature, or auxiliary input. Ideal for computer input or remote readout and recording. Mating connector included.

Probe and Auxiliary I/O Connector. Accepts probe input or auxiliary inputs (-MA option) from other transducers such as OMEGA's HX92 Humidity Transmitter and PX150 Differential Pressure Transmitter

Digital Display. 16-character alphanumeric LCD readout. Display measurement mode (e.g., VEL, TEMP, AVG, AUX or REL), 4-½ numerical digits, and English or metric measurement units. Stores 200 points permanently; up to 1000 with power left on.

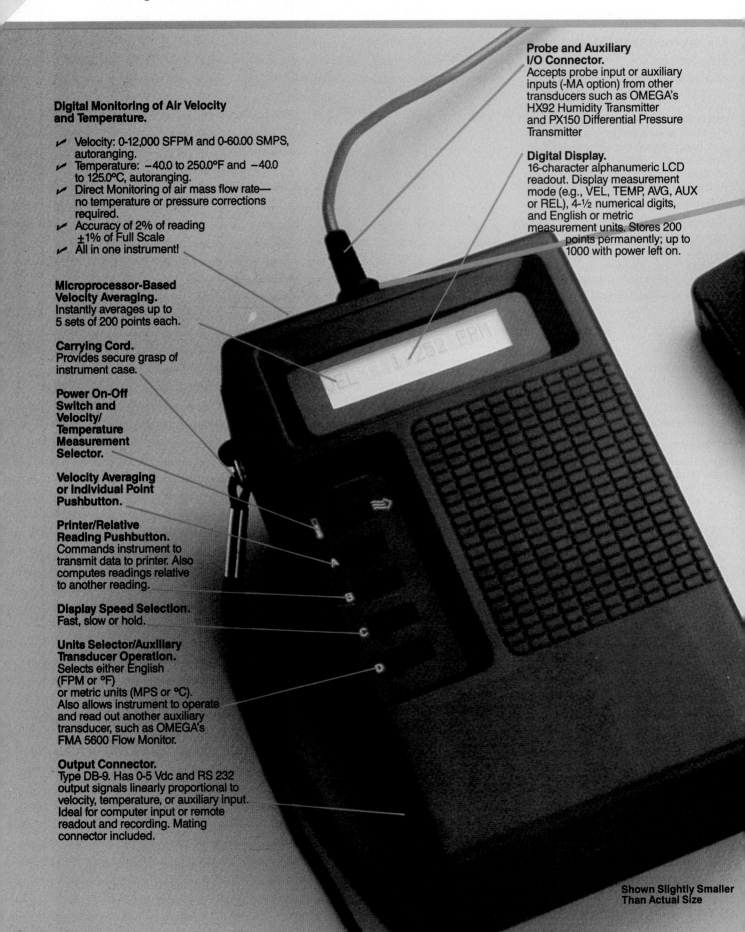

Shown Slightly Smaller Than Actual Size

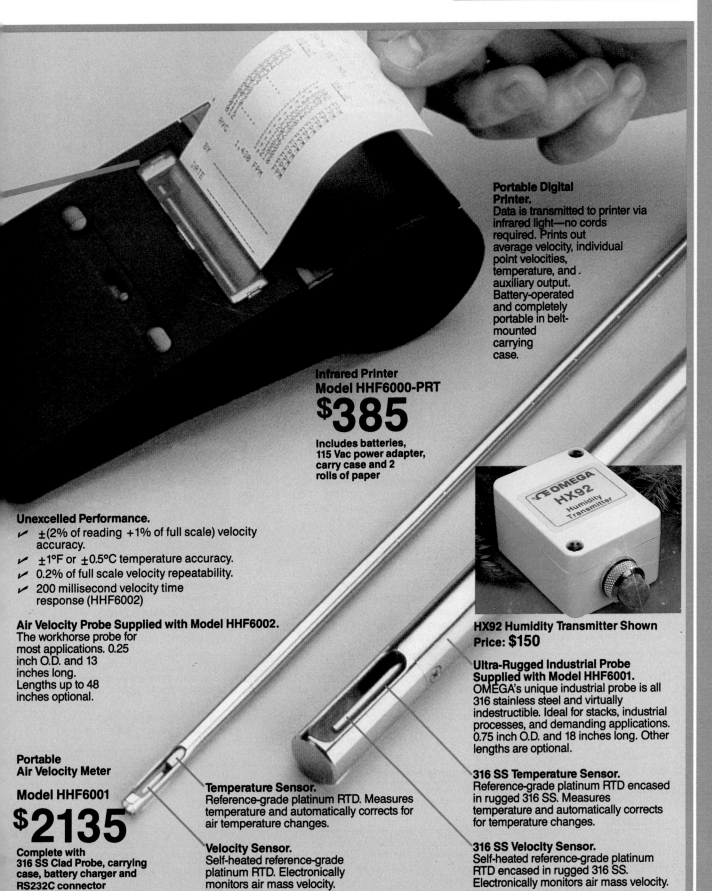

Portable Digital Printer.
Data is transmitted to printer via infrared light—no cords required. Prints out average velocity, individual point velocities, temperature, and auxiliary output. Battery-operated and completely portable in belt-mounted carrying case.

Infrared Printer Model HHF6000-PRT

$385

Includes batteries, 115 Vac power adapter, carry case and 2 rolls of paper

HX92 Humidity Transmitter Shown Price: $150

Unexcelled Performance.
- ±(2% of reading +1% of full scale) velocity accuracy.
- ±1°F or ±0.5°C temperature accuracy.
- 0.2% of full scale velocity repeatability.
- 200 millisecond velocity time response (HHF6002)

Air Velocity Probe Supplied with Model HHF6002.
The workhorse probe for most applications. 0.25 inch O.D. and 13 inches long. Lengths up to 48 inches optional.

Ultra-Rugged Industrial Probe Supplied with Model HHF6001.
OMEGA's unique industrial probe is all 316 stainless steel and virtually indestructible. Ideal for stacks, industrial processes, and demanding applications. 0.75 inch O.D. and 18 inches long. Other lengths are optional.

316 SS Temperature Sensor.
Reference-grade platinum RTD encased in rugged 316 SS. Measures temperature and automatically corrects for temperature changes.

Portable Air Velocity Meter

Model HHF6001

$2135

Complete with 316 SS Clad Probe, carrying case, battery charger and RS232C connector

Temperature Sensor.
Reference-grade platinum RTD. Measures temperature and automatically corrects for air temperature changes.

Velocity Sensor.
Self-heated reference-grade platinum RTD. Electronically monitors air mass velocity.

316 SS Velocity Sensor.
Self-heated reference-grade platinum RTD encased in rugged 316 SS. Electronically monitors air mass velocity.

Environmental Monitoring Anemometer
Microprocessor-Based

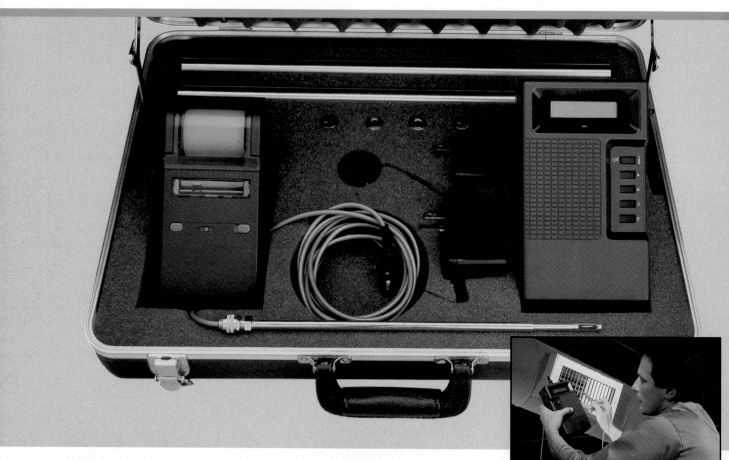

SPECIFICATIONS

Accuracy	Air Velocity	Temp.
0 to 50°C	±2% of reading + 1% of full scale	±0.4°F
−40 to 0°C, 50 to 125°C	±3% of reading + 1% of full scale	±1°F
HT1,2 options −40 to 250°C	±4% of reading + 1% of full scale	±4°F

Time response: Velocity HHF6001: 1 second; HHF6002: 200 milliseconds. 15 seconds for temperature for both.

Probe Pressure: HHF6002 probe 150 psig, HHF6001 probe 1000 psig max.

Electronics temperature: 32 to 122°F

Output signal: 0 to 5 Vdc with 0.005 Vdc resolution

Power source: Six "C" size rechargeable Ni-Cad batteries. Battery life is 11 hours at 0 SFPM, 4 hours at 12,000 SFPM. Recharger included.

Net wt of instrument and probe: 2.7 lb. nominally

Carrying case: Black plastic, padded. Size 21 × 15 × 5 in.

Optional Infrared Printer

Operating temperature: 32 to 122°F, 5 to 95% RH

Printer enclosure: Plastic, size 3.5 × 7.3 × 2.4 in.

Net weight: 1.0 lb

Model No.	Price	Description
HHF6001	$2135	Includes 316SS, 18″ long, 316SS clad velocity/temperature probe with 15′ of cable for −40 to 250°F; handheld display/storage unit; rugged carry case; and battery charger for 115/230 VAC, 50-60 Hz with 6′ of cable. Includes RS232C connector.
HHF6002	1630	Includes chrome-plated brass, 13″ long, ceramic/glass clad velocity/temperature probe with 15′ of cable for −40 to 250°F; handheld display/storage unit; rugged carry case; and battery charger for 115/230 VAC, 50-60 Hz with 6′ of cable. Includes RS232C connector.
HHF6002-HT1	1755	HHF6002 with probe for for −40 to 500°F air flow
HHF6001-HT2	2260	HHF6001 with probe for for −40 to 500°F air flows

Add suffix "-MAX" for 4-20 mA auxiliary input option for use with other transmitters. Display reads 0-100% of full scale. Add $85 to price. Example: Model HHF6001-MAX calls for a portable air velocity meter with 4-20 mA input option, price is $2220.

Accessories

Model No.	Price	Description
HHF6001-EXT	$125	18″ probe extenders for HHF6001 ONLY; up to 4 can be used. (price shown is per extender)
HHF6000-PRT	385	Infrared printer with (4) 1.5V AA alkaline batteries. 115 VAC power adaptor with 8′ cable, carry case. and 2 rolls of paper.

Compact Electronic Recorders

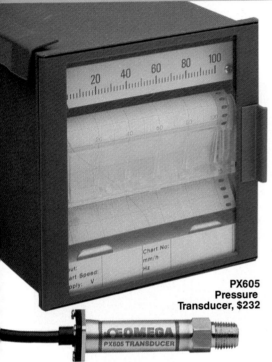

PX605 Pressure Transducer, $232

✓ **100 mm (4″) Chart Width**
✓ **Only 7.3″ Rear Panel Space Required**
✓ **Selectable Chart Speeds**
✓ **Optional Alarm/Control Relays**

The compact OMEGA RD170 Series single pen recorders, available for pH and millivolt inputs, measure only 5.7″ square and require just 7.3″ panel depth. Optional alarm/control relays can be supplied, offering a choice of six different modes of operation. The appropriate variant is chosen by simple dual-in-line switches. Setpoints are easily adjusted on-site by moving pointers on the scale.

RD170 Series pH and mV Input Models

RD170 Series From

$805

1 YEAR WARRANTY — **MADE IN USA**

Specifications
pH Input
Inputs: two, pH and RTD
Range: 0 to 14 pH
Input Amplifier Stability: Better than ±0.1 pH in 24h at constant temp.; non-cumulative temp. coeff. <0.1 pH/10°C
Input Impedance: >10^{12} Ohms at 20°C
Resolution: 0.2 pH
Accuracy: ±1% span
Temp. Compensation: Auto/manual selection via internal switch; automatic using Pt100 RTD; manual via potentiometer, 0 to 100°C
Slope Factor Correction: Variable from 80 to 100% by potentiometer accessible via recorder scale (100% fully clockwise)
Electrode Pair Zero Potential Point: 7 pH
Isopotential Point: 7 pH, factory pre-set

mV, other Inputs
Inputs: 1
Range: 0 to 100 mV, other ranges available on special request
Base Specifications
Chart Paper: 100 mm (4″), 15 m (50′)

Chart Speed: Selectable, 20/60/180 mm/hr
Alarm: 2 setpoints, 2 relays
Relay Contacts: 250 Vac, 5 A
Relay Action: Relay energized above or below setpoint, on/off, 3-state or latching
Power: 110 V nominal 60 Hz; 10 to 15 VA
Operating Temperature Range: 32 to 130°F
Operating Humidity Range: 0 to 80% RH
Dimensions: 5.7″W × 5.7″H × 7.7″D (145 × 145 × 196 mm); 7.3″ (185 mm) behind panel depth
Panel Cutout: 5.4″ (138 mm) square
Case: Sheet steel, door hinged left
Weight: 9.9 lb (4.5 kg)

For a complete selection of pH electrodes, see Section D.

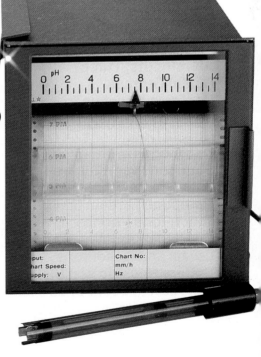

To Order (Specify Model Number)

Model No.	Price	Description
RD170	$805	1-pen recorder, pH input
RD170-ALM	900	1-pen recorder, pH input with two alarm relays
RD173	560	1-pen recorder, millivolt input
RD173-ALM	655	1-pen recorder, millivolt input with two alarm relays
RDX-170-RD	12	Pens, pkg. of 3
RDX-170-0-14	25	Paper, 0-14 pH, pkg. of 5 rolls
RDX-170-0-100	25	Paper, 0-100 mV, pkg. of 5 rolls

Supplied complete with pen, roll of paper, and user's manual.

Voice Synthesized Environmental Monitoring Data Logging Systems

OMEGASAYS™ Models OMA-P3300 and OMA-P4300

From **$780**

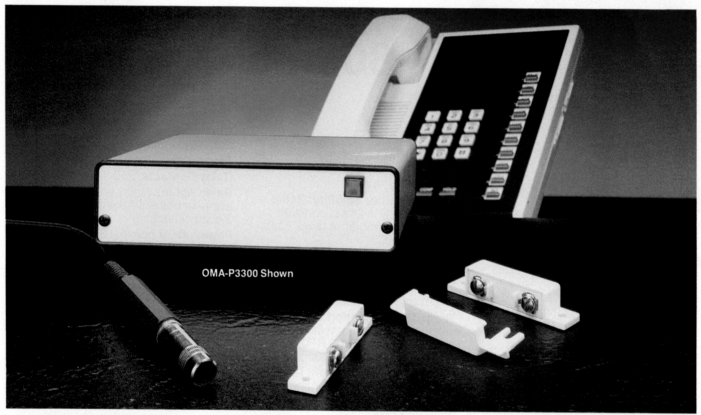

OMA-P3300 Shown

- ✔ **Integral Temperature Sensor and ac Power Failure Detection**
- ✔ **One 4-20 mA Analog Input; Three Dry Contact Alert Inputs; Three Digital Outputs**
- ✔ **Contacts You at up to Three Locations if Unsafe Conditions Occur**
- ✔ **Data Logging of Timed Stamped Alarm States**
- ✔ **Fully Programmable by Computer Modem or Touch-Tone Phone**
- ✔ **Continual Updates of all Levels and Conditions**
- ✔ **Battery Back Up and Dial Out Alert in Event of ac Power Failure**

Now you can prevent problems even when you can't be there! Monitor conditions such as temperature, humidity, tank levels, water incursion, smoke, and sound. The OMEGA OMA-P3300 and OMA-P4300 environmental monitoring systems let you keep track of important facilities and processes and actually enter control commands over standard phone lines. These advanced systems contact you by phone to advise you of unsafe conditions. The monitors can communicate in either voice-synthesized English or ASCII text through a computer serial port. Both units can be programmed through a computer or touch-tone phone. The OMA-P4300 is also locally programmable by a front key panel. The compact, key-lock OMA-P4300 is protected in a NEMA type 1 steel housing.

Inputs which are capable of dial-out alerts include an integral temperature sensor, a 4-20 mA

input, and three digital inputs. There are three additional digital inputs whose state may be determined during a status poll. Six dry-contact digital inputs are used to monitor any area or process. Three of those inputs can be programmed to automatically dial out if levels exceed your specified limits. The OMA-P3300/P4300 can be interfaced with a 300 baud computer to provide the increased versatility of computer data control.

The OMA-P3300/P4300 also includes three digital outputs that can be used to control external devices. The optional OMA-PX101 control module provides relays to handle 1 A loads to the three outputs. In addition to its 'dial out on alert' capability, the unit may be polled from computer or touch-tone phone for the present status of the inputs, and up to 32 alert history points may be stored for periodic downloading to a computer.

OMA-P4300 Protected by a NEMA 1
Steel Housing

Specifications

Inputs: one integral temperature (–20 to 150°F); one 4-20 mA; three digital inputs (alert inputs); three digital inputs (non-alert)

Outputs: Three digital outputs (TTL voltage levels, 20 mA max. sink current)

Battery System: OMA-P3300: 0.08 Amp-hour sealed rechargeable, life approx. 30 min with ac off. OMA-P4300: 1.9 Amp-hour sealed rechargeable, life approx. 20 hours with ac off

AC Connection: wall transformer with 6 ft cord

Telephone Connection: Standard modular connector (RHIIC) with a 6 ft cord

Operating Temp.: 20 to 120°F (6 to 60°C)

Dimensions: OMA-P3300: 5.5″ W x 1.5″ H x 8″ D (127 x 38 x 203 mm); OMA-P4300: 10.375″ W x 10.5″ H x 4.125″ D (263.5 x 266.7 x 105 mm)

Weight: OMA-P3300: 2 lbs, 5 oz (1.05 kg); OMA-P4300: 12 lbs (5.4 kg)

OMA-PX06 Magnetic Reed Switch, $10

Microphone Included with OMA-P4300

To Order *(Specify Model Number)*		
Model No.	**Price**	**Description**
OMA-P3300	$780	Environmental monitoring system with integral temperature sensor and ac power detection.
OMA-P4300	980	Locally programmable environmental monitoring system with temperature (remote) sensor, microphone, ac power detection, and NEMA 1 enclosure
OMA-PX101	160	1 Amp relay control module
OMA-PX06	10	Magnetic reed switch
OMA-PX04	40	Water detection switch
OMA-PX22	60	Temperature switch
OMA-PX31	50	Terminal communication software

OMA-P3300 comes with an integral temperature sensor and ac power detection. OMA-P4300 comes with a remote temperature sensor, microphone and ac power detection.

We Take Great Ideas . . .
& Make Them Even Better™

J-18

Voice Synthesized Monitoring and Control Systems

for Environmental and Operating Conditions

1 YEAR WARRANTY

MADE IN USA

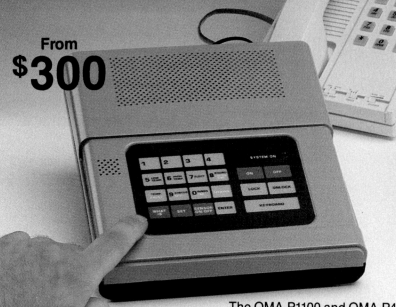

From **$300**

It Speaks to You in Plain English!

Specifications

Temperature Limit Range: +2°F to 126°F ; primary temp. alert occurs when temp. exceeds programmable Hi or Lo limits

AC Power: UL listed plug-in, Class 2 transformer with a 6 ft cord, 105-124 Vac, 8 watt input/9 Vac 600 mA output

Batteries: OMA-P1100 uses six 1.5 V alkaline batteries (not included), provides up to 12 hr continuous operation with ac power off. OMA-P4100 uses a 1.9 Amp-hour gelled electrolyte battery (included) with constant trickle recorder. 20 hour battery backup with ac power off.

Phone Connection: plugs into a standard RJ-11 telephone jack; works with rotary or pulse dialing systems

Operating Temp. Range: +40°F to +100°F (operate in a clean, dry environment)

Dimensions: OMA-P1100: 2″ H x 7 ¾″ W x 8 ⅝″ D (51 x 196 x 219 mm) OMA-P4100: 10 ¼″ H x 10 ⅜″ W x 4 ½″ D (260 x 264 x 108 mm)

Weight: OMA-P1100: 2 lbs with batteries (0.91 kg); OMA-P4100: 10 lb 6 oz with batteries (4.7 kg)

OMEGASAYS™

OMA-P1100 and OMA-P4100

- ✔ **Dials up to Four Phone Numbers to Deliver Alert Message**
- ✔ **Monitors Temperature, ac Power, and High Level Sound**
- ✔ **Three Digital Inputs for Switch Closure Sensing**
- ✔ **Operates Over Standard Phone Equipment**
- ✔ **OMA-P4100 has NEMA Enclosure**
- ✔ **Battery Backup**

The OMA-P1100 and OMA-P4100 from OMEGA provide cost-effective monitoring and control of environmental and security conditions in industrial, office, and residential locations. Housed in a NEMA type enclosure, the OMA-P4100 is an industrial version of the OMA-P1100. Both units monitor up to six environmental conditions including ac power, temperature, and high sound level (i.e., smoke or fire alarms) plus three digital inputs for hook-up to switch closure sensors.

When an Alert condition occurs the unit will automatically dial up to four user-programmed numbers to deliver its alert message in English. It continues to call until the alert message is properly acknowledged. You can call in from any anywhere for a complete status report on all monitored conditions. The unit also provides a live 'listen-in' feature to monitor actual sounds on-site.

OMA-P4100 Industrial Monitor with NEMA Enclosure, $600.

To Order *(Specify Model Number)*

Model No.	Price	Description
OMA-P1100	$300	Desktop monitor with integral temperature sensor
OMA-P4100	600	Industrial monitor with NEMA enclosure and remote temp. sensor
OMA-PX06	10	Magnetic reed switch
OMA-PX05	20	Remote temp. sensor (included with OMA-P4100)
OMA-PX04	40	Water detection switch
OMA-PX22	60	Temperature switch

Batteries
Energy to Spare!

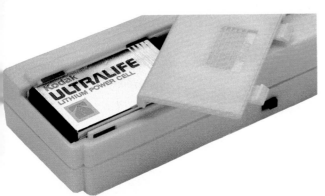

- ✔ **Wide Range of Styles Available**
- ✔ **Alkaline**
- ✔ **Long-Life Lithium**
- ✔ **Mercury**
- ✔ **Silver Oxide**

From extra long-life lithium to those tiny silver oxide cells—OMEGA has the battery you need. Look in the tables below for the correct replacement battery for your OMEGA instrument. Many units require more than one battery, so be sure to check how many you need before placing an order.

Alkaline and Lithium

To Order *(Specify Model Number)*	Model No.	Standard Size	Voltage	Price	Compatible OMEGA Units	
	MN1500-6	AA (alkaline)	1.5 V	$3.00	CT-410 Series CT-420 Series MM-1 OS71	PHH-47 PHB-51 and 52 PHB-62 T150
	MN1400	C (alkaline)	1.5 V	4.00	OmniAmp IIA, IIB	
	MN1300	D (alkaline)	1.5 V	3.00	CT485 Series DP-171 DP-172	DP-173 DP-174
	MN1600-4 MN1604	K9V (alkaline)	9 V	3.00	383 CL-303 CL-304	CL-305 CL-306 HH-30
	U9VL	U9VL (lithium)	9V	4.90	Handheld units accepting a 9V battery, except those listed above for 9V alkaline battery.	

Mercury and Silver Oxide

To Order *(Specify Model Number)*	Model No.	Voltage	Price	Compatible OMEGA Units	
	RM401R	1.35 V (mercury)	$3.00	CJ Series	
	PX625	3.55 V (silver oxide)	3.00	LXCJ MCJ Series OmniAmp I	
	PH-BATT-1	1.5 V (silver oxide)	1.00	CDH-1 CDH-2 PHH-1	PHH-1X PH-TC PH-TF
	RM12R	1.35 V (mercury)	4.00	OmniAmp IIB LXCJ Series	

Temperature Sensors and Probes

PFA* Coated Thermocouple Probes

PFA* Coated Probes are the perfect solution when there is a need to measure the temperature of caustic or corrosive chemical solutions in industrial and laboratory environments. Corrosion resistance of PFA allows you to measure the temperature of sulfuric, hydrochloric, nitric and chromic acids.

The PFA Probes are made standard in 12″ lengths with an OST quick disconnect connector at the cold end.

PFA* Perfluoro Alkoxy

To Order: *(Specify Model Number)*

Part Number	Price	Probe Dia.	Calibration	
ICSS-116G-12-PFA	$47	¹⁄₁₆″	**J**	Iron Constantan
ICSS-18G-12-PFA	47	⅛″		
CASS-116G-12-PFA	47	¹⁄₁₆″	**K**	Chromel Alumel
CASS-18G-12-PFA	47	⅛″		
CPSS-116G-12-PFA	47	¹⁄₁₆″	**T**	Copper Constantan
CPSS-18G-12-PFA	47	⅛″		
CXSS-116G-12-PFA	47	¹⁄₁₆″	**E**	Chromel Constantan
CXSS-18G-12-PFA	47	⅛″		

400 Series Precision Thermistor Probes

OMEGA Series "400" Probes are for use in laboratory applications. All models have an accuracy of ±0.1°C and are 225Ω @ 25°C. Each sensor is supplied with a 10-foot vinyl cable and phone plug connector. For use with Model 865 and 866 Thermometers. (See the OMEGA Complete Temperature Measurement Handbook and Encyclopedia®)

Configuration	Model	Description	Temp. Rating	Application	Price
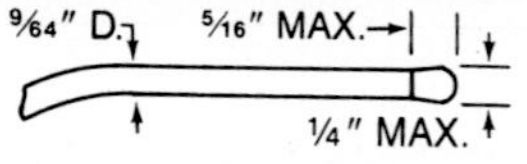 ⁹⁄₆₄″ D. ⁵⁄₁₆″ MAX. ¼″ MAX.	**ON-401-PP**	**General Purpose.** Vinyl tipped, most rugged probe. Used for short-term water and sub-soil readings. Waterproof construction available on special order.	212°F 100°C	Buried	**$50**
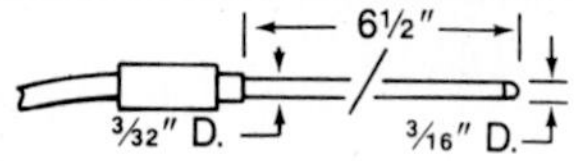 6½″ ³⁄₃₂″ D. ³⁄₁₆″ D.	**ON-402-PP**	**Small, Flexible.** Vinyl sheath and tip. Cuvette temperatures. General purpose measurement.	212°F 100°C	General Purpose	**$75**
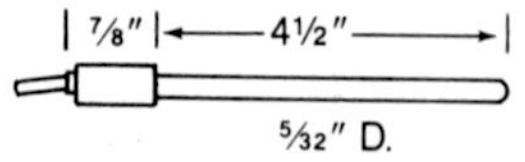 ⅞″ 4½″ ⁵⁄₃₂″ D.	**ON-403-PP**	**Tubular.** Stainless steel probe for rugged duty. Often used for liquid immersion. Probe is immersible only to cap.	212°F 100°C	Liquid	**$70**
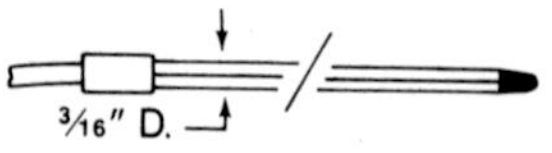 ³⁄₁₆″ D.	**ON-404-PP**	**Tubular-Glass.** Chemically inert for liquid immersion use. Thermometric titration. Freezing point determination. Pyrex, 5″ long.	212°F 100°C	Liquid	**$75**
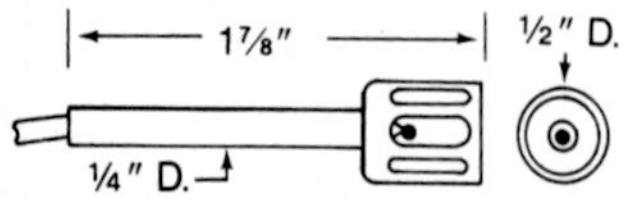 1⅞″ ½″ D. ¼″ D.	**ON-405-PP**	**Air Temperature.** Stainless steel probe suitable for test rooms, incubators, remote air readings, monitoring of gas streams, etc.	212°F 100°C	Gas	**$70**
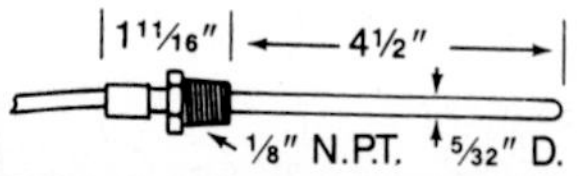 1¹¹⁄₁₆″ 4½″ ⅛″ N.P.T. ⁵⁄₃₂″ D.	**ON-410-PP**	**Tubular With Fitting.** Rugged, stainless steel probe with pipe fitting. Suitable for taking readings in pipes or inside closed vessels.	212°F 100°C	Gas, Liquid	**$70**

Quick Disconnect Thermocouple Assemblies

OST Thermocouple Probe Assemblies

To Order (Specify Model Number)

THERMOCOUPLE ALLOY		SHEATH DIA.	MODEL NO. 12″ LENGTH	PRICE G*/E*	U*	MODEL NO. 18″ LENGTH	PRICE G*/E*	U*	MODEL NO. 24″ LENGTH	PRICE G*/E*	U*	PRICE PER ADD'L FT.
IRON-CONSTANTAN 304 SS Sheath	J	1⁄16″	JQSS-116(*)-12	$22	$27	JQSS-116(*)-18	$22.80	$27.80	JQSS-116(*)-24	$23.55	$28.55	$1.55
		1⁄8″	JQSS-18(*)-12	23	27	JQSS-18(*)-18	23.90	27.90	JQSS-18(*)-24	24.85	28.85	1.85
		3⁄16″	JQSS-316(*)-12	25	28	JQSS-316(*)-18	26.60	29.60	JQSS-316(*)-24	28.15	31.15	3.15
		1⁄4″	JQSS-14(*)-12	27	30	JQSS-14(*)-18	29.50	32.50	JQSS-14(*)-24	32.00	35.00	5.00
CHROMEL-ALUMEL 304 SS Sheath	K	1⁄16″	KQSS-116(*)-12	22	27	KQSS-116(*)-18	22.80	27.80	KQSS-116(*)-24	23.55	28.55	1.55
		1⁄8″	KQSS-18(*)-12	23	27	KQSS-18(*)-18	23.90	27.90	KQSS-18(*)-24	24.85	28.85	1.85
		3⁄16″	KQSS-316(*)-12	25	28	KQSS-316(*)-18	26.60	29.60	KQSS-316(*)-24	28.15	31.15	3.15
		1⁄4″	KQSS-14(*)-12	27	30	KQSS-14(*)-18	29.50	32.50	KQSS-14(*)-24	32.00	35.00	5.00
COPPER-CONSTANTAN 304 SS Sheath	T	1⁄16″	TQSS-116(*)-12	22	27	TQSS-116(*)-18	22.80	27.80	TQSS-116(*)-24	23.55	28.55	1.55
		1⁄8″	TQSS-18(*)-12	23	27	TQSS-18(*)-18	24.30	28.30	TQSS-18(*)-24	25.50	29.50	2.50
		3⁄16″	TQSS-316(*)-12	25	28	TQSS-316(*)-18	26.60	29.60	TQSS-316(*)-24	28.15	31.15	3.15
		1⁄4″	TQSS-14(*)-12	27	30	TQSS-14(*)-18	29.50	32.50	TQSS-14(*)-24	32.00	35.00	5.00

* *Specify junction type: E (Exposed), G (Grounded) or U (Ungrounded)*

Ordering Example: KQSS-14G-12, **$27.** *Molded junction quick disconnect probe, type K (Chromel-Alumel), 304SS sheath, ¼″ O.D., grounded junction, 12″ length*

Subminiature Thermocouple Probe Assemblies

Quick Disconnect Subminiature Probes

To Order (Specify Model Number)

Thermocouple Alloy		Sheath Dia.	Model No. 6″ Length	Price G*/E*	U*	Model No. 12″ Length	Price G*/E*	U*	Price Per Add'l 6″
IRON-CONSTANTAN 304 SS Sheath	J	0.010″	JMQSS-010(*)-6	$48	$68	JMQSS-010(*)-12	$49.25	$69.25	$1.25
		0.020″	JMQSS-020(*)-6	28	30	JMQSS-020(*)-12	28.65	30.65	.65
		0.032″	JMQSS-032(*)-6	28	30	JMQSS-032(*)-12	28.65	30.65	.65
		0.040″	JMQSS-040(*)-6	28	30	JMQSS-040(*)-12	28.65	30.65	.65
		0.062″	JMQSS-062(*)-6	24	26	JMQSS-062(*)-12	24.80	26.80	.80
		0.125″	JMQSS-125(*)-6	24	26	JMQSS-125(*)-12	24.95	26.95	.95
CHROMEL-ALUMEL 304 SS Sheath	K	0.010″	KMQSS-010(*)-6	48	68	KMQSS-010(*)-12	49.25	69.25	1.25
		0.020″	KMQSS-020(*)-6	28	30	KMQSS-020(*)-12	28.65	30.65	.65
		0.032″	KMQSS-032(*)-6	28	30	KMQSS-032(*)-12	28.65	30.65	.65
		0.040″	KMQSS-040(*)-6	28	30	KMQSS-040(*)-12	28.65	30.65	.65
		0.062″	KMQSS-062(*)-6	24	26	KMQSS-062(*)-12	24.80	26.80	.80
		0.125″	KMQSS-125(*)-6	24	26	KMQSS-125(*)-12	24.95	26.95	.95
COPPER-CONSTANTAN 304 SS Sheath	T	0.020″	TMQSS-020(*)-6	28	30	TMQSS-020(*)-12	28.65	30.65	.65
		0.032″	TMQSS-032(*)-6	28	30	TMQSS-032(*)-12	28.65	30.65	.65
		0.040″	TMQSS-040(*)-6	28	30	TMQSS-040(*)-12	28.65	30.65	.65
		0.062″	TMQSS-062(*)-6	24	26	TMQSS-062(*)-12	24.80	26.80	.80
		0.125″	TMQSS-125(*)-6	24	26	TMQSS-125(*)-12	24.95	26.95	.95

* *Specify junction type: E (Exposed), G (Grounded) or U (Ungrounded)*
Ordering Example: KMQSS-040G-6, **$28.** *Subminiature quick disconnect probe type K stainless steel sheath, 0.040″ O.D., 6″ long, grounded junction.* **To Order Inconel Sheath,** *change "SS" in part no. to "IN", no additional charge. Example: KMQIN-040G-6,* **$28.**

Quick Disconnect Handle/Probe Sets
With 6 Custom Measuring Tips

Standard probe/handle sets are equipped with either a high impact plastic handle, style SDX, or with a rugged aluminum handle, style HDX. Either handle is equipped with a one foot long retractable cable (expands to five feet) and with an OMEGA SMP subminiature connector for use with many handheld thermocouple thermometers. Other connector styles are also available. Consult Sales for ordering information.

HDX Aluminum Handle Not Shown

SDX Plastic Handle

GP
General Purpose
Our most popular style

12″ Length; ⅛″ O.D. Stainless Steel Sheath

Model No.	Price	Handle
SDX-SET-GP-(*)-SMP	$42	SDX
HDX-SET-GP-(*)-SMP	47	HDX

NP
Penetration Style

12″ Length ³⁄₁₆″ O.D. Conical Point

Model No.	Price	Handle
SDX-SET-NP-(*)-SMP	$55	SDX
HDX-SET-NP-(*)-SMP	60	HDX

RT
Fast Response Style

12″ Length; Reduced to ¹⁄₁₆″ O.D.

Model No.	Price	Handle
SDX-SET-RT-(*)-SMP	$60	SDX
HDX-SET-RT-(*)-SMP	65	HDX

FSP
Flexible Tip Surface Probe

12″ Length ¼″ O.D.

Model No.	Price	Handle
SDX-SET-FSP-(*)-SMP	$85	SDX
HDX-SET-FSP-(*)-SMP	90	HDX

AP
Air Probe

12″ Length ³⁄₁₆″ O.D. Radiant Energy Shield

Model No.	Price	Handle
SDX-SET-AP-(*)-SMP	$ 95	SDX
HDX-SET-AP-(*)-SMP	100	HDX

SM
Subminiature

6″ Length; ¹⁄₃₂″ O.D. Stainless Steel Sheath

Model No.	Price	Handle
SDX-SET-SM-(*)-SMP	$43	SDX

* Insert Calibration Type J: Iron- Constantan; K: Chromel-Alumel; T: Copper-Constantan; E: Chromel-Constantan

Ten Channel Digital Bench Thermometer

Model DSS-199

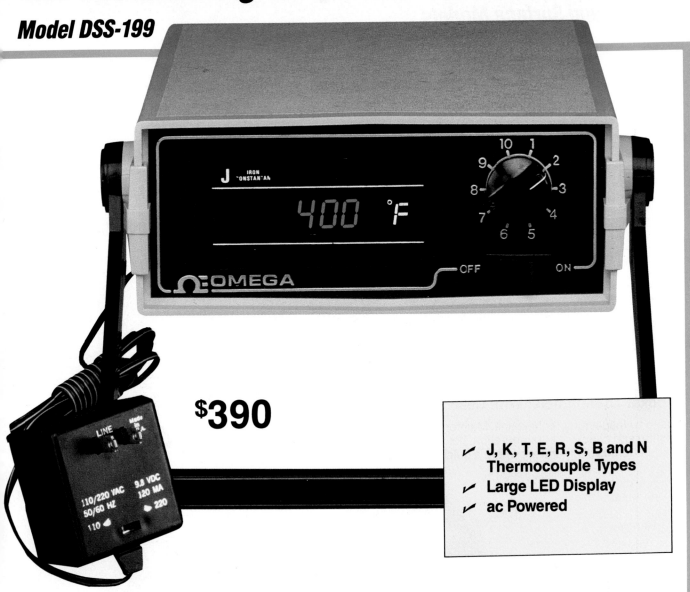

$390

✔ **J, K, T, E, R, S, B and N Thermocouple Types**
✔ **Large LED Display**
✔ **ac Powered**

To Order *(Specify Model Number)*

Model No.	Price	Input Type		Range	Accuracy
DSS-199AJC DSS-199AJF	$390	J	Iron-Constantan	− 180 to 760°C − 170 to 1400°F	± 1.5°C ± 1.5°F
DSS-199AKC DSS-199AKF	390	K	Chromel-Alumel	− 50 to 1250°C − 50 to 1999°F	± 2.1°C ± 2.5°F
DSS-199ATC DSS-199ATF	390	T	Copper-Constantan	− 150 to 400°C − 245 to 750°F	± 1.5°C ± 2.5°F
DSS-199AEC DSS-199AEF	390	E	Chromel-Constantan	− 95 to 840°C − 75 to 1440°F	± 2.1°C ± 2.5°F
DSS-199ARC	390	R	Pt/13% Rh-Pt	300 to 1750°C	± 2.5°C
DSS-199ASC	390	S	Pt/10% Rh-Pt	335 to 1750°C	± 2.3°C
DSS-199ABC	390	B	Pt/6% Rh-Pt/30% Rh	745 to 1820°C	± 1.9°C
DSS-199ANC	390	N	Omegalloy™	− 15 to 1300°C	± 2.1°C

The DSS-199 Digital Thermometer is a thermocouple meter mounted in a heavy-duty bench case. A 10-position terminal block, located on the back of the meter, is capable of monitoring up to 10 thermocouples of the same calibration. A 10-position rotary switch located on the front panel allows the user to select the thermocouple channel to be read.

For additional bench style meters and specifications, refer to the OMEGA® Complete Temperature Measurement Handbook and Encyclopedia®.

Stainless Steel DialTemp™ Thermometers
Pocket and Surface Models

K Series
Thin Stem Pocket Thermometer

This handy little Pocket Thermometer is great for spot checking temperatures accurately and quickly. Driven by a sensitive bi-metal helix coil, it gives precise temperature measurement within 1% of Full Scale.

Model	Range	Model	Range
K-79-2	−40 to 160°F	K-79-5	50 to 550°F
K-79-3	0 to 220°F	K-79-7	−10 to 110°C
K-79-4	25 to 125°F	K-79-8	0 to 150°C

**Model K
All Models**

$20

1″ Head
5″ Stem

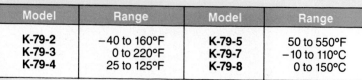

QP Series
Pocket Thermometer With Case

Used by Inspectors, Technicians, Maintenance and Service men for general testing and checking of refrigeration, hot asphalt, dairy and food products and hundreds of other uses where a quick temperature is needed.

**Model QP
All Models**

$24

**1 5/32″ Head
5″ Stem**

Ranges

25-125°F	50-500°F
−40-160°F	0-250°F
0-150°C	

To Order, Specify Model Number and Range.

Example: QP-0 150C

SUR Series
Surface Thermometer

This unique, handy little gage is great for use in sensing the temperature of almost any surface. The bi-metal sensing element is exposed to allow quick, accurate response.

Model SUR-15	Model SUR-25
0-150°F	0-250°F
−20-65°C	−20-120°C
Model SUR-50	**Model SUR-75**
0-500°F	50-750°F
−20-260°C	10-400°C

All Models # $23

2″ Head
2 Rear Mounting Magnets

For Additional Information Refer to the OMEGA® Complete Temperature Measurement Handbook and Encyclopedia™, Section S.

Non-Reversible Temperature Labels
Single and Multiple Dot

To Order Labels Specify Model Number Below

Single Dot Round Labels
$5.50 pack of 30

Model No.	°F Range	Model No.	°F Range	Model No.	°F Range	Model No.	°F Range
TL-S-100	100	TL-S-190	190	TL-S-300	300	TL-S-410	410
TL-S-105	105	TL-S-200	200	TL-S-310	310	TL-S-420	420
TL-S-110	110	TL-S-210	210	TL-S-320	320	TL-S-435	435
TL-S-115	115	TL-S-220	220	TL-S-330	330	TL-S-450	450
TL-S-120	120	TL-S-230	230	TL-S-340	340	TL-S-465	465
TL-S-130	130	TL-S-240	240	TL-S-350	350	TL-S-480	480
TL-S-140	140	TL-S-250	250	TL-S-360	360	TL-S-490	490
TL-S-150	150	TL-S-260	260	TL-S-370	370	TL-S-500	500
TL-S-160	160	TL-S-270	270	TL-S-380	380	TL-S-543	543
TL-S-170	170	TL-S-280	280	TL-S-390	390		
TL-S-180	180	TL-S-290	290	TL-S-400	400		

├─ ³⁄₈″ ─┤

4 Dot Labels
$11.00 pack of 10

Model No.	Temperature Range °F				Model No.	Temperature Range °F			
TL-C-105	105	110	115	120	TL-C-290	290	300	310	320
TL-C-130	130	140	150	160	TL-C-330	330	340	350	360
TL-C-170	170	180	190	200	TL-C-370	370	380	390	400
TL-C-210	210	220	230	240	TL-C-410	410	420	435	450
TL-C-250	250	260	270	280	TL-C-465	465	480	490	500

├─ ⁹⁄₁₆″ ─┤

3 Dot Labels
$13.00 pack of 10

Model No.	Temperature Range °F			Model No.	Temperature Range °F		
TL-T-105	105	110	115	TL-T-300	300	310	320
TL-T-120	120	130	140	TL-T-330	330	340	350
TL-T-150	150	170	180	TL-T-360	360	370	380
TL-T-180	180	190	200	TL-T-390	390	400	410
TL-T-210	210	220	230	TL-T-420	420	435	450
TL-T-240	240	250	260	TL-T-465	465	480	490
TL-T-270	270	280	290				

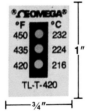

8 Dot Labels
$30.00 pack of 10

Model No.	Temperature Range °F							
TL-E-105	105	110	115	120	130	140	150	160
TL-E-170	170	180	190	200	210	220	230	240
TL-E-250	250	260	270	280	290	300	310	320
TL-E-330	330	340	350	360	370	380	390	400
TL-E-410	410	420	435	450	465	480	490	500

5 Dot Labels
$19.00 pack of 10

Model No.	Temperature Range °F				
TL-F-105	105	110	115	120	130
TL-F-140	140	150	160	170	180
TL-F-190	190	200	210	220	230
TL-F-240	240	250	260	270	280
TL-F-290	290	300	310	320	330
TL-F-340	340	350	360	370	380
TL-F-390	390	400	410	420	435
TL-F-450	450	465	480	490	500

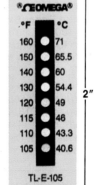

* All labels except TL-C Series show the °C equivalent to the °F rating.

Non-reversible temperature labels have a self-adhesive backing that enables them to be attached to a variety of surfaces to provide a permanent record of overheating. Indicator spot turns black at critical temperature. Available in choice of size, shape and number of indicator dots.

Single Dot Labels

TL-S labels are designed for low cost, single temperature operation. They are compact round labels, only ³⁄₈″ diameter, and are perfect for use in limited spaces. TL-S labels are supplied in packages of 30.

4-Dot Labels

TL-C labels feature four temperature ratings in a single, compact, round design. These labels are especially suited for use in areas with limited space. TL-C indicators are supplied 10 to a package.

3-Dot Labels

TL-T labels have three temperature ratings on a single label, which give the user more information about the maximum temperature of the label. Use these labels to bracket the maximum temperature. TL-T labels are supplied 10 to a package.

8-Dot Labels

TL-E labels have 8 different temperature ratings on a single label, which give the user the most information about the highest temperature reached. These indicators are supplied 10 to a package.

5-Dot Labels

TL-F labels have five temperature dots aligned in a straight line. This design gives the user the maximum temperature, with just a quick glance. The TL-F series labels are supplied 10 to a package.

Off-the-shelf Delivery!

Mix and Match Discounts	
Order Value	**Discount**
below $100	**Net**
$100 to 200	**10%**
$200.25 to 300	**20%**
$300.25 to 400	**30%**
$400.25 to 500	**40%**
over $500.00 . . . Consult Sales Department	

Portable Strip Chart Recorders
Models 141 and 142

Compact Single Channel

Model 141
$1180

Model 142
$1405

with Built-in Rechargeable Battery Pack

All models complete with protective door. (not shown)

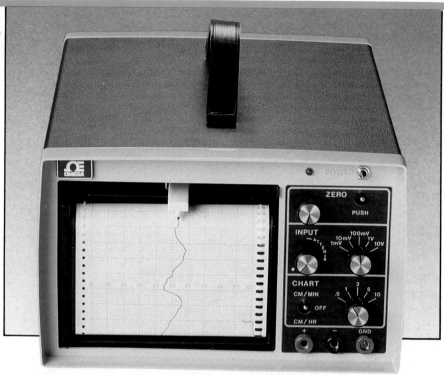

The **Model 141** is a small, portable ac powered recorder which offers multiple span input ranges from 1 mV through 10 volts with a variable attenuator to 100 volts. The chart drive has ten speeds ranging from 0.5 cm/hour to 10 cm/minute.

This unit features a unique servo drive system that practically eliminates dead band, plus an electronic servo "shutdown" for off-scale protection.

The **Model 142** is identical in appearance and specifications to the Model 141. However, this unit is powered by an internal battery pack. Many hours of recording can be done on a fully charged battery which is rechargeable by just plugging it into a wall receptacle, and up to 200 charges can be made on one battery.

Being battery operated and only eleven pounds light, it will be easy to carry this recorder into the field for necessary tests where ac power is not available.

Precision Design
- **100 mm Chart Width**
- **10 Chart Speeds**
- **5 Input spans, 1 mV to 10 Volts**
- **100% Zero Suppression**
- **100% Full Scale Zero**
- **Model 142 Battery Operated**

General Specifications

Number of Channels: 1
Full Scale Span (Switch Selected): 1, 10, and 100 mV; 1 and 10 Volts with variable 10:1 attenuator to 100 Volts dc
Input Type: Single ended (floating, up to ±100 V)
Input Impedance: 2.5 M Ω
Chart Width: 100 mm
Chart Speeds: 0.5, 1, 2, 5, 10 cm/minute and cm/hour
Writing Method: Disposable fiber-tipped pens

Accuracy: Overall limit of error $< \pm0.5\%$
Response Time: <0.5 sec. full scale
Zero Adjust: Continuously adjustable from -100% to $+100\%$
Power: Model 141-115/230 V ac Model 142- +12 V dc battery, recharges on 115/230 V ac
Battery Life: (Model 142) 6 hours to over 1 week (dependent on chart speed and recording rate)
Weight: Model 141: 9.5 lb. (4.3 kg) Model 142: 11 lb. (5 kg)
Dimensions: H: 6.25" (158.8 mm) x W: 8.75" (222 mm) x D: 11.5" (292.1 mm)
Accessories Furnished: One disposable pen, one roll chart paper, one instruction manual. Model 142 — one rechargeable battery (internal)

To Order:
Specify **Model 141 $1180**
Specify **Model 142**
  Battery operated **$1405**
Specify pens, paper, probes, or options by number.
Consult Sales Department for **Ice Point References, Thermocouples** and **Thermocouple Wire.**

Accessories: *Keep extra pens and paper on hand.*

Chart Paper:	0-100 grid, 30 meters long	No. 0100-0011	6 rolls/**$36**
Z-Fold Paper:	100 mm Wide	No. 0100-0028	1 pkg/**$10**
Disposable Pens:	Blue	No. 0100-0105	6 pack/**$10.75**
	Red	No. 0100-0106	6 pack/**$10.75**
	Black	No. 0100-0107	6 pack/**$10.75**
	Green	No. 0100-0108	6 pack/**$10.75**
Dust Cover:	Clear	No. 0100-0203	each **$20**

Models 141 and 142 can be used in conjunction with the pH to Analog Converter, Model PHCV-1. See page J-4 for ordering information and specifications.

Flatbed Strip Chart Recorders
Models 156 and 555

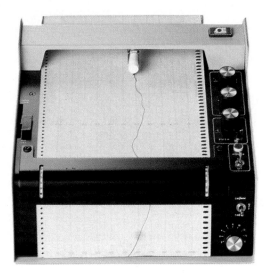

Compact Single Channel Flatbed

- **Precision Design**
- **125 mm Chart Width**
- **1 mV to 10 V Span — 5 Settings**
- **22 Chart Speed Settings**
- **< 1% Limit of Error**
- **> 50 cm/sec Pen Response**
- **Remote Chart On/Off Standard**

Standard features of the Model 156 Single Channel Strip Chart Recorder include multiple chart speeds from 1 cm/hour to 30 cm/minute, multiple input spans from 1 mV to 10 volts dc. It is switch selectable between 115 Vac or 230 Vac at 50/60 Hertz.

This recorder incorporates the fine features of the Model 555, 250 mm chart recorder but offers a compact chart width of 125 mm. Also Model 156 has ±100% full scale zero suppression to allow up to 2 times the input of any range desired.

Simplicity, reliability, small size and low cost make this recorder a necessity when bench space is at a premium.

Model 156
$875
Includes one pen, one roll of chart paper and operator's manual.

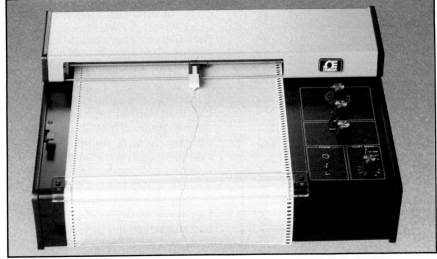

Model 555
$1190
Includes one pen, one roll of chart paper and operator's manual.

Models 156 and 555 can be used to record and measure pH in conjunction with the pH to Analog Converter, Model PHCV-1. See page J-4 for ordering information and specifications.

Every possible feature has been included in this versatile recorder to provide the user with optimum flexibility, accuracy and long-term reliability.

Features include 22 chart speeds from 1 cm/hour to 30 cm/minute, adjustable zero setting, electronic "servo kill", remote chart programming (TTL), < 0.5% limit of error and 100% suppression.

Single Channel with Built-In Attenuator

- **Large 250 mm Chart**
- **22 Chart Speeds**
- **12 Input Spans**
- **±100% Zero Suppression**
- **1 mV to 50 Volt — Variable Attenuator**
- **0.5 Second Pen Response**
- **Crystal Controlled Stepper Chart Drive**
- **Pulse-modulated Servo System**

> **Additional Specifications, Options, and Accessories can be found in the OMEGA® Complete Temperature Measurement Handbook and Encyclopedia®, Section N.**

Medium Temperature Heating Tapes

MADE IN **USA**

SRT Series

- ✔ **Continuous Exposure Rating up to 500°F**
- ✔ **Short-Term Exposure Temperature (De-energized) up to 600°F**
- ✔ **Uniform Heat Distribution**
- ✔ **Time-Tested**
- ✔ **Moisture and Chemical Resistant***
- ✔ **Integrally Molded Separable Plug**

How to Order

Watts	W/in²	Volts	Size	Catalog No.	Price
52	4.3	120	½″ × 2′	SRT051-020	$ 37
104	4.3	120	½″ × 4′	SRT051-040	43
156	4.3	120	½″ × 6′	SRT051-060	49
209	4.3	120	½″ × 8′	SRT051-080	58
261	4.3	120	½″ × 10′	SRT051-100	63
313	4.3	120	½″ × 12′	SRT051-120	69
104	4.3	120	1″ × 2′	SRT101-020	48
209	4.3	120	1″ × 4′	SRT101-040	63
313	4.3	120	1″ × 6′	SRT101-060	77
418	4.3	120	1″ × 8′	SRT101-080	92
522	4.3	120	1″ × 10′	SRT101-100	102
627	4.3	120	1″ × 12′	SRT101-120	113
731	4.3	120	1″ × 14′	SRT101-140	127
836	4.3	120	1″ × 16′	SRT101-160	138
940	4.3	120	1″ × 18′	SRT101-180	150
1045	4.3	120	1″ × 20′	SRT101-200	162
209	4.3	120	2″ × 2′	SRT201-020	64
418	4.3	120	2″ × 4′	SRT201-040	93
627	4.3	120	2″ × 6′	SRT201-060	133
836	4.3	120	2″ × 8′	SRT201-080	163
1045	4.3	120	2″ × 10′	SRT201-100	184
1254	4.3	120	2″ × 12′	SRT201-120	199
1463	4.3	120	2″ × 14′	SRT201-140	209
1672	4.3	120	2″ × 16′	SRT201-160	241
1881	4.3	120	2″ × 18′	SRT201-180	272
2090	4.3	120	2″ × 20′	SRT201-200	295

Note 1: All tapes ½″ or wider are available in 240V without plug. Add 10% to heater price, and add suffix "/240V" to catalog no.

* Contact OMEGALUX for specific vapor and solvent resistance. Call 1-800-USA-HEAT

APPLICATIONS

Silicone rubber extruded heating tapes can be used in direct contact with a metal or conductive surface.

SPECIFICATIONS

Heating Elements: 36-40 gage finely stranded resistance wire
Heating Element Insulation: double-braided fiberglass yarn
Dielectric Strength: in excess of 2000V
Lead Wires: 16 AWG high temperature 600V silicone rubber insulated lead wire emerging from opposite ends of the heating tape into separate sides of integrally molded separable plug

OMEGALUX Silicone Rubber Extruded Heating Tapes are low-watt density electrical resistance heaters designed for temperature maintenance in applications requiring moisture and chemical resistance. Silicone rubber tapes are constructed of finely stranded resistance wires fully insulated with braided fiberglass and knitted into flat tape with fiberglass yarn. These tapes are encapsulated in a void-free silicone rubber sheath.

Integrally Molded Separable Plug Shown

High Temperature Heating Tapes

FGS, FGH, FWH Series
- ✔ Reliable
- ✔ Integral Molded Separable Plug
- ✔ Rated to 900°F Continuous
- ✔ Short-term Exposure Temperature (de-energized) up to 950°F
- ✔ Fiberglass Insulated
- ✔ Fast Themal Response
- ✔ Moisture and Chemical Resistant **

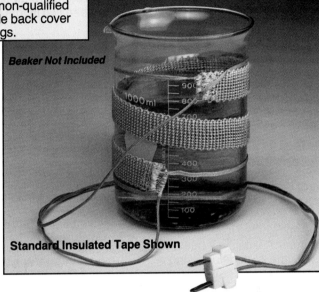

CAUTION AND WARNING!
Fire and electrical shock may result if products are used improperly or installed or used by non-qualified personnel. See inside back cover for additional warnings.

Beaker Not Included

Standard Insulated Tape Shown

Standard tapes are made from fine gage stranded resistance wires that are double insulated with braided fiberglass and knitted into flat tapes for maximum flexibility. A heavy insulated tape is made by taking a standard tape and braiding it between layers of fiberglass yarn. Wide tapes are made from two or more standard tapes that are sewn between two layers of fiberglass cloth.

APPLICATIONS
Wide and Heavy Duty insulated tapes are good for direct contact on conductive surfaces. Do not use standard insulated tapes on a conductive surface.

SPECIFICATIONS
Heating Elements: 36-40 gage resistance wire.
Lead Wires: emerge from opposite ends into separate sides of an integrally molded separable plug.
Heating Element Insulation: double-braided fiberglass
Dielectric Strength: in excess of 2000V

How to Order — HIGHLIGHTED MODELS STOCKED

Wide Heavy Insulated Tapes

Watts	W/in²	Volts	Size	Catalog No.	Price
208	4.9	120	1¾" × 2'	FWH171-020	$62
416	4.9	120	1¾" × 4'	FWH171-040	92
624	4.9	120	1¾" × 6'	FWH171-060	124
832	4.9	120	1¾" × 8'	FWH171-080	146
1040	4.9	120	1¾" × 10'	FWH171-100	168
314	5.2	120	2½" × 2'	FWH251-020	73
628	5.2	120	2½" × 4'	FWH251-040	102
942	5.2	120	2½" × 6'	FWH251-060	148
1256	5.2	120	2½" × 8'	FWH251-080	187
1570	5.2	120	2½" × 10'	FWH251-100	204
418	5.3	120	3¼" × 2'	FWH321-020	82
836	5.3	120	3¼" × 4'	FWH321-040	118
1256	5.3	120	3¼" × 6'	FWH321-060	175
1672	5.3	120	3¼" × 8'	FWH321-080	241
2092	5.3	120	3¼" × 10'	FWH321-100	265

How to Order — HIGHLIGHTED MODELS STOCKED

Standard Insulated Tapes

Watts	W/in²	Volts	Size	Catalog No.	Price
38	8.6	120	7/16" × 8'	FGS0041-006	$17
46	8.6	120	3/8" × 12'	FGS0031-010	17
104	8.6	120	½" × 2'	FGS051-020	19
109	8.6	120	½" × 4'	FGS051-040	22
313	8.6	120	½" × 6'	FGS051-060	29
418	8.6	120	½" × 8'	FGS051-080	34
522	8.6	120	½" × 10'	FGS051-100	40
209	8.6	120	1" × 2'	FGS101-020	21
418	8.6	120	1" × 4'	FGS101-040	30
627	8.6	120	1" × 6'	FGS101-060	36
836	8.6	120	1" × 8'	FGS101-080	50
1045	8.6	240	1" × 10'	FGS102-100*	61

Heavy Insulated Tapes

Watts	W/in²	Volts	Size	Catalog No.	Price
104	8.6	120	½" × 2'	FGH051-020	$24
209	8.6	120	½" × 4'	FGH051-040	30
313	8.6	120	½" × 6'	FGH051-060	39
418	8.6	120	½" × 8'	FGH051-080	48
522	8.6	120	½" × 10'	FGH051-100	59
209	8.6	120	1" × 2'	FGH101-020	31
418	8.6	120	1" × 4'	FGH101-040	44
627	8.6	120	1" × 6'	FGH101-060	55
836	8.6	120	1" × 8'	FGH101-080	67
1040	8.6	240	1" × 10'	FGH102-100*	77

Note1: All Tapes ½" or wider are available in 240V without plug. Add 10% to heater price, and add suffix "/240V" to catalog no.
* 240V Heaters are not supplied with plugs.
** Contact OMEGALUX for specific vapor and solvent resistance. Call 1-800-USA-HEAT

Ultra-High Temperature Heating Tapes

SST, STH, SWH Series

- ✔ **Premium Quality**
- ✔ **Rated to 1400°F Continuous**
- ✔ **Short-term Exposure Temperature (de-energized) up to 1450°F**
- ✔ **Moisture and Chemical Resistant****
- ✔ **Samox® Insulated**
- ✔ **Integrally Molded Separable Plug**

Standard tapes are made from fine gage stranded resistance wires that are double insulated with braided Samox® and knitted into flat tapes for maximum flexibility. A heavy insulated tape is made by taking a standard tape and braiding it between layers of Samox yarn. Wide tapes are made from two or more standard tapes that are sewn between two layers of Samox cloth.

APPLICATIONS

Laboratory: Wide and Heavy Insulated tapes are good for direct contact on conductive surfaces. Do not use standard insulated tapes on a metal or conductive surface.

SPECIFICATIONS

Heating Elements: 36-40 gage stranded resistance wire
Heating Element Insulation: double-braided Samox
Dielectric Strength: In excess of 2000V
Lead Wires: Emerge from opposite ends into separate sides of integrally molded separable plug

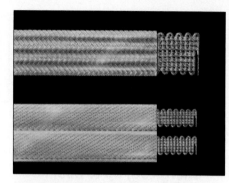

Heavy Insulated and Wide Heavy Insulated Tapes Shown

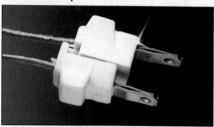

Integrally Molded Separable Plug Shown

How to Order   *HIGHLIGHTED MODELS STOCKED FOR FAST DELIVERY!*

Watts	W/in²	Volts	Size	Heavy Insulated Tapes Catalog Number	Price	Standard Insulated Tapes Catalog Number	Price
156	13	120	½″ × 2′	STH051-020	$ 28	SST051-020	$ 20
313	13	120	½″ × 4′	STH051-040	35	SST051-040	25
470	13	120	½″ × 6′	STH051-060	46	SST051-060	33
627	13	120	½″ × 8′	STH051-080	55	SST051-080	39
783	13	240	½″ × 10′	STH052-100*	66	SST052-100*	46
940	13	240	½″ × 12′	STH052-120*	80	SST052-120*	57
313	13	120	1″ × 2′	STH101-020	35	SST101-020	24
627	13	120	1″ × 4′	STH101-040	49	SST101-040	34
940	13	240	1″ × 6′	STH102-060*	63	SST102-060*	40
1256	13	240	1″ × 8′	STH102-080*	76	SST102-080*	57

Watts	W/in²	Volts	Size	Wide Heavy Insulated Tapes Catalog Number	Price
314	13	120	1¾″ × 2′	SWH171-020	$ 76
628	13	120	1¾″ × 4′	SWH171-040	104
942	13	120	1¾″ × 6′	SWH171-060	143
1256	13	120	1¾″ × 8′	SWH171-080	187
1570	13	240	1¾″ × 10′	SWH172-100*	201
470	13	120	2½″ × 2′	SWH251-020	92
940	13	120	2½″ × 4′	SWH251-040	133
1410	13	120	2½″ × 6′	SWH251-060	188
1880	13	120	2½″ × 8′	SWH251-080	226
2350	13	240	2½″ × 10′	SWH252-100*	239
628	13	120	3¼″ × 2′	SWH351-020	105
1256	13	120	3¼″ × 4′	SWH351-040	153
1884	13	120	3¼″ × 6′	SWH351-060	207
2512	13	120	3¼″ × 8′	SWH351-080	291
3140	13	240	3¼″ × 10′	SWH352-080*	338

Note 1: All tapes ½″ or wider are available in 240V without plug. Add 10% to heater price, and add suffix "/240V" to catalog no.

*240V Heaters are not supplied with plugs.

**Contact OMEGALUX for specific vapor and solvent resistance. Call 1-800-USA-HEAT

CAUTION AND WARNING!
Fire and electrical shock may result if products are used improperly or installed or used by non-qualified personnel. See inside back cover for additional warnings.

Self-Standing Laboratory Heating Mantles

MADE IN
USA

LHM Series
- ✔ Uniform Heat Distribution
- ✔ Temperature Ratings to 900°F
- ✔ Low Watt Density Heat
- ✔ Rectangular Shape for Easy Storage and Stacking
- ✔ Vinyl Exterior Cover is Easily Cleaned

OMEGALUX Laboratory Heating Mantles are fiberglass insulating heating jackets specifically designed for heating laboratory vessels. OMEGALUX's Standard Laboratory Heating Mantles are available in eight different sizes. There is a size and power capacity to meet any of your flask heating requirements from 50 ml to 5000 ml. With OMEGALUX's proven ''self'' standing design, you are able to place a soft, form fitting mantle directly on your counter top. No more hassle with jack stands, support rings or bulky metal case units. Magnetic stirring is easily performed through the heating mantle.

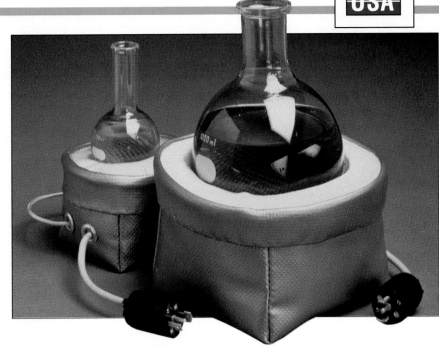

By using our variable output CPP Series temperature controller (see page G1-9), exact repeatable results can be achieved. The unique serpentine constructed heating element provides evenly distributed, low-watt density heat making these mantles ideal for highly sensitive applications.

CAUTION AND WARNING!
Fire and electrical shock may result if products are used improperly or installed or used by non-qualified personnel. See inside back cover for additional warnings.

How to Order

HIGHLIGHTED MODELS STOCKED FOR FAST DELIVERY!

Holds Flask Size (ml)	Volts	Amps	Watts./ Sq. in.	A	B	C	D	Catalog No.	Price	Shipping Weight lbs.
50	120	0.43	52	7.95	10.20	5.10	6.35	LHM0050-VF1	$ 59	0.5
50	240	0.22	52	7.95	10.20	5.10	6.35	LHM0050-VF2	68	0.5
100	120	0.58	70	9.20	11.70	6.35	7.65	LHM0100-VF1	64	0.5
100	240	0.29	70	9.20	11.70	6.35	7.65	LHM0100-VF2	73	0.5
250	120	1.19	143	11.10	15.00	8.57	8.90	LHM0250-VF1	73	0.75
250	240	0.60	143	11.10	15.00	8.57	8.90	LHM0250-VF2	80	0.75
500	120	1.75	210	13.35	17.00	10.50	9.55	LHM0500-VF1	80	1.00
500	240	0.88	210	13.35	17.00	10.50	9.55	LHM0500-VF2	89	1.00
1000	120	3.14	377	14.60	18.55	14.00	10.20	LHM1000-VF1	89	1.25
1000	240	1.57	377	14.60	18.55	14.00	10.20	LHM1000-VF2	97	1.25
2000	120	4.33	520	16.50	21.10	16.20	11.45	LHM2000-VF1	93	1.75
2000	240	2.17	520	16.50	21.10	16.20	11.45	LHM2000-VF2	102	1.75
3000	120	4.58	550	18.40	24.50	18.40	15.20	LHM3000-VF1	126	2.00
3000	240	2.29	550	18.40	24.50	18.40	15.20	LHM3000-VF2	134	2.00
5000	120	5.17	620	21.00	27.20	22.50	15.25	LHM5000-VF1	133	2.00
5000	240	2.58	620	21.00	27.20	22.50	15.25	LHM5000-VF2	139	2.00

Automatic Dialing Remote Monitoring System OMA Series

- ✓ **Monitors 4 Channels Plus Internal AC Power**
- ✓ **Synthesized Voice Messages**
- ✓ **Remote Status Inquiry from any Telephone with Security Code to Prevent Unauthorized Tampering**
- ✓ **Automatic Alarm Calling**
- ✓ **Easy to Program**
- ✓ **Remote Programming**

From
$1200

The OMA Series Monitor is an automatic dialing remote monitoring system that keeps you in direct touch with your distant facility. The OMA Series continuously monitors the inputs connected to the system and if an alarm condition occurs, it dials up to eight field programmable phone numbers and identifies the specific problem in plain English. When you want to receive a complete status report, you may dial it from any telephone allowing direct touch with a remote or unattended facility. Easy to program, the voice synthesizer asks for input. All you do is enter up to 8 dial out phone numbers. All other operating parameters (alarm criteria, alarm and normal messages, alarm trip delay, etc.) are preprogrammed, but

may be altered from their default values to meet your needs. The following parameters may be programmed over a wide range on the keyboard: alarm trip delay, time between alarm calls, alarm rest time, telephone answer response time, alarm criteria (alarm on open contacts, alarm on closed contacts or no alarm) run time meters on/ off, tone/pulse dialing, number of message repeats. Nonvolatile memory keeps your programming intact and a rechargeable gel cell battery keeps the system operating in the event of a power failure. The OMA Series is easy to hook up-it operates on a standard telephone line, and will work with any telephone system and most paging systems.

Communication with called parties is via a highly intelligible voice synthesizer, station identification plus alarm and normal messages from each channel are programmable from the approximately 200 or 400 word vocabulary. In addition, a built-in microphone permits a caller to listen to local sounds and to have a two-way conversation with personnel at the dealer site. Models are available to monitor from 4 to 32 dry contacts plus a 120 Vac power source, and all models are provided with remote programming to allow the operator to call the unit and program a wide variety of functions of the system.

- Non Volatile Memory keeps your programming intact, even in extended power failures

- Sturdy screw-clamp terminal strips for easy installation

- Superior surge protection on power, phone and all alarm input lines

- Solid state speech synthesizer eliminates moving tape loop mechanisms

- FCC approved phone line coupler

- Includes a gel cell battery with precision charger. Maintains operation during power failures.

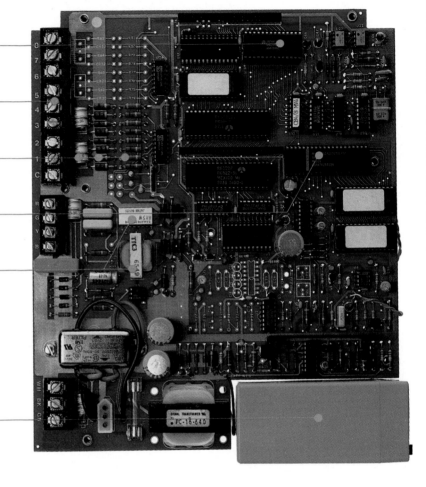

Specifications

ELECTRICAL

Power: 105-135 Vac, 50/60 Hz, 15 W max

Battery charging: precision voltage controlled, including automatic rapid recharge after drain

Battery backup: 6 h on OMA-C4, OMA-C8; others 24 h

Input Sensing: Open contacts see 5 Vdc, closed contacts see 10 mA dc

Physical Surge protection: integral gas tube and solid-state protectors on all phone, power and signal lines

Weight: 8 lb Dimensions: 11⅝" H x 9⅝" W x 3¾" D

Mounting centers: 10¼" vertical by 8¼" horizontal

ENVIRONMENTAL

Temperature Range: 0 to 130°F
Humidity: 0 to 95%, non-condensing

TELEPHONE

Rotary pulse or tone dialing, keyboard selectable. Dials up to 8 different numbers, each up to 16 digits long. Allows programming of PBX relays in 1 second increments FCC Registration #EMR539-14954-AL-R, "Ringer Equivalence" 0.3 A Alarm acknowledgment is by Touch Tone™ key or calling back. Built-in microphone allows two way conversation. Speech Messages Unit comes standard programmed with standard "alarm/normal" speech messages. Custom messages (including station ID) may be keyboard programmed from the internal memory

NOVRAM Nonvolatile Memory

User-entered programming is kept intact for up to ten years, even when all power is removed from the unit.

Rugged Construction

The OMA Monitor is built to last. An all solid state design, quality components, and a heavy-duty metal enclosure ensure a long life of service. All keyboard and front panel switches are sealed to prevent contamination by dust and moisture.

How to Order		
Model No.	Price	Number Dry Contacts Monitored
OMA-C4	$1200	4
OMA-C8	1600	8
OMA-C16	2575	16
OMA-C24	3175	24
OMA-C32	3775	32

Touch Tone™- is a trademark of AT&

K-3	K-11	K-15
OM900 SERIES MODULAR INTERFACE	**WHITE BOX® PLUG IN COMPUTER INTERFACE**	**OM270 SERIES TREND RECORDERS/ DATA LOGGERS**

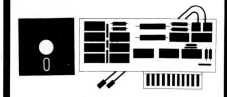
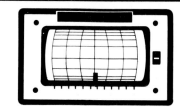

K

DATA ACQUISITION

Stand-Alone Interface System
That's A Snap
Model OM-900

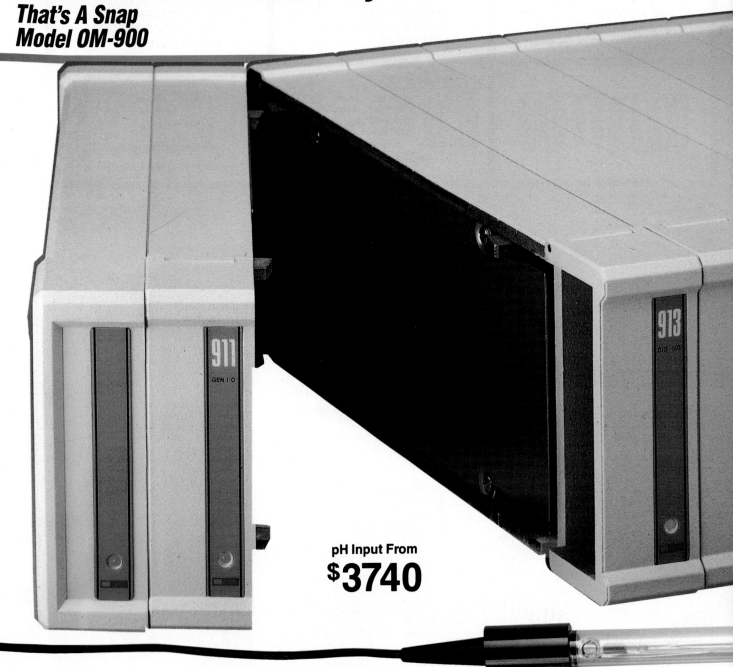

pH Input From
$3740

Electrode Sold Separately, See Section D

The OM-900 monitors your incoming data rapidly and accurately, and it provides excitation for and works directly with all common transducers measuring temperature, pressure, position, flow, etc. It automatically calibrates, linearizes, scales and converts to your engineering units. The OM-900 can acquire data at 20 thousand data points and then store the data built-in RAM memory for by your host computer, perform its own statistical analyses: averaging, obtaining maxima or minima, etc. It controls external parameters with analog and digital output signals. It works with all common languages, or no language at all using LABTECH NOTEBOOK™, and its modular, snap together multichannel construction allows you to purchase and configure only the system you need at the time and place you need it. It features advanced technological innovations such as isolated, floating input, output and excitation channels, 12 and 16 bit A/D conversion, and complete self-checking of its functions every time it is used.

Moreover, after initial system start-up, the OM-900's distributed intelligence sets your personal computer free to perform any of your other usual functions, from word processing to spreadsheet analysis, while it continues to perform all of its programmed tasks. And since all communications between the OM-900 and your PC are via industry-standard RS-232, RS-422 or IEEE-488 ports, your system can be plugged together and operational

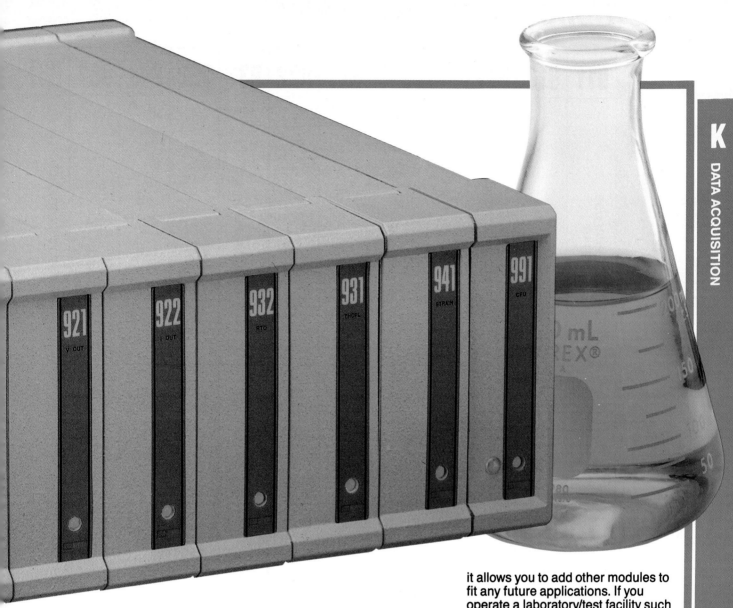

in just minutes, without extensive knowledge of either hardware or software.

Then you're ready to put the power of the OM-900 to work. While you're word processing a report on your PC, for example, your OM-900 can be silently gathering the data you need, automatically linearizing it, scaling it, and storing it in its own memory until you retrieve it…at your convenience…for examination and analysis.

Designed for the growing laboratory, industrial research facility, production test operation, incoming inspection area and other measurement

and control applications, the OM-900 system features a fully modular design that permits gradual expansion to match your increasing data acquisition requirements. You can start with a highly economical, yet powerful, basic system: the 992 CPU Microprocessor Module, Power Supply Module, and a third module of your choice, depending on the processes you will be monitoring. For less than you probably invested in a personal computer, you'll have all the speed, power and time-saving convenience of an advanced-technology, data acquisition and control system. Yet, you still retain total access to your PC for performing other important tasks.

The OM-900's economical, modular design lets you purchase only the low-cost modules you need today, without sacrificing flexibility, sophistication or ease-of-use. Then,

it allows you to add other modules to fit any future applications. If you operate a laboratory/test facility such as a: Chemistry Laboratory, Pilot Plant Application, Electronic Test/Analysis Facility, Chromatography/Spectroscopy/Physiology Laboratory, Vibration/Catastrophic Failure/Stress Analysis Facility, Quality Control/Incoming Inspection Operation, an OM-900 system can be your silent partner—quietly, efficiently and economically collecting vast amounts of data that would otherwise require hours of tedious manual keystroking to enter on your personal computer. With an OM-900 system, you have more time to spend analyzing you newfound data because you don't spend time keying it in…or correcting troublesome keystroke errors that mean even further delays. Add the capability to perform many statistical functions on its own and you have an ideal combination of computing power and time-saving convenience.

Stand-Alone Interface System

OM-900 MODULES

	911	912	913	915	916	921	922	931	932	941	951	961
	GENERAL PURPOSE INPUT/OUTPUT	HIGH RESOLUTION ANALOG INPUT	DIGITAL INPUT/OUTPUT*	MULTIPLEXER*	ANALOG INPUT	ANALOG VOLTAGE OUTPUT	ANALOG CURRENT OUTPUT	THERMOCOUPLE INPUT	RTD INPUT	STRAIN GAGE INPUT	LVDT INPUT	pH/ION CONCENTRATION INPUT
$	1595	1750	1050	1095	1550	1650	1650	1350	1350	1475	1375	1795
ANALOG INPUT	4	8	—	—	8	—	—	8	8	6	6	3
ANALOG OUTPUT	4	—	—	—	—	8	8	—	—	—	—	—
DIGITAL INPUT	8	—	60	—	8	8	8	—	—	4	—	—
DIGITAL OUTPUT	8	—	—	—	8	8	8	—	—	4	—	—
A/D CONVERTER	12	16	—	—	12	—	—	16	16	12	13	17
CONVERSION TIME	50 μs	100 ms	—	—	50 μs	—	—	50 ms	400 ms	50 μs	66.6 ms	120 ms
D/A CONVERTER	12	—	—	—	—	12	12	—	—	—	—	—
UPDATE FREQUENCY	5 kHz	—	—	—	—	5 kHz	5 kHz	—	—	—	—	—
INPUT RANGE	±200 mV ±2V ±20V	±200 mV ±2V ±20V	1 MHz +Event 5V	32 RELAYS + COMMON (8 BLOCKS OF 4)	±200 mV ±2V ±20V	—	—	±65 mV	327.67 Ω	0-40 0-80 mV	0-1.6V 0-.16V 0-.016V	0-14 pH
ACCURACY	±0.1% +1C	±0.007% ±2C	—		±0.1% +1C	—	—	.24% Base Metal	±0.3°C	.1% RDG ±80 μV +2C	.1% RDG + .05% FS	±.001 pH
OUTPUT RANGE	±10V	—	500 kHz +1μs Pulse 5V		TTL	±10V	50 mA	—	—	TTL	—	—
ACCURACY	+0.05% +1C	—	—		—	±0.05% +1C	0.025% +1C	—	—	—	—	—

* Both the OM-913 and OM-915 are now supplied with an auxiliary terminal panel with 6 ft. cabling

The OM-900 may be programmed in any common computer language. Typically, the standard PRINT and INPUT statements implemented in BASIC are used to communicate with the OM-900 Data Acquisition and Control System. For example, the IBM PC uses the "PRINT #. . ." statement to send commands to the OM-900 system and the "INPUT #. . ." statement to receive data from the OM-900. Any OM-900 system command may be sent to the OM-900 Data Acquisition and Control System using the PRINT statement under BASIC. In the following program, the OPEN "COM 1: . . ."statement is required by PC BASIC in order to open the RS-232 serial port for data input and output.

EXAMPLES — WHEN PROGRAMMING THE OM-900

As an illustration of just how simple and easy the OM-900 system is to use, the following simple program is all that is required in order to output signal data from the OM-900 Data Acquisition and Control System with the IBM PC under BASIC.

The response is a list of all modules installed in the system and the respective addresses.

Line 10 OPENs the COMmunications port as file #1.
Line 20 prints the OM-900 command VERSION to file #1 (RS-232 port).

```
10 OPEN "COM1:9600,N,8,
   CS,DS" AS #1
20 PRINT #1, "@NAME"
30 INPUT #1, X$
40 PRINT X$
50 CLOSE #1
60 END
```
Sample communications program for the IBM PC

Line 30 "looks" for an input from file #1 and returns it to the variable X$. Since the response to the command name will be a series of ASCII characters terminated by a carriage return, we must use a "string" variable (denoted by $) to hold the ASCII characters.
Line 40 displays the contents of the string variable X$ on the CRT screen.
Line 50 & 60 CLOSEs file #1 (the RS-232 port) and ENDs the program.

If you are using an APPLE computer with a super serial card the APPLESOFT™ program is very similar. In order to access the Super Serial Card (or any other APPLE BUS compatible serial card) you must know which APPLE expansion slot the card is plugged into. In the examples below, we have a Super Serial Card plugged into expansion slot number 2.

Once we have accessed the Serial card, we will want to send instructions to and receive information from the OM-900. The following short program displays the configuration of the OM-900 system.

```
10 PRINT CHR$(4); "PR#2"
20 PRINT "@NAME"
30 PRINT CHR$(4); "PR#0"
40 PRINT CHR$(4); "IN#2"
50 INPUT X$
60 PRINT CHR$(4); "PR#0"
```
Sample communications program for the Apple II

Line 10 accesses slot number 2 for command output to the OM-900
Line 20 sends (prints) the command @NAME to the CPU (OM-991).
Line 30 closes all APPLE expansion slots.
Line 40 accesses slot number 2 for input of the CPU response.
Line 50 gets the CPU response and displays it on the CRT screen.
Line 60 closes all APPLE slots.

* NOTE: The input statement in line number 50 automatically displays all input data on the CRT screen so that there is no need for a separate print statement under APPLESOFT BASIC.

How To Order

To Assemble a Complete OM-900 System, Order
1. OM-992 Processor
2. Power Supply Module (OM-902 or 903)
3. Up to 15 Input/Output Modules (see modules chart)
4. Software
5. Required Sensors and Cables

Minimum configuration of each system includes one power supply and one OM-992 CPU with at least one I/O module.

Accessories
OM-900-RM $295 19" Rack mount adaptor kit for up to 10 modules 7" H.

OM-900-RMS $195 Slides for rack mount kit.

Optional memory expands module buffer beyond standard 2k RAM (available on new module purchases only, factory installed). Add suffix to module number and increase module price:

/32 k. $450
Note: not available with OM-902, 903, 913, 915, 917, 921, 922, 951 or 992

Input and Output Modules

Module No.	Price	Description
OM-911	$1595	General Purpose
OM-912	1750	High Res. Analog In
OM-913	1050	Digital I/O
OM-915	1095	Multiplexer
OM-916	1550	Analog & Digital I/O
OM-917	575	Multiplexer Controller
OM-917-LLEM	600	Relay Board for OM-917
OM-921	1650	Voltage Output
OM-922	1650	Current Output
OM-931	1350	Thermocouple Input
OM-932	1350	RTD Input
OM-941	1475	Strain Gage Input
OM-951	1375	LVDT/RVDT Input
OM-961	1795	pH/Ion Concentration

STAND-ALONE INTERFACE SYSTEM
OM-900 Series

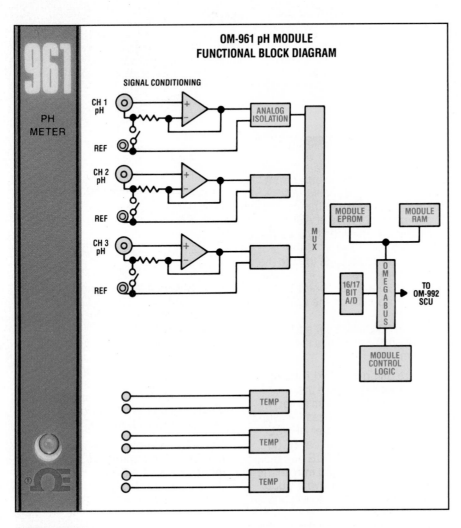

OM-961 pH MODULE
FUNCTIONAL BLOCK DIAGRAM

961
PH METER

SIGNAL CONDITIONING

CH 1 pH
REF
CH 2 pH
REF
CH 3 pH
REF

ANALOG ISOLATION

MUX

MODULE EPROM
MODULE RAM

16/17 BIT A/D

OMEGABUS

TO OM-992 SCU

MODULE CONTROL LOGIC

TEMP
TEMP
TEMP

common-mode voltages. The OM-961 module allows automatic statistical data collection and contains a background conversion mode, permitting data collection and storage while other independent operations are performed elsewhere in the OM-900 system.

Specifications (@ 23°C ±5°C)

pH/Ion Inputs: 3 channels, individually isolated and floating

pH/Ion Input Impedance: 10^{12} Ohms

pH Range: 0 to 14

pH Resolution: 0.001 pH @ 16 bits, 0.0005 pH @ 17 bits

Accuracy: better than ±0.01 pH

Temperature Range: -200 to +600°C

Temperature Sensing: 100Ω 2-wire platinum RTD (alpha = 0.00385)

Temperature Resolution: 0.16°C @ 16 bits, 0.06°C @ 17 bits

Temperature Accuracy: better than 0.31°C

Maximum CMV: 100 V

Sensing Electrode Connection: Teflon-insulated male BNC

Reference Electrode Connection: tip jack

RTD Connection: screw terminals

On-Board Memory: 8K std./32K optional

Power Consumption: 4 W maximum

Environmental: 0-45°C, 0-85% RH non-condensing

OM-961 pH/Ion Concentration Module $1795

✔ **3 Channels**

✔ **±0.001 pH Accuracy**

✔ **User-Definable Probe Slopes**

✔ **On-Board Linearization to pH Units**

The OM-961 is a three-channel, high impedance analog input module for high resolution measurement of pH and ion selective probes. The unit performs all signal conditioning, multiplexing, and digitizing for up to three high impedance probes per module. A 17-bit, dual-slope integrating A/D converter provides high normal-mode rejection capability. Each channel of the module can determine the ion concentration of a test solution by measuring the voltage of a specific ion probe relative to an associated reference probe.

Temperature compensation is performed automatically, based on either the measured temperature of the solution, on a default temperature of 25°C, or on a value entered by the operator via software. The OM-961 module accepts a two-wire platinum RTD sensor for each pH input channel, providing temperature accuracy of better than ±0.31°C.

The input channels are individually floating and isolated from each other and from ground, a feature that provides maximum noise immunity in the presence of ground loops or high

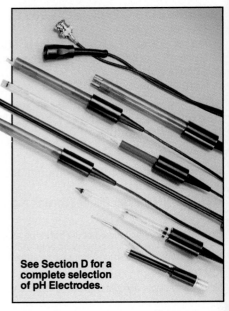

See Section D for a complete selection of pH Electrodes.

917

MUX

OM-917 EXPANSION MULTIPLEXER SUBSYSTEM
FUNCTIONAL BLOCK DIAGRAM

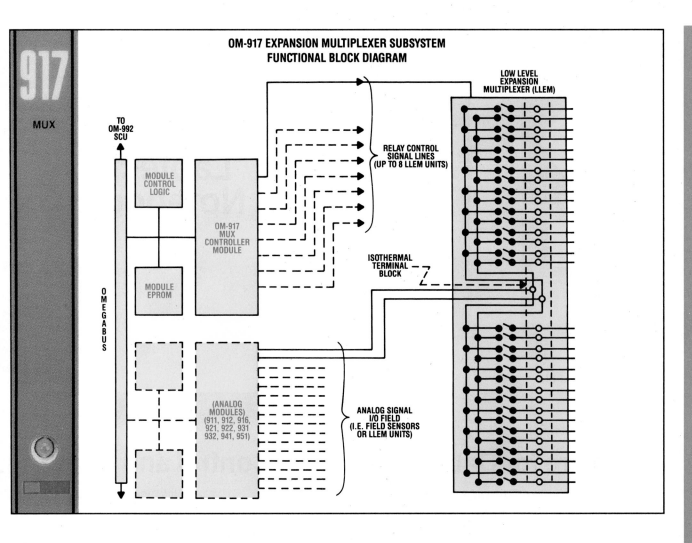

OM-917 Low Level Multiplexer Controller $575

OM-917-LLEM Low Level Multiplexer Relay Board $600

- ✔ **Up to Eight Low-Level Expansion Multiplexers**
- ✔ **Up to 128 Differential Channels**
- ✔ **Isothermal Screw-Terminal Signal Inputs**

OM-917/OM-917-LLEM multiplexer system allows you to create high channel capacity OM-900 systems for a very low dollar per channel cost. The OM-917-LLEM contains 16 differential input channels and a single output channel. Via a serial link, the serial OM-917 controller instructs the OM-917-LLEM to connect one of the 16 input channels to the output channel. The output channel can then be connected to a module, such as the OM-931 thermocouple module, which will perform the analog to digital conversion. Up to eight OM-917-LLEM's can be connected to one OM-917 controller, for a throughput of 128 channels.

Specifications (@23°C ±5°C)
Relay Selection: Any one of 16 differential pairs
Switching Voltage: 150 V maximum
Switching Current: 0.25 A peak into resistive load

Switching Power: 5 VA, maximum, into resistive load
Contact Resistance: 0.3Ω, maximum, single contact
Thermal Voltage: 5 μV, maximum, differential
Dielectric Strength: 250 V
Operating Time: < 20 msec
LLEM Control Connection: Via 6″ modular cable
Signal Connections: Isothermal screw terminals
On-Board Memory: None
Power Consumption: 2 W maximum
Environmental: 0 to 45°C, 0 to 85% RH non-condensing
LLEM Dimensions: 1.5″ H x 6.25″ W x 10″ D (38 x 159 x 254 mm)
Module Dimensions: 5.2″ H x 1.7″ W x 14″ D (132 x 43 x 356 mm)

Labtech® Notebook

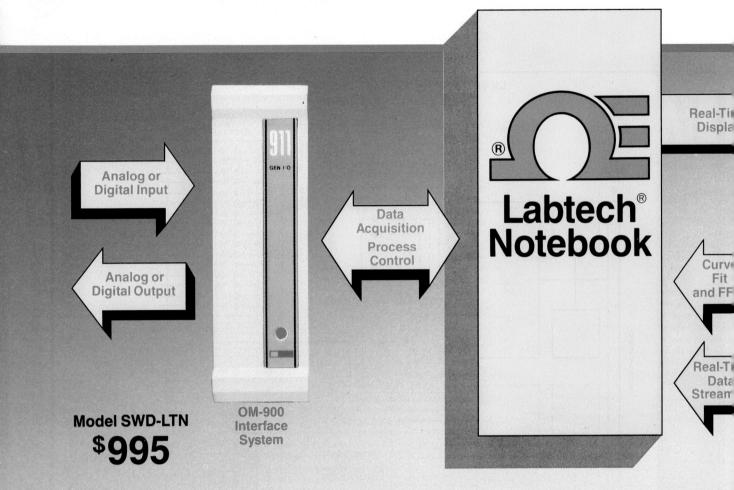

Model SWD-LTN

$995

OM-900
Interface
System

Software for Data Acquisition, Control and Analysis

- **No Programming Required**
- **Real-Time Graphic Data Display**
- **Menu Driven Software— Similar Style to Popular Spreadsheets**
- **Advanced Non-linear Curve Fitting**
- **Fast Fourier Transforms**
- **Interfaces to 1-2-3 or Symphony for Analysis, File Management and Graphics**
- **Complete On-line Tutorial and Help Screens**
- **For IBM PC, XT, AT and Compatibles**

Labtech Notebook software increases laboratory research productivity the same way personal computers increase productivity for the office. This integrated, general purpose software package for data acquisition, process control, monitoring, and data analysis runs on the IBM PC, XT, or AT, and other PC compatibles. This software is designed to complement the OM-900 intelligent interface system, fully utilizing its advanced capabilities. Designed for the novice or programmer, Labtech Notebook needs no programming. Everything is presented in an easy-to-use menu system.

Labtech Notebook allow the personal computer to be used for other programs while collecting data. After initiating a run, the user may run another program, while the system continues collecting data. When this program is completed, the graphic displays are updated with the data which was collected during background operation. This

capability means the computer can be used for other functions during long tests.

Because this is a menu-driven software package, and is extremely easy to learn and use, it requires no computer skills on the part of the operator. Each acquisition run may be set up differently or as previously specified. Each setup conditions may be stored, and recalled at a later date for further use.

Although Labtech Notebook is user-friendly, it does not sacrifice any of the performance potential of the OM-900 system. Data collection may be at any rate supported by the OM-900. For flexibility, each channel of the OM-900 can be set up with different characteristics. Sampling rates may vary from channel to channel, and the rate may vary at different times during a run. For control functions, open and closed-loop control algorithms are readily implemented.

Labtech Notebook includes two

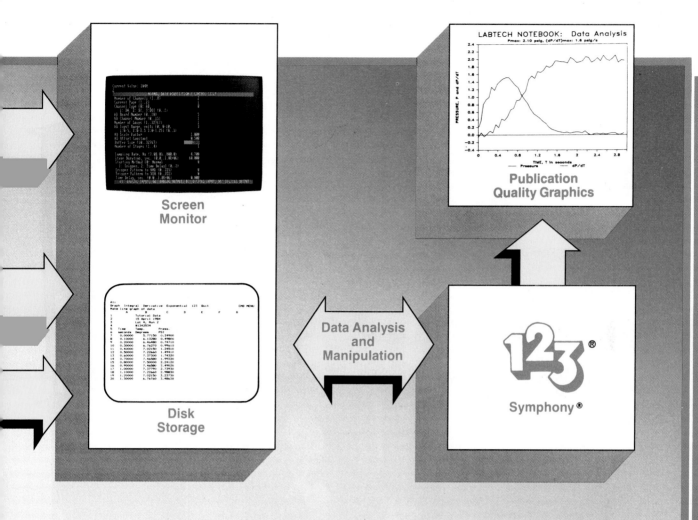

Screen Monitor

Disk Storage

Data Analysis and Manipulation

Publication Quality Graphics

Symphony®

sophisticated analytical routines: non-linear curve-fitting and fast fourier transforms. Both these programs take advantage of the optional 8087 or 80287 math coprocessors of the PC if they are present, but do not require them.

By interfacing Labtech Notebook with a spreadsheet such as 1-2-3 or Symphony, the user may go from data collection to the final report without ever writing down or keying-in a single piece of data.

A tutorial section demonstrates how

data acquisition can be set up and run. A software simulation of an A/D converter creates a real-time display of a data file without installing the OM-900 system. The novice can learn how to set up an acquisition run, analyze, reduce and graph the data. Also, on-line help screens are available to the user at different points throughout the program.

Plug-In Interface Systems
With Applications Software for Apple and IBM PCs

From
$745

- **RTD Measurement with Optional Screw Terminal Panel**
- **Easy to Use Menu Driven Software for Operation Without Programming**
- **Standard 12-Bit Resolution with 16-Bit Models for High Precision Measurements**
- **All Cards Contain Independently Selectable Digital Input and Output Channels**

- **Complete System with Plug-In Card, Terminal Box and Software**
- **Software Selectable Input Types Include Thermocouples, mV and V**

The White Box interface system provides both the hardware and software for a computerized data acquisition and control system. Included is a card which plugs into one of the internal slots of an IBM PC XT, AT or compatible, a terminal box which resides externally to the computer for easy hook-up to sensors and a user-friendly menu driven software package. All you need is a computer and sensors to complete the system.

The Hardware

The hardware provides the ability to interface with a wide variety of analog signals including thermocouples, millivolts, volts, currents and even RTD's. The standard model, the WB-FAI, features 12-bit A/D resolution, and includes a battery backed clock and on-board current shunts for easy measurement of milliamp signals. The WB-FAI is available in two models, with either 8 or 16 analog input channels. The WB-AAI includes all features of the WB-FAI with improved accuracy and resolution (16-bit) for high precision applications. As an economical alternative, the WB-ASC is a half card version of the WB-FAI lacking only the battery backed clock and on-board current shunts. In addition to the analog input channels, all models include a number of digital I/O channels. Each of these channels may be independently selected through software as digital inputs for switch sensing type applications or digital outputs for alarm or control purposes.

The Software

Included with the White Box System is a menu-driven data acquisition and control software package for easy operation without programming. The software includes many featues such as graphical and tabular display of real-time data, control of alarm conditions, datalogging to printer or disk (in a format that can be easily imported to most spreadsheet programs for further data analysis) as well as many other features. The software is written in BASIC for those who may want to customize it for a special application. OMEGA also offers many other software packages that also work with the hardware. See the software section of the catalog for a complete description.

Each menu in the control software is a step-by-step procedure for fast, easy system installation and operation

The software provides a tabular display of inputs with continuous updating. The user can select names, engineering units, and data logging to both disk and printer

Graphics capabilities of the WB-AAI, FAI and ASC allow inputs to be plotted in real time against the control setpoint and alarm limits

For accurate control, digital outputs can be configured quickly and easily in menus

White Box® Computer Interfaces For Apple II

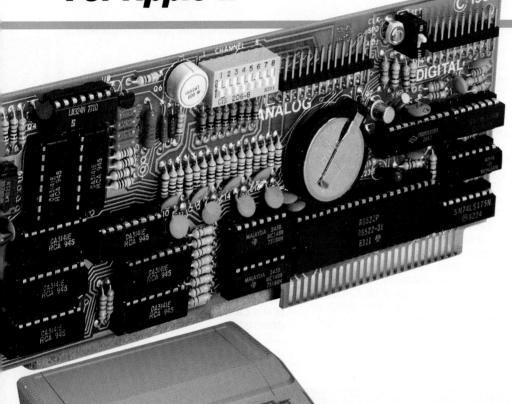

Each unit includes:

- Plug-in A/D Board
- Terminal Board(s) With Isothermal Plate
- Connection Cables
- Data Acquisition Software
- Comprehensive User's Manual
- 100' Type K Thermocouple Wire

WB-AIO-A $ 890   8 channel

$890

WB-AIO-A requires
Apple II+, IIe; 48K RAM

Resolution	Cycle Time, 8 Channels	
	Read & Control	Read, Control & Datalog
14 bit, 0.006%	8 sec	18 sec
13 bit, 0.012%	6 sec	16 sec
12 bit, 0.024%	5 sec	15 sec
11 bit, 0.05%	4 sec	14 sec
10 bit, 0.1%	4 sec	14 sec
9 bit, 0.2%	4 sec	14 sec
8 bit, 0.4%	4 sec	14 sec

Analog Ranges	Resolution	Accuracy—larger of	
		% of range	% of rdg
−5 to 50 mV	3 μV	0.04	—
−25 to 25 mV	3 μV	0.08	—
−50 to 500 mV	30 μV	0.05	0.1
−250 to 250 mV	30 μV	0.05	0.1
−1 to 10 V	600 μV	0.05	0.1
−5 to 5 V	600 μV	0.05	0.3
−0.5 to 5 mA	0.3 μA	0.2	1
−2.5 to 2.5 mA	0.3 μA	0.2	1
−5 to 50 mA	3 μA	0.2	1
−25 to 25 mA	3 μA	0.2	1

Input Type	Range	Resol.	Accuracy
J	−80 to 100°C 100 to 760°C	0.2°C 0.1°C	±0.9°C ±0.6°C
K	−110 to 0°C 0 to 1260°C	0.2°C 0.1°C	±1.0°C ±0.8°C
T	−120 to 0°C 0 to 400°C	0.2°C 0.1°C	±1.2°C ±0.8°C
E	−60 to 150°C 150 to 680°C	0.1°C 0.1°C	±0.7°C ±0.5°C
R	0 to 200°C 200 to 1770°C	0.5°C 0.3°C	±4.0°C ±2.5°C
S	0 to 200°C 200 to 1770°C	0.5°C 0.3°C	±4.0°C ±2.5°C
B	200 to 300°C 300 to 500°C 500 to 1000°C 1000 to 1820°C	0.8°C 0.5°C 0.3°C 0.3°C	±10.0°C ±6.0°C ±4.0°C ±2.2°C
G	25 to 200°C 200 to 2315°C	0.5°C 0.2°C	±6.0°C ±2.5°C
C	−20 to 2315°C 100 to 1500°C	0.3°C 0.2°C	±3.0°C ±2.0°C
D	−20 to 2315°C 150 to 1500°C	0.5°C 0.2°C	±3.0°C ±2.0°C

Standard screw terminal input with isothermal block for thermocouple input. Included with WB-AIO, WB-AAI, WB-FAI and WB-ASC.

High Speed, High Resolution and Half Sized Cards for the IBM PC

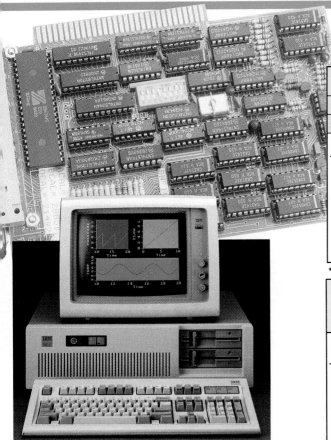

Model	WB-AAI High Resolution		WB-FAI High Speed	WB-ASC Short Card
Digital I/O	16 Channels		16 Channels	12 Channels
Scan Frequency	1 channel / 8 channels		1 channel / 8 channels	
Low Noise	60 Hz	7 Hz	60 Hz	7 Hz
16 bit, 0.0015%	225 Hz	25 Hz	—	—
15 bit, 0.003%	440 Hz	45 Hz	—	—
14 bit, 0.006%	830 Hz	80 Hz	—	—
13 bit, 0.012%	1500 Hz	120 Hz	—	—
12 bit, 0.024%	2500 Hz	160 Hz	2500 Hz	160 Hz
11 bit, 0.05%	—	—	5000 Hz	200 Hz
10 bit, 0.1%	—	—	7500 Hz	220 Hz
9 bit, 0.2%	—	—	10 KHz	240 Hz

*1Hz = 1 sample per second

Analog Ranges	WB-AAI			WB-FAI, WB-ASC		
	Resol.	Accuracy-larger of:		Resol.	Accuracy-larger of:	
		% range	% of rdg		% range	% of rdg
−5 to 50 mV	0.8 µV	0.04	—	12 µV	0.08	—
±25 mV	0.8 µV	0.08	—	12 µV	0.16	—
−50 to 500 mV	8 µV	0.01	0.05	120 µV	0.05	0.2
±250 mV	8 µV	0.01	0.05	120 µV	0.05	0.2
−1 to 10 V	150 µV	0.01	0.05	2.4 mV	0.05	0.2
−5 to 5 V	150 µV	0.01	0.10	2.4 mV	0.05	0.3
−0.2 to 2 mA*	0.03 µA	0.1	0.3	0.5 µA	0.2	0.5
−1 to 1 mA*	0.03 µA	0.1	0.3	0.5 µA	0.2	0.5
−2 to 20 mA*	0.3 µA	0.02	0.3	5 µA	0.1	0.5
±10 mA*	0.3 µA	0.02	0.3	5 µA	0.1	0.5
±50 mA*	6 µA	0.02	0.3	100 µA	0.1	0.5

* Requires user-supplied shunt resistor with WB-ASC

Model No.	Price	Description
WB-FAI-B8	$1190	12-bit resolution 8 input: T/C, mV, V, mA 8 digital I/O
WB-FAI-B16	1690	12-bit resolution 16 input: T/C, mV, V, mA 16 digital I/O
WB-AAI-B8	1690	16-bit resolution 8 input: T/C, mV, V, mA 8 digital I/O
WB-AAI-B16	2290	16-bit resolution 16 input: T/C, mV, V, mA 16 digital I/O
WB-ASC-GP	745	12-bit short card 8 input: mV, V 8 digital I/O
WB-ASC-TC	895	12-bit short card 8 input: T/C, mV, V 8 digital I/O
WB-ASC-RTD	780	12-bit short card 8 input: Pt RTD 8 digital I/O
SWD-LTN-2	995	Labtech Notebook Data Acquisition Software

Thermocouple Type	Range	WB-AAI		WB-FAI, WB-ASC	
		Resol.	Accuracy	Resol.	Accuracy
J	− 80 to 100°C	0.02°C	± 0.9°C	0.3°C	± 1.6°C
	100 to 760°C	0.01°C	± 0.6°C	0.2°C	± 1.2°C
K	− 110 to 0°C	0.03°C	± 1.0°C	0.4°C	± 1.9°C
	0 to 1260°C	0.02°C	± 0.8°C	0.3°C	± 1.5°C
E	− 60 to 150°C	0.01°C	± 0.7°C	0.3°C	± 1.3°C
	150 to 680°C	0.01°C	± 0.5°C	0.2°C	± 1°C
T	− 120 to 0°C	0.03°C	± 1.2°C	0.4°C	± 2°C
	0 to 400°C	0.02°C	± 0.8°C	0.3°C	± 1.5°C
R	0 to 200°C	0.1°C	± 4.0°C	2°C	± 8°C
	200 to 1770°C	0.08°C	± 2.5°C	1°C	± 5°C
S	0 to 200°C	0.1°C	± 4.0°C	2°C	± 8°C
	200 to 1770°C	0.08°C	± 2.5°C	1°C	± 5°C
B	200 to 300°C	0.3°C	± 10°C	5°C	± 20°C
	300 to 500°C	0.2°C	± 6°C	3°C	± 12°C
	500 to 1000°C	0.1°C	± 4°C	2°C	± 8°C
	1000 to 1820°C	0.1°C	± 2.2°C	1°C	± 5°C
G	25 to 200°C	0.2°C	± 6°C	3°C	± 15°C
	200 to 2315°C	0.06°C	± 2.5°C	1°C	± 5°C
C	− 20 to 2315°C	0.06°C	± 3°C	1.5°C	± 5°C
	100 to 1500°C	0.05°C	± 2.0°C	1°C	± 3.5°C
D	− 20 to 2315°C	0.1°C	± 3°C	1.5°C	± 5°C
	150 to 1500°C	0.04°C	± 2.0°C	1°C	± 3.5°C

Requires: IBM PC, XT, AT; 192K RAM; Color Graphics adaptor required for graphic displays.

Precision Dataloggers
Expanded OM-270 Series

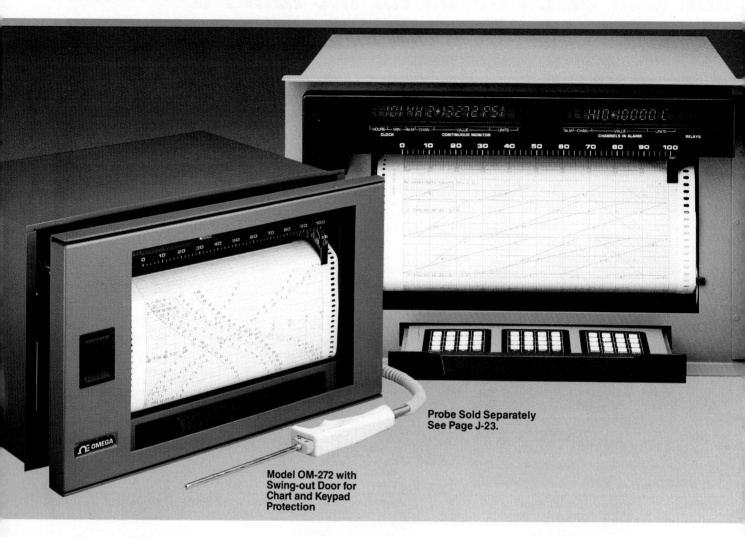

Probe Sold Separately
See Page J-23.

Model OM-272 with
Swing-out Door for
Chart and Keypad
Protection

Model OM-272

- 32 Character Alphanumeric Display
- Full RS-232C Communications
- Linear Scaling for Any Input with Floating Point Arithmetic
- Optional 12 Alarm Relays Assignable to Any Channel(s) with AND/OR Logic
- Full Mathematics
- 255 mm Chart

Model OM-372

- OM-272 in a Portable Package
- Only 27 lb, with Built-In Handle
- RS-232C Interface at up to 19,200 Baud
- Full Mathematics, Including:
  — Averaging
  — Integration
  — Mass Flow
  — Square Root Extraction
  — Floating Point Arithmetic

Model OM-472

- Desk Top 32 Channel Computer Interface
- Accepts Thermocouple, Voltage or Current Inputs
- 32 Character Alphanumeric Display
- RS-232-C Communications up to 19,200 Baud or Active or Passive 20 mA Current Loop
- Full Mathematics
- Accepts Optional OM-372-ALM Board with 12 Additional Alarm Relays

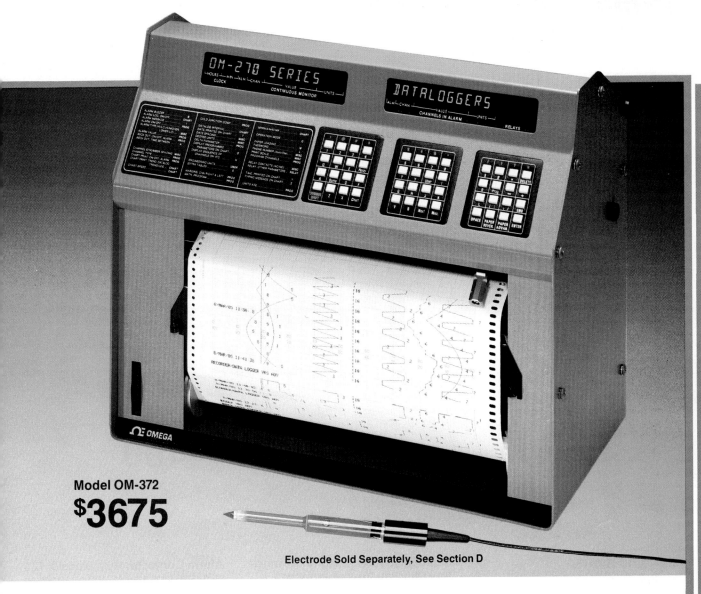

Model OM-372

$3675

Electrode Sold Separately, See Section D

Trend or Data Display

All OM-270 Series models record the trend of every selected channel in under 2 second cycles. In addition, they can be converted into a data logger either from the keyboard or remotely. In this mode, the various input signals are digitized and printed in a five-column format across the chart. A printout of all 32 channels takes approximately 60 seconds and includes the time and date. Print frequency can be programmed from once each minute to once every 5000 minutes.

All 32 channels are scanned every 2 seconds and compared to the stored alarm values. When an alarm is detected, either high or low, the appropriate alarm relay is activated. During every scan cycle, the internal reference source is used to check both zero and full scale values and make calibration adjustments automatically if needed.

The OM-270 Trend/Data Loggers meet most process and laboratory applications by utilizing the versatility in signal conditioning that only a microprocessor can provide. Each channel can be individually programmed for range and sensor type, without the need for range cards or special hardware. The parameters of any channel may be changed at any time by a command from the keyboard. The design gives the user optimum performance in a dependable and easy-to-service package. To maximize reliability, mechanical parts have been kept to a minimum; only the chart drive and thermal print head assembly contain moving parts. The OM-270 accepts inputs from 12 thermocouple types, and other process sensors with up to a 10 V full scale output. In addition, current output sensors may also be used (sensing resistor required).

The OM-272 and OM-372 models combine a datalogger, computer interface adn alarm/control unit in one package. These models feature an RS-232C computer interface, a large, easy-to-read digital display, mathematic capabilities including float point arithmetic, and 12 alarm relays which can be used with any channel or channels, using and/or logic (optional). Both the OM-272 and 372 have full scaling capability, using zero and offset, to configure the input to any desired engineering units.

For Additional Information Refer to the OMEGA Complete Temperature Measurement Handbook and Encyclopedia®.

Precision Dataloggers
Expanded OM-270 Series

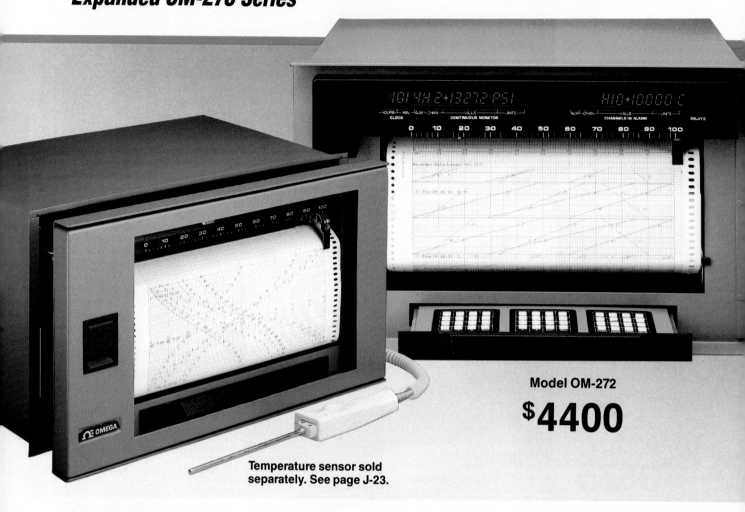

Model OM-272

$4400

Temperature sensor sold
separately. See page J-23.

Specifications

Inputs: 32 channels

Input Types: Any full scale voltage from 1 mV to 10 V; any current input by installation of proper shunt resistor (user supplied); Thermocouple types J,K,T,E,R,S,B,G,C,D,N,Pt II; RTD 0.00385 and 0.00392 100 ohm Pt, 120 ohm Ni, 10 ohm Cu — external current source required (Model OM-270-R32)

Time Averaging: Up to 8 inputs over programmed time period from 24 min. to 254 hrs.

Group Averaging: Average of 2 to 31 channels may be displayed as a separate channel.

Math Functions: Integration, mass flow rate, square root extraction, floating point arithmetic

Prompting: Prompting of all channel parameters for ease of use

Computer Interface: OM-271: 300 baud, passive serial ASCII; OM-272, 372: RS-232C communications at various baud rates up to 19,200

Digital Display: Alphanumeric display for setup prompting, time, channel number, alarm status, up to 5 digits of data with units, and alarm display

Engineering Units: Scaling factor for any channel, using span and zero suppression of
$Y = MX + B$

Alarm Contacts: ALM Models: 12 relays assignable to any channel or channels, using and/or logic.

Accuracy: >0.1% full scale, for all ranges over 1 mV; >1% full scale for 1 mV range

Scan Cycle Time: 2 sec.

Print Cycle Time: Under 6 sec.

Common Mode Voltage: ±15 V

Input Impedance: >1M ohm at dc

CMRR: >120 dB

NMRR: >45 dB at 60 Hz

Dimensions: OM-272: 10.5″ H x 17.75″ W x 14″ D; OM-372: 14″ H x 17″ W x 9″ D

Weight: OM-272: 48 lb; OM-372: 27 lbs.

For Additional Information Refer to the OMEGA Complete Temperature Measurement Handbook & Encyclopedia®.

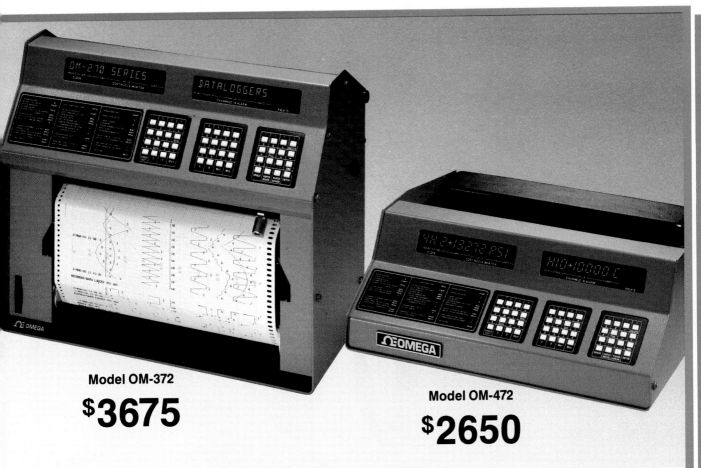

Model OM-372

$3675

Model OM-472

$2650

Also Available!
OM-472 Interface

The OM-472 is a truly versatile 32 channel computer interface, for both laboratory and industrial environments. As with the OM-272 datalogger, each channel is set up individually as either thermocouple, current or voltage, and no range cards are required. To make the OM-472 easy to use, all channel and other programming is prompted by a 32 character vacuum fluorescent display, which results in a true user friendly design. In addition to 12 thermocouple linearizations, any voltage/current channel may be linearly scaled, using scale and offset of Y = mX + B. Or, the user may create up to 16 linearizations for other nonlinear input signals. And, calculations on the raw data, such as floating point arithmetic, averaging, rate of change integration and mass flow may be performed on any channel, with the results transmitted. Communications between the OM-472 and the host

computer is either RS-232C, or active or passive 20mA current loop. Baud rates from 50 to 19,200 are possible, with various communication data formats. Also, the optional OM-372-ALM alarm board for the OM-472 adds 12 alarm relays, which may be assigned to any channel (or channels, using and/or logic).

How To Order   *HIGHLIGHTED MODELS IN STOCK FOR FAST DELIVERY*

Model No.	Price	Description
OM-272	4400	Trend/data recorder with display and RS-232C interface
OM-272-ALM	4700	OM-272 with alarm package
OM-372	3675	Portable trend/data recorder
OM-472	2650	32 channel computer interface
OM-372-ALM	4075	OM-372 with alarm package
OM-270-R32	1050	32 channel current source for RTD's
OM-270-R16	700	16 channel current source for RTD's
OM-TR27E	18	English chart paper, 100 ft. roll
OM-TR27M	18	Metric chart paper, 100 ft. roll
OM-JS27	75	Panel mount jack screw kit

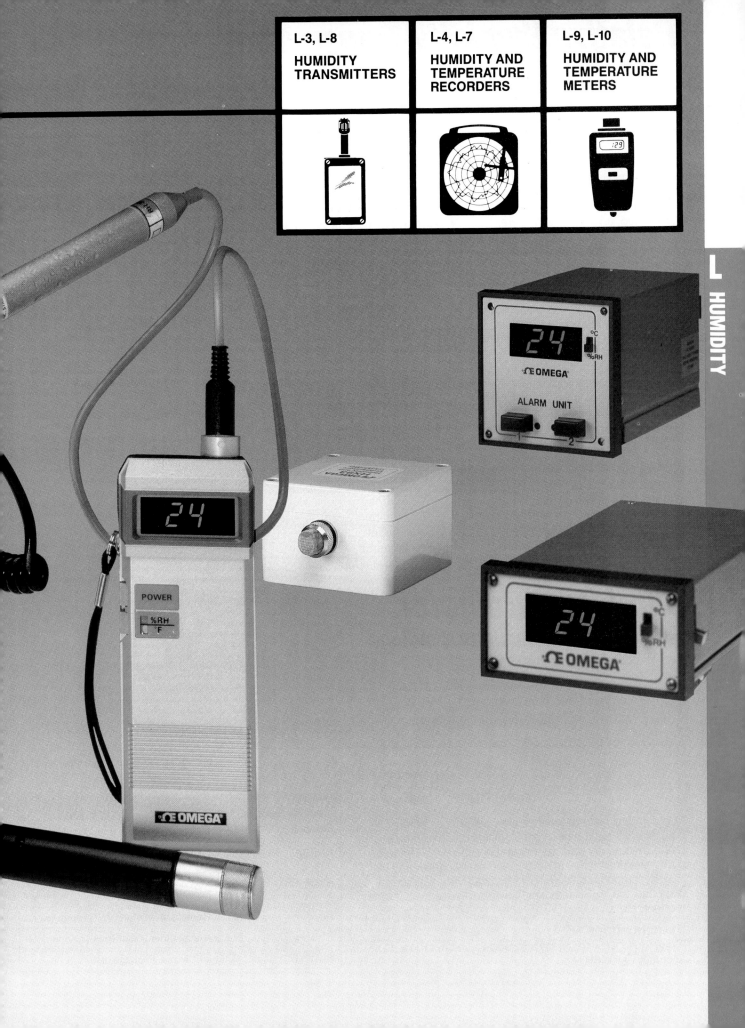

L-3, L-8

HUMIDITY TRANSMITTERS

L-4, L-7

HUMIDITY AND TEMPERATURE RECORDERS

L-9, L-10

HUMIDITY AND TEMPERATURE METERS

L

HUMIDITY

POWER

%RH
°F

ΩE OMEGA®

ΩE OMEGA®

ALARM UNIT

ΩE OMEGA®

Relative Humidity Transmitter

The model HX92 is an economical humidity transmitter, providing on-site continuous monitoring of relative humidity. It is a 2-wire transmitter with either voltage or current output. The transmitter output is linearized, and RH readings are temperature compensated. A thin-film polymer capacitor senses relative humidity. The sensor is protected by a stainless mesh-type filter that is easily removable for cleaning. The case and wiring connectors provide gland nut weathertight protection, and screws are provided for mounting the unit via internal holes. An unusually low minimum voltage of 6 V allows the use of large impedances for longer wire runs. The HX93, on the previous page, is a similar unit that provides transmitter outputs for both humidity and temperature.

- **Models Available with Either Voltage or Current Output**
- **Compact Size**
- **Watertight Enclosure**
- **Accurate to 2% RH and 0.6°C**

Model HX92
$150

Specifications
Input Voltage Range: 24 Vdc nominal (6 to 30 Vdc)
Range: 3 to 95% RH
Accuracy: ±2% RH
RH Temperature Compensation: −4 to 167°F
Output, HX92C: 4 to 20 mA for 0 to 100% RH

Shown Smaller than Actual Size

Output, HX92V: 0 to 1 Vdc for 0 to 100% RH
RH Time Constant (90% response at 25°C, in moving air at 1 m/s): >10 s, 10 to 90% RH; >15 s, 90 to 10% RH
Repeatability: ±1% RH, 0.5°F
Housing: ABS plastic watertight enclosure; meets NEMA 1, 2, 3, 3R, 4, 4X, 5, 12 and 13 specifications
Connections: liquid-tight nylon with neoprene gland, for 0.09 to 0.265″ dia. cable; Internal 4-pin terminal block accepts 14-22 AWG wire
Dimensions: 1.96″ x 2.55″ x 1.37″
Weight: 8 oz

How To Order

Model No.	Price	Description
HX92C	$150	Humidity Transmitter, 4-20 mA output
HX92V	150	Humidity Transmitter, 0-1 Vdc output
HX92-CAL	60	Calibration kit, 11 and 75% standards
PSU-24	40	Unregulated 24 Vdc, 100 mA power supply

Sling Psychrometer
For Economical Humidity Readings

Shown Smaller than Actual Size

Model RHSP $55

This compact instrument accurately determines relative humidity, without the need of consulting complex tables. Using wet and dry bulb measurements, the RHSP features slide rule construction to quickly and easily convert the wet and dry temperatures to relative humidity. For fast thermal response, the RHSP features thin bulb design thermometers.

Specifications
Range: 10 to 100% RH for dry bulb temperatures from 30 to 100°F
Accuracy: ±5% RH

How To Order

Model No.	Price	Description
RHSP-F	$55	Psychrometer with Mercury filled Thermometer
RHSP-FR	55	Psychrometer with Red Spirit filled Thermometer
RHSP-FT	12	Replacement Mercury Thermometer
RHSP-FRT	12	Replacement Red Spirit Thermometer
RHSP-W	7	10″ Wicks, Package of 4

Microprocessor-Based Temperature/Humidity Recorder

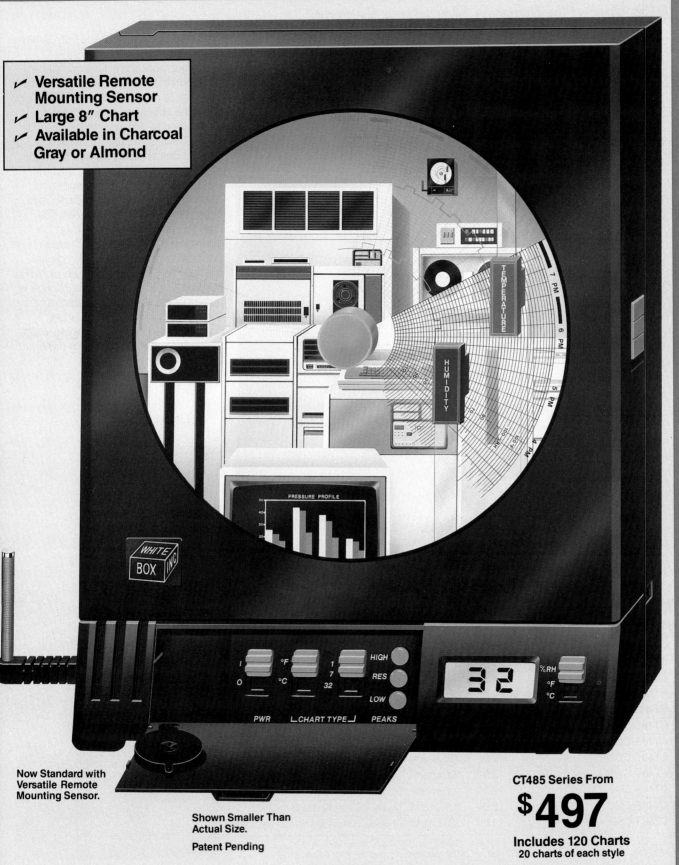

- ✔ **Versatile Remote Mounting Sensor**
- ✔ **Large 8″ Chart**
- ✔ **Available in Charcoal Gray or Almond**

Now Standard with Versatile Remote Mounting Sensor.

Shown Smaller Than Actual Size.

Patent Pending

CT485 Series From

$497

Includes 120 Charts
20 charts of each style

Microprocessor-Based Temperature/Humidity Recorder

With Versatile Remote Mounting Sensor

Shown with sensor, also includes 6′ extension cord for remote sensing applications.

Dual LCD display and large 8″ chart for accurate indication of temperature and humidity

The new Model CT485RS from White Box® sets a new standard in hygrothermography. This completely self-contained temperature/humidity recorder is microprocessor-based for accurate indication of temperature and humidity, along with the current time. Unrivaled in the industry, this rugged unit enables storage of high and low peak values (max. and min.) for both temperature and humidity. Each function of the recorder is easily accessible via the front panel. The user may select 1, 7 or 32 day operation of the large, 8″ chart, in addition to programming the digital display for °F/°C temperature or %RH humidity indication. The chart drive is quartz controlled for precision, and the CT485RS includes a unique spring-loaded chart positioning knob to eliminate the possibility of paper tear.

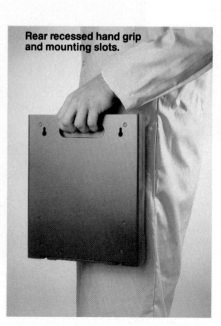

Rear recessed hand grip and mounting slots.

To Order *(Specify Model Number)*

Model No.	Price	Description
CT485RS-110V	$497.00	charcoal gray color recorder-110 Vac
CT485RS-110V-W	525.00	almond color recorder-110 Vac
CT485-PR	4.50	red pen (temperature)
CT485-PB	4.50	blue pen (humidity)
CT-485-PS	8.00	pen set, red and blue
CT485-CDF	12.00	100 charts, 1 day, °F (printed both sides)
CT485-CDC	12.00	100 charts, 1 day, °C (printed both sides)
CT485-CWF	12.00	100 charts, 7 day, °F (printed both sides)
CT485-CWC	12.00	100 charts, 7 day, °C (printed both sides)
CT485-CMF	12.00	100 charts, 32 day, °F (printed both sides)
CT485-CMC	12.00	100 charts, 32 day, °C (printed both sides)
CT485-CSP	15.00	120 charts, 20 of each style (printed both sides)

For 220V option, replace "110 V" in part no. with "220 V" and add $20 to price.
Example: CT485RS-220V, calls for 220V version of the recorder in charcoal gray. **Price: $517**

Slim profile design. Ideal for wall mounting.

Convenient front panel selection of all functions, including 1, 7, or 32 day operation and current time display.

For placing orders, Call
1-800-TC-OMEGA
1-800-82-66342

The CT485RS demonstrates its impressive versatility and rugged performance by allowing both laboratory and portable operation. A swing-out desk stand provides added stability for benchtop use, or wall mount the recorder using the rear recessed mounting slots. A standard 110 Vac power transformer is supplied for permanent installation along with (4) "D" cell batteries for easy field use.

To handle a variety of measurement applications the unit now includes a versatile remote mounting sensor with 6 feet of cable as standard equipment. The recorder is available in two attractive colors: charcoal gray or almond.

Also Available in Almond. Model CT485RS-110V-W, Price $525

The CT485RS Includes:

QTY	DESCRIPTION
1	Package of 120 charts (20 of each style)
1	Remote mounting sensor and 6' extension cord
1	AC adaptor/power cord
4	"D" cell batteries
1	Wall mounting template with mounting hardware
1	Temperature pen (red)
1	Humidity pen (blue)
1	Operator's Manual

Microprocessor-Based Temperature/Humidity Recorder

SPECIFICATIONS

MEASUREMENT INPUTS temperature and humidity, with plug-in external sensor, removeable for remote location (up to 6 ft). Extension cable included.

TEMPERATURE
Range: 2 to 120°F, −17 to 49°C
Accuracy: ±1°C
Sensor: solid state
Response Time: 5 minutes for 63% step change
Display Resolution: 1°F/1°C

HUMIDITY
Range: 2 to 98% RH
Accuracy: ±3% @ 25°C, between 20 and 90% of range (±5% below 20% and above 90% @ 25°C)
Sensor: resistive polymer
Response Time: 5 minutes for a 30 to 80% step change
Display Resolution: 1% RH

DISPLAY
Display One: 2½ digit LCD, 0.5″, low battery and parameter indication
Display Two: Time-of-day and date clock
Display Modes: user-switchable between °F, °C and %RH for continuous display; max/min storage for both temperature and humidity

ELECTRONICS
Type: Microprocessor-controlled and linearized High and Low Peak Hold for both Temperature and Humidity Re-calibrates Position at Every Chart Change

CHART
Type: 8″ circular, with linear radial divisions; 1, 7 and 32 day with both °F and °C scales

CHART DRIVE
Type: quartz clock stepper drive
Ranges: 1, 7, 32 day; switchable
Accuracy: 1% of rotation
Chart Paper Hold Down: magnetic hub lock

RECORDING PENS
Type: disposable fiber tip; red-temperature, blue-humidity

PEN DRIVES
Type: motorized linear screw drive
Deadband: 1.5°F, 1.5% RH
Zero: automatic zero during chart change
Penlift: automatic on door opening; pens are door mounted and swing clear of the chart when door opens.
Pen Arms: clear plastic to allow full chart viewing

OPERATING CONDITIONS (Recorder)
Temperature: 32 to 122°F (0 to 50°C)
Humidity: 0 to 90% RH, non-condensing

POWER: four D cells or 6V/110V power supply (all provided)
Battery Life: More than 2 months continuous operation in 32 day mode (average conditions).
Power Requirements: 400 mA "normal" during pen movement; 1.5 A max. surge
DC Power Jack Voltage: 7.2 to 14 Vdc, 1.25 A; 9V, 1 A wall transformer supplied

OPERATING RANGE (Sensor):
Operates from 0 to 122°F (−20 to 99°C), 0 to 98% relative humidity

MECHANICAL
Dimensions: 12″H x 10″W x 2.5″D
Weight: approx. 7 lbs, including Alkaline batteries
Mounting: t-slots for wall mount
Case: rugged ABS plastic, charcoal gray or almond
Miscellaneous: retractable handle, swing-out desk stand for benchtop use, 6 foot sensor extension cord for remote sensing

Relative Humidity Transmitter
With Temperature Output

$180

Model HX93
- **Models Available with Either Voltage or Current Output**
- **Compact Size**
- **Watertight Enclosure**
- **Accurate to 2% RH and 0.6°C**

The model HX93 provides on-site continuous monitoring of relative humidity and temperature. It is a 2-wire transmitter with either voltage or current output for both humidity and temperature. All outputs are linearized, and RH readings are temperature compensated. A thin-film polymer capacitor senses relative humidity, and the temperature sensor is thin-film permalloy RTD. The sensors are protected by a stainless mesh-type filter that is easily removed for cleaning. The case and wiring connectors provide gland nut weathertight protection, and screws are provided for mounting the unit via internal holes. An unusually low minimum voltage of 6 V allows the use of large impedances for longer wire runs. The HX92, shown on the other side, is a similar unit, without the temperature output.

Works with Loop Powered Indicators!

Model TX82
$165

Specifications
Input Voltage Range: 24 Vdc nominal (6 to 30 Vdc)
Range, RH: 3 to 95% RH
Range, Temperature: −4 to 167°F (−20 to 75°C)
Accuracy, RH: ±2% RH
Accuracy, Temperature: ±1°F
RH Temperature Compensation: −4 to 167°F
Output, HX93C: 4 to 20 mA for 0 to 100% RH; 4 to 20 mA for −20 to 75°C
Output, HX93V: 0 to 1 Vdc for 0 to 100% RH; 0 to 1 Vdc for −20 to 75°C

RH Time Constant (90% response at 25°C, in moving air at 1 m/s): >10 s, 10 to 90% RH; >15 s, 90 to 10% RH
Repeatability: ±1% RH, 0.5°F
Housing: ABS plastic watertight enclosure; meets NEMA 1, 2, 3, 3R, 4, 4X, 5, 12 and 13 specifications
Connections: liquid-tight nylon with neoprene gland, for 0.09 to 0.265″ dia. cable; Internal 4-pin terminal block accepts 14-22 AWG wire
Dimensions: 3.14″ x 3.22″ x 2.16″
Weight: 8 oz

How To Order

Model No.	Price	Description
HX93C	$180	Humidity/temperature transmitter, 4-20 mA output
HX93V	180	Humidity/temperature transmitter, 0-1 Vdc output
HX92-CAL	60	Calibration kit, 11 and 75% standards
PSU-24	40	Unregulated 24 Vdc, 100 mA power supply

Hand Held Hygrometer Kit
Model RH-201

Shown smaller than actual size.

- **0 to 97% Relative Humidity with 2% Accuracy**
- **0.7% of Reading Temperature Accuracy**
- **Standard Recorder Output for both RH and Temperature**
- **ac Adaptor Included**
- **Fast Response**

RH-201-CAL Kit sold separately. $125

Model RH-201
$495

RH-201 Kit Includes:
- Combination Humidity/Temperature Probe
- ac Adaptor
- Carrying Case
- Recorder Output Leads

The RH-201 Combination Relative Humidity/Temperature Meter eliminates the need for charts, tables, and interpretations. This precision handheld instrument measures humidity up to 97% RH, with 2% accuracy. For temperature measurements, the standard RH/Temperature probe measures up to 104°F, and with other standard type K (chromel-alumel) thermocouples, the RH-201 can measure up to 900°F.

The RH-201 instruments are supplied with a standard recorder output for both humidity and temperature measurements. Any millivolt recorder can be used with the RH-201 to record either temperature or humidity.

Specifications

Range, Humidity: 0 to 97% RH
Range Temperature: −22° to 900°F
Accuracy, Humidity: ±2% RH
Accuracy Temperature: ±(0.7% rdg +1°F)
Resolution: 1% RH, 1° F or C
Ambient Operating Range, RH Probe: 32° to 160°F

Ambient Operating Range, instrument: 32° to 104°F
Display: 0.5″ LCD, 3 digits
Battery: 9V lithium, 50 hrs. typical life
Recorder Output: 1 mV per %RH or degree (C or F)
Accessories Supplied: ac adaptor, carrying case, recorder leads, combination RH/temperature sensor with 3 ft. extension lead

To Order: *(Specify Model Number)*

Model No.	Price	Temperature Range
RH-201F	$495	−22 to 900°F
RH-201C	495	−30 to 480°C
RH-201-CAL	125	Calibration Kit

Hand Held Hygrometer
Model RH-200

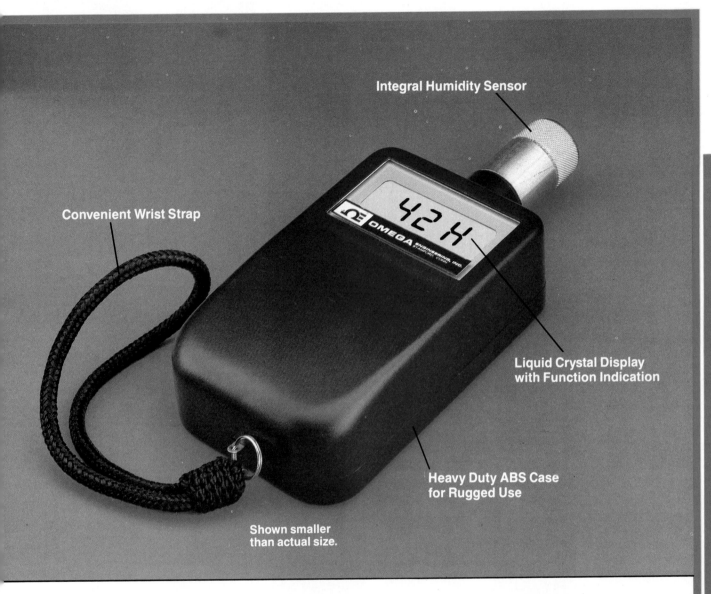

Integral Humidity Sensor

Convenient Wrist Strap

Liquid Crystal Display with Function Indication

Heavy Duty ABS Case for Rugged Use

Shown smaller than actual size.

The RH-200 handheld relative humidity meter gives quick, accurate checks of the humidity in any environment. With the integral RH sensor, the RH-200 goes anywhere you do. The large, easy-to-read display gives a clear indication of the environmental humidity. The size of the RH-200 makes it perfect for the hand, and it comes with a convenient wrist strap.

Specifications
Range: 0 to 97% RH
Accuracy: ±2% RH
Resolution: 1% RH
Ambient Operating Range: 32° to 104°F
Display: 0.5″ LCD
Battery: 9V lithium
Battery Life: 50 hrs., typical
Dimensions: 4.5″ H x 2.75″ W x 1.5″ D
Weight: 8.6 oz., with battery

- **Compact Humidity Meter with Integral Sensor**
- **0 to 97% RH with 2% Accuracy**
- **Large, Easy-to-Read LCD Display**
- **High Accuracy Thin-Film Capacitance Sensor**
- **Fast Response**

Model RH-200
$295

For Additional Information Refer to the OMEGA Complete Temperature Measurement Handbook and Encyclopedia®.

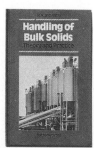

HANDLING OF BULK SOLIDS, THEORY AND PRACTICE
ORDER NO. CM-0494 $49.95

FLEXIBLE MANUFACTURING
ORDER NO. MS-0917 $79.95

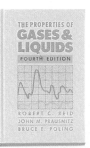

THE PROPERTIES OF GASES AND LIQUIDS, 4TH ED.
ORDER NO. CM-0142 $56.00

ELECTRONIC PRODUCT DESIGN FOR AUTOMATED MANUFACTURING
ORDER NO. EE-1057 $89.75

PROCESS INSTRUMENTS AND CONTROLS HANDBOOK
ORDER NO. MS-0333 $102.00

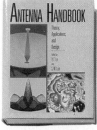

ANTENNA HANDBOOK
ORDER NO. EE-1078 $140.00

LASERS IN MANUFACTURING
ORDER NO. GE-0549 $59.00

FILTRATION; PRINCIPLES AND PRACTICES, PART II
ORDER NO. CM-0485 $99.75

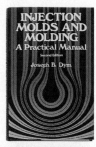

POWER ELECTRONICS: DEVICES, DRIVERS, AND APPLICATIONS
ORDER NO. EE-1009 $51.95

INJECTION MOLDS AND MOLDING: A PRACTICAL MANUAL
ORDER NO. CM-0463 $44.95

CONCISE ENCYCLOPEDIA OF SCIENCE & TECHNOLOGY
ORDER NO. GS-0002 $110.00

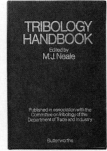

TRIBOLOGY HANDBOOK
ORDER NO. ME-0811 $125.00

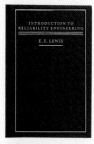

INTRODUCTION TO RELIABILITY ENGINEERING
ORDER NO. ME-0734 $63.50

ON-LINE ELECTRICAL TROUBLESHOOTING
ORDER NO. EE-1075 $34.50

MACHINE DESIGNS CALCULATIONS REFERENCE GUIDE
ORDER NO. ME-0713 $32.50

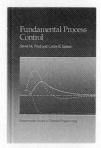

FUNDAMENTAL PROCESS CONTROL
ORDER NO. CM-0495 $57.95

REFERENCE MANUAL FOR TELECOMMUNICATIONS ENGINEERING
ORDER NO. EE-0077 $95.00

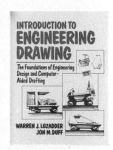

INTRODUCTION TO ENGINEERING DRAWING
ORDER NO. GE-0535 $49.95

OPTIMIZATION USING PERSONAL COMPUTERS
ORDER NO. EE-1040 $49.95

WHAT EVERY ENGINEER SHOULD KNOW ABOUT FINITE ELEMENT ANALYSIS
ORDER NO. MS-0920 $39.75

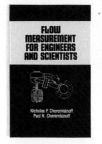

FLOW MEASUREMENT FOR ENGINEERS AND SCIENTISTS
ORDER NO. MS-0918 $99.75

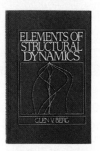

ELEMENTS OF STRUCTURAL DYNAMICS
ORDER NO. ME-0826 $40.00

MC GRAW-HILL ENCYCLOPEDIA OF ELECTRONICS AND COMPUTERS
ORDER NO. EE-0409 $75.00

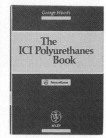

THE ICI POLYURETHANES BOOKS
ORDER NO. CM-0508 $74.95

WELDING, FAILURE ANALYSIS, AND METALLOGRAPHY
ORDER NO. MM-0750 $70.00

FUNDAMENTALS OF TEMPERATURE, PRESSURE AND FLOW MEASUREMENTS
ORDER NO. OP-6 $69.95

VISCOUS FLOWS: THE PRACTICAL USE OF THEORY
ORDER NO. CM-0498 $52.95

DESIGN OF REINFORCED CONCRETE STRUCTURES
ORDER NO. ME-0825 $42.00

EMERGENCY RESPONSE TO CHEMICAL ACCIDENTS
ORDER NO. MS-0907 $39.50

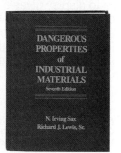

DANGEROUS PROPERTIES OF INDUSTRIAL MATERIALS
ORDER NO. MS-0388 $395.00

To Order Your Books, Dial These Convenient Toll-Free Numbers

Books Hot Line
(For Book Orders Only)

1-800-222-BooK™
1-800-222-2665

To Order Books and Instruments

1-800-826 6342
1-800-TC OMEGA

In CT Dial **(203) 359-1660**

Why You Should Order From Book of Books®

✔ **No Shipping Charges on Pre-Paid Orders**

✔ **No Handling Charges Ever**

✔ **One Source for All your Technical and Scientific Books**

✔ **Order by Calling Toll-Free in the USA**

✔ **ASM Members get ASM books at ASM Member Prices. Please give Your ASM Membership Number When Ordering!!!**

ΩP OMEGA PRESS

One Omega Drive, P.O. Box 4182 Stamford, CT 06907

CABLE: OMEGA   24 HR. FAX: (203) 357-7700
TELEX: 996404   EASYLINK: 62968934

Category		Pages
Popular Reference Texts		Y-3 Thru Y-4
Chemistry/Chemical Engineering		Y-5 Thru Y-13
Civil Engineering		Y-14
Industrial Engineering		Y-15 Thru Y-16
Mechanical Engineering		Y-17 Thru Y-21
Electrical Engineering		Y-22 Thru Y-27
Safety		Y-28
Self-Help		Y-29
Computing		Y-30 Thru Y-37
General Engineering		Y-38 Thru Y-43
Mathematics		Y-44 Thru Y-45
ASM International Texts		Y-46 Thru Y-53
Index		Y-54 Thru Y-56

BOOK OF BOOKS® YOUR SOURCE FOR

Over 10,000 Titles Available, Call Us with Your Book Request Today!

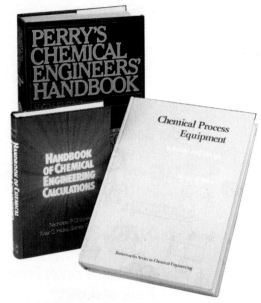

THE CHEMIST'S COMPANION
Gordon, Ford
WILEY
ISBN 0-471-31590-7
ORDER NO. CH-0169 **$55.00**

HANDBOOK OF REACTIVE CHEMICAL HAZARDS, 3RD ED.
Bretherick
BUTTERWORTHS
ISBN 0-408-01388-5
ORDER NO. CM-0480 **$128.00**

HAZARDOUS CHEMICALS DESK REFERENCE
Sax, Lewis
VAN NOSTRAND REINHOLD
ISBN# 0-442-28208-7
ORDER NO. CM-0452 **$79.95**

PROCESS INSTRUMENTS AND CONTROLS HANDBOOK
Considine
MCGRAW-HILL
ISBN 0-07-012436-1
ORDER NO. MS-0333 **$102.00**

HANDBOOK OF CHEMISTRY AND PHYSICS, 69TH ED.
Weast
CRC PRESS
ISBN 469-8493-0469-5
ORDER NO. SD-0503 **$89.95**

VAN NOSTRAND REINHOLD ENCYCLOPEDIA OF CHEMISTRY 4TH ED.
Considine, Considine
ISBN 0-442-22572-5
ORDER NO. CM-0160 **$107.95**

PERRY'S CHEMICAL ENGINEERS' HANDBOOK, 6TH ED.
Perry, Green
MCGRAW-HILL
ISBN 0-07-049479-7
ORDER NO. CM-0102 **$105.00**

HANDBOOK OF CHEMICAL ENGINEERING CALCULATIONS
Chopey, Hicks
MCGRAW-HILL
ISBN 0-07-10805-6
ORDER NO. CM-0100 **$62.00**

CHEMICAL PROCESS EQUIPMENT, SELECTION AND DESIGN
Walas
BUTTERWORTHS
ISBN 0-409-90131-8
ORDER NO. CM-0490 **$89.95**

CHEMICAL INSTRUMENTATION: A SYSTEMATIC APPROACH, 3RD ED.
Strobel, Heineman
WILEY
ISBN 0471-61223-5
ORDER NO. CM-0512 **$49.95**

INSTRUMENTATION REFERENCE BOOK
Noltingk
BUTTERWORTHS
ISBN 0-408-01562-4
ORDER NO. GE-0500 **$220.00**

VOGEL'S QUALITATIVE INORGANIC ANALYSIS, 6TH ED.
Svehla
WILEY
ISBN 0-582-45090-X
ORDER NO. CH-3070 **$38.95**

QUANTITATIVE ANALYSIS USING CHROMATOGRAPHIC TECHNIQUES
Katz
WILEY
ISBN 0-471-91406-1
ORDER NO. CH-3056 **$99.95**

INFRARED SPECTROSCOPY
George, McIntyre
WILEY
ISBN 0471-91383-9
ORDER NO. CH-4105 **$38.95**

TECHNICAL AND SCIENTIFIC BOOKS

KIRK-OTHMER ENCYCLOPEDIA OF CHEMICAL TECHNOLOGY 3RD ED.
ISBN# 0-471-80104-6
Editorial Board: Herman F. Mark, Polytechnic Institute of New York; Donald F. Othmer, Polytechnic Institute of New York; Charles G. Overberger, University of Michigan; and Glenn T. Seaborg, University of California, Berkeley

The 3RD ED. of the "bible" of chemical technology is now available in 26 volumes, including Index and Supplement.
Complete 26-Volume Set: $4,650.00
Price per volume purchased separately: $200.00

ORDER NO. CH-4000

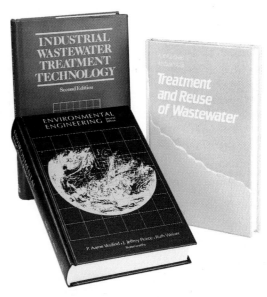

RECENT DEVELOPMENTS IN CHEMICAL PROCESS AND PLANT DESIGN
Liu, McGee, Epperly
WILEY
ISBN 0-471-84780-1
ORDER NO. CM-0506 **$80.00**

PUMP HANDBOOK, 2ND ED.
Karassik, Krutzsch, Fraser, Messina
MCGRAW-HILL
ISBN 0-07-033302-5
ORDER NO. ME-0341 **$96.00**

THE PROPERTIES OF GASES & LIQUIDS, 4TH ED.
Reid, Prausnitz, Poling
MCGRAW-HILL
ISBN 0-07-051799-1
ORDER NO. CM-0142 **$56.00**

FUNDAMENTAL PROCESS CONTROL
Prett, Garcia
BUTTERWORTHS
ISBN 0-409-90082-6
ORDER NO. CM-0492 **$39.95**

METERING PUMPS
Poynton
MARCEL DEKKER
ISBN 0-8247-1759-7
ORDER NO. MS-0919 **$59.75**

INDUSTRIAL WASTEWATER TREATMENT TECHNOLOGY, 2ND ED.
Patterson
BUTTERWORTHS
ISBN 0-409-90002-8
ORDER NO. CM-4012 **$64.95**

ENVIRONMENTAL ENGINEERING
Vesilind, Peirce, Weiner
BUTTERWORTHS
ISBN 0-409-90050-8
ORDER NO. CE-0652 **$39.95**

TREATMENT AND REUSE OF WASTEWATER
Biswas, Arar
BUTTERWORTHS
ISBN 0-408-02335-X
ORDER NO. GE-0654 **$90.00**

Chemical Engineering

PERRY'S CHEMICAL ENGINEERS' HANDBOOK, 6TH ED.
Perry, Green
MCGRAW-HILL
ISBN 0-07-049479-7
ORDER NO. CM-0102 **$105.00**

CHEMICAL PROCESS EQUIPMENT, SELECTION AND DESIGN
Walas
BUTTERWORTHS
ISBN 0-409-90131-8
ORDER NO. CM-0490 **$89.95**

THERMOMECHANICAL PROCESSING OF HIGH STRENGTH LOW ALLOY STEELS
Tamura, Ouchi, Tanaka, Sekine
BUTTERWORTHS
ISBN 0-408-11034-1
ORDER NO. CM-0497 **$120.00**

LUBRICATION FUNDAMENTALS
Wills
MARCEL DEKKER
ISBN 0-8247-6976-7
ORDER NO. CM-0486 **$69.75**

$89.95

$105.00

$120.00

$69.75

HANDLING OF BULK SOLIDS, THEORY AND PRACTICE
Shamtou
BUTTERWORTHS
ISBN 0-407-01180-3
ORDER NO. CM-0494 **$49.95**

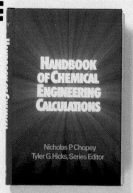

HANDBOOK OF CHEMICAL ENGINEERING CALCULATIONS
Chopey, Hicks
MCGRAW-HILL
ISBN 0-07-10805-6
ORDER NO. CM-0100 **$62.00**

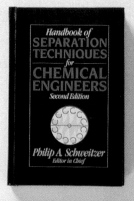

HANDBOOK OF SEPARATION TECHNIQUES FOR CHEMICAL ENGINEERS, 2ND ED.
Schweitzer
MCGRAW-HILL
ISBN 0-07-055808-6
ORDER NO. CH-3081 **$79.50**

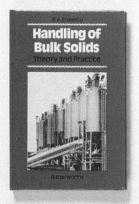

HAWLEY'S CONDENSED CHEMICAL DICTIONARY, 11TH ED.
Sax, Lewis
VAN NOSTRAND REINHOLD
ISBN 0-442-28097-1
ORDER NO. CM-0177 **$57.95**

CONSTITUTIVE EQUATIONS FOR POLYMER MELTS AND SOLUTIONS
Larson
BUTTERWORTHS
ISBN 0-409-90119-9
ORDER NO. CM-0491 **$39.95**

CHEMICAL INSTRUMENTATION: A SYSTEMATIC APPROACH, 3RD ED.
Strobel, Heineman
WILEY
ISBN 0471-61223-5
ORDER NO. CM-0512 **$49.95**

SHELL PROCESS CONTROL WORKSHOP
Prett, Morari
BUTTERWORTHS
ISBN 0-409-90136-9
ORDER NO. CM-0496 **$45.00**

ΩE OMEGA Recommended

Chemical Engineering

RUBBER COMPOUNDING, PRINCIPLES, MATERIALS, AND TECHNIQUES
Barlow
MARCEL DEKKER
ISBN 0-8247-7851-0
ORDER NO. CM-0488 **$99.75**

PLASTICS TECHNOLOGY HANDBOOK
Chanda, Roy
MARCEL DEKKER
ISBN 0-8247-7851-0
ORDER NO. CM-0487 **$115.00**

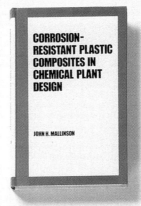

CORROSION RESISTANT PLASTIC COMPOSITES IN CHEMICAL PLANT DESIGN
Mallinson
MARCEL DEKKER
ISBN 0-8247-7687-9
ORDER NO. CM-0484 **$99.75**

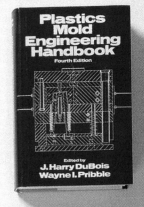

PLASTICS MOLD ENGINEERING HANDBOOK, 4TH ED.
DuBois, Pribble
VAN NOSTRAND REINHOLD
ISBN 0-442-21897-4
ORDER NO. CM-0469 **$59.95**

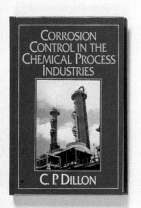

CORROSION CONTROL IN THE CHEMICAL PROCESS INDUSTRIES
Dillion
MCGRAW-HILL
ISBN 0-07-016940-3
ORDER NO. CM-0112 **$48.00**

HANDBOOK OF FILLERS FOR PLASTICS
Katz, Milewski
VAN NOSTRAND REINHOLD
ISBN 0-442-26024-5
ORDER NO. CM-0465 **$69.95**

HANDBOOK OF REINFORCEMENTS FOR PLASTICS
Milewski, Katz
VAN NOSTRAND REINHOLD
ISBN 0-442-26475-5
ORDER NO. CM-0468 **$69.95**

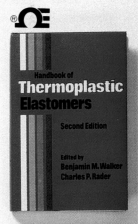

HANDBOOK OF THERMOPLASTIC ELASTOMERS, 2ND ED.
Walker, Rader
VAN NOSTRAND REINHOLD
ISBN 0-442-29184-1
ORDER NO. CH-3080 **$86.95**

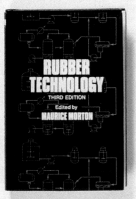

RUBBER TECHNOLOGY, 3RD ED.
Morton
VAN NOSTRAND REINHOLD
ISBN 0-442-26422-4
ORDER NO. CM-0464 **$42.95**

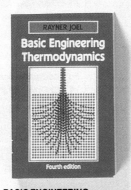

BASIC ENGINEERING THERMODYNAMICS, 4TH ED.
Joel
WILEY
ISBN 0-470-21075-3
ORDER NO. ME-0834 **$34.95**

PLASTICS ENGINEERING HANDBOOK, 4TH ED.
Frados
VAN NOSTRAND REINHOLD
ISBN 0-442-22469-9
ORDER NO. MM-0232 **$62.95**

To Order, Call Toll-Free
Book Hot Line (to Order Books Only)
1-800-222-BooK ™
1-800-222-2665

For Instruments and Books
1-800-TC-OMEGA
1-800-82 66342

In CT Dial (203) 359-1660

ΩE OMEGA Recommended

FILTRATION, PRINCIPLES AND PRACTICES PART II
Orr
MARCEL DEKKER
ISBN 0-8247-6763-2
ORDER NO. CM-0485   **$99.75**

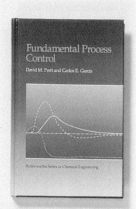

FUNDAMENTAL PROCESS CONTROL
Prett, Garcia
BUTTERWORTHS
ISBN 0-409-90082-6
ORDER NO. CM-0492   **$39.95**

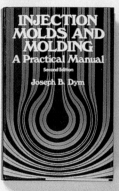

INJECTION MOLDS AND MOLDING, A PRACTICAL MANUAL, 2ND ED.
Dym
VAN NOSTRAND REINHOLD
ISBN 0-442-21785-4
ORDER NO. CM-0463   **$44.95**

PHASE EQUILIBRIA IN CHEMICAL ENGINEERING
Walas
BUTTERWORTHS
ISBN 0-409-95162-5
ORDER NO. CM-0495   **$57.95**

GAS SEPARATION BY ADSORPTION PROCESS
Yang
BUTTERWORTHS
ISBN 0-409-90004-4
ORDER NO.CM-0493   **$54.95**

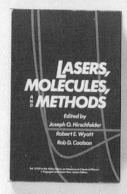

LASERS, MOLECULES, AND METHODS
Hirschfelder, Wyatt, Coalson
WILEY
ISBN 0-471-62457-8
ORDER NO. CM-0504   **$125.00**

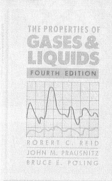

THE PROPERTIES OF GASES & LIQUIDS, 4TH ED.
Reid, Prausnitz, Poling
MCGRAW-HILL
ISBN 0-07-051799-1
ORDER NO. CM-0142   **$56.00**

STATISTICAL THERMODYNAMICS OF NONEQUILIBRIUM PROCESSES
Keizer
SPRINGER-VERLAG
ISBN 0-387-96501-7
ORDER NO. ST-0611   **$54.00**

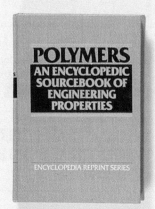

POLYMERS, AN ENCYCLOPEDIC SOURCEBOOK OF ENGINEERING PROPERTIES
Kroschwitz
WILEY
ISBN 0-471-85652-5
ORDER NO. GE-0501   **$67.95**

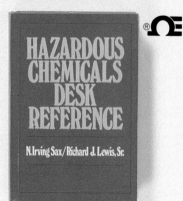

HAZARDOUS CHEMICALS DESK REFERENCE
Sax, Lewis
VAN NOSTRAND REINHOLD
ISBN 0-442-28208-7
ORDER NO. CM-0452   **$69.95**

ΩE **OMEGA Recommended**

Chemical Engineering

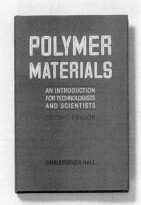

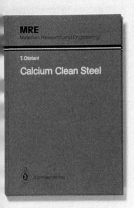

CALCIUM CLEAN STEEL
Ototani
SPRINGER-VERLAG
ISBN 0-387-16346-8
ORDER NO. MM-0636 **$84.00**

POLYMERS MATERIALS, AN INTRODUCTION FOR TECHNOLOGISTS AND SCIENTISTS, 2ND ED.
Hall
WILEY
ISBN 0-470-21092-3
ORDER NO. GE-0546 **$39.95**

SURFACTANTS IN CHEMICAL/ PROCESS ENGINEERING
Wasan, Ginn, Shah
MARCEL DEKKER
ISBN 0-8247-7830-8
ORDER NO. CM-0489 **$99.75**

BATCH PROCESS AUTOMATION
Rosenof, Ghosh
VAN NOSTRAND REINHOLD
ISBN 0-442-27708-3
ORDER NO. CM0462 **$44.00**

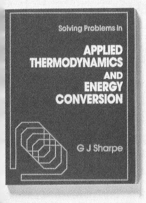

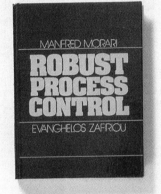

SOLVING PROBLEMS IN APPLIED THERMODYNAMICS AND ENERGY CONVERSION
Sharpe
WILEY
ISBN 0-582-28647-6
ORDER NO. ME-0730 **21.95**

ROBUST PROCESS CONTROL
Morari, Zafiriou
PRENTICE HALL
ISBN 0-13-782153-0
ORDER NO. CM-0505 **$45.00**

VISCOUS FLOWS, THE PRACTICAL USE OF THEORY
Churchill
BUTTERWORTHS
ISBN 0-409-95185-4
ORDER NO. CM-0498 **52.95**

CORROSION AND CORROSION PROTECTION HANDBOOK, 2ND ED.
Schweitzer
MARCEL DEKKER
ISBN 0-8247-7998-3
ORDER NO. CM-0482 **84.00**

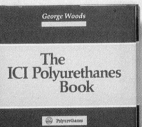

THE ICI POLYURETHANES BOOK
Woods
WILEY
ISBN 0-471-914266
ORDER NO. CM-0508 **$74.95**

CORROSION RESISTANCE TABLES, METALS, PLASTICS, NONMETALICS, AND RUBBER, 2ND ED.
Schweitzer
MARCEL DEKKER
ISBN 0-8247-7541-4
ORDER NO. CM-0483 **$185.00**

RECENT DEVELOPMENTS IN CHEMICAL PROCESS AND PLANT DESIGN
Liu, McGee, Epperly
WILEY
ISBN 0-471-84780-1
ORDER NO. CM-0506 **$80.00**

ΩE OMEGA Recommended

Chemistry/Chemical Engineering

KIRK-OTHMER ENCYCLOPEDIA OF CHEMICAL TECHNOLOGY 3RD ED.
Editorial Board: Herman F. Mark, Polytechnic Institute of New York; Donald F. Othmer, Polytechnic Institute of New York; Charles G. Overberger, University of Michigan; and Glenn T. Seaborg, University of California, Berkeley

The 3RD ED. of the "bible" of chemical technology is now available in 26 volumes, including Index and Supplement. Complete 26-Volume Set: $4,650.00.
Price per volume purchased separately: $200.00
ISBN 0-471-80104-6
ORDER NO. CH-4000 $4,650.00

Complete Set $4,650.00

Price per volume if purchased separately $200.00 each. Call Book of Books for details!

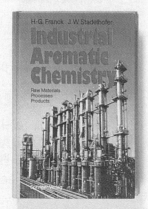

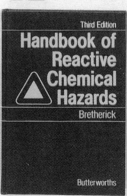

INDUSTRIAL AROMATIC CHEMISTRY
Franck, Stadelhofer
SPRINGER-VERLAG
ISBN 0-387-18940-8
ORDER NO. CM-0509 $79.00

SUPERCONDUCTIVITY SOURCEBOOK
Hunt
WILEY
ISBN 0-471-61706-7
ORDER NO. CH-4017 $34.95

HANDBOOK OF REACTIVE CHEMICAL HAZARDS, 3RD ED.
Bretherick
BUTTERWORTHS
ISBN 0-408-01388-5
ORDER NO. CM-0480 $128.00

Chemistry/Chemical Engineering

Why You Should Order From Book of Books®

✓ No Shipping Charges on Pre-Paid Orders
✓ No Handling Charges Ever
✓ One Source for All Your Technical and Scientific Books
✓ Order by Calling Toll-Free in the USA

THE CHEMIST'S COMPANION
Gordon, Ford
WILEY
ISBN 0-471-31590-7
ORDER NO. CH-0169 **$55.00**

FUNDAMENTALS OF CHEMICAL REACTION ENGINEERING, 2ND ED.
Holland, Anthony
PRENTICE HALL
ISBN 0-13-335639-6
ORDER NO. CE-0651 **$66.00**

FIRST-ORDER PARTIAL DIFFERENTIAL EQUATIONS: VOLUME II
Ku Rhee, Aris, Amundson
PRENTICE HALL
ISBN 0-13-319237-7
ORDER NO. GE-0505 **$60.00**

THE MEASUREMNET OF APPEARANCE, 2ND ED.
Hunter, Harold
WILEY
ISBN 0-471-83006-2
ORDER NO. CH-4018 **$65.00**

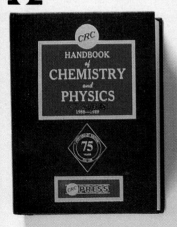

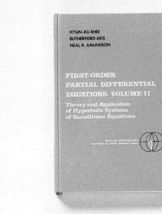

HANDBOOK OF CHEMISTRY AND PHYSICS, 70TH ED.
Weast
CRC PRESS
ISBN 469-8493-0469-5
ORDER NO. SD-0503 **$95.00**

HANDBOOK ON TOXICITY OF INORGANIC COMPOUNDS
Seiler, Sigel, Sigel
MARCEL DEKKER
ISBN 0-8247-7727-1
ORDER NO. CH-4006 **$195.00**

LANGE'S HANDBOOK OF CHEMISTRY, 13TH ED.
Dean
MCGRAW-HILL
ISBN 0-07-016192-5
ORDER NO. CH-1000 **$73.00**

ΩE OMEGA Recommended

Chemistry

$114.00

CHEMISTRY OF CLAYS AND CLAY MINERALS

Edited by A.C.D.NEWMAN

VOGEL'S QUALITATIVE INORGANIC ANALYSIS
REVISED BY G SVEHLA
SIXTH EDITION

$34.95

PRACTICAL SPECTROSCOPY SERIES   VOLUME 6

Infrared Microspectroscopy
Theory and Applications

edited by
Robert G. Messerschmidt · Matthew A. Harthcock

$85.00

CHEMISTRY OF CLASYS AND MINERALS
Newman
WILEY
ISBN 0-471-01141-X
ORDER NO. CH-3052 **$114.00**

VOGEL'S QUALITATIVE INORGANIC ANALYSIS, 6th Ed.
Svehla
WILEY
ISBN 0-582-45090-X
ORDER NO. CH-3070 **$34.95**

INFRARED MICROSPECTROSCOPY, THEORY AND APPLICATIONS
Messerschmidt, Harthcock
MARCEL DEKKER
ISBN 0-8247-8003-5
ORDER NO. CH-4007 **$85.00**

ΩE OMEGA Recommended

COMPUTERIZED QUALITY CONTROL
Programs for the analytical laboratory
T. F. Hartley

COMPUTERIZED QUALITY CONTROL
Hartley
WILEY
ISBN-0-470-20761-2
ORDER NO. CH-3069 **$44.95**

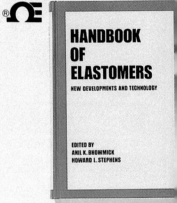

Quantitative Analysis using Chromatographic Techniques
E.KATZ

QUANTITATIVE ANALYSIS USING CHROMATOGRAPHIC TECHNIQU
Katz
WILEY
ISBN 0-471-91406-1
ORDER NO. CH-3056 **$99.9**

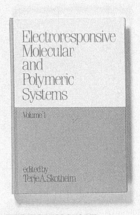

Electroresponsive Molecular and Polymeric Systems
Volume 1

edited by
Terje A.Skotheim

ELECTRORESPONSIVE MOLECULAR AND POLYMERIC SYSTEMS, VOLUME 1
Skotheim
MARCEL DEKKER
ISBN 0-8247-7968-1
ORDER NO. CH-4002 **$99.95**

®ΩE

HANDBOOK OF ELASTOMERS
NEW DEVELOPMENTS AND TECHNOLOGY

EDITED BY
ANIL K. BHOWMICK
HOWARD L. STEPHENS

HANDBOOK OF ELASTOMERS, N DEVELOPMENTS AND TECHNOLOGY
Bhowmick, Stephens
MARCEL DEKKER
ISBN 0-8247-7800-6
ORDER NO. CH-4005 **$150.**

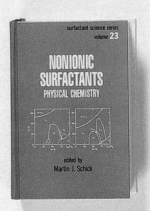

surfactant science series
volume 23
NONIONIC SURFACTANTS
PHYSICAL CHEMISTRY

edited by
Martin J. Schick

NONIONIC SURFACTANTS PHYSICAL CHEMISTRY, VOLUME 23
Schick
MARCEL DEKKER
ISBN 0-8247-7530-9
ORDER NO. CH-4009 **$225.00**

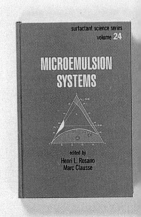

surfactant science series
volume 24
MICROEMULSION SYSTEMS

edited by
Henri L. Rosano
Marc Clausse

MICROEMULSION SYSTEMS, VOLUME 24
Rosano, Clausse
MARCEL DEKKER
ISBN 0-8247-7439-6
ORDER NO. CH-4008 **$120.**

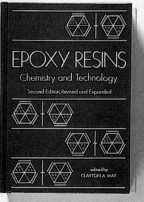

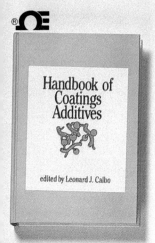

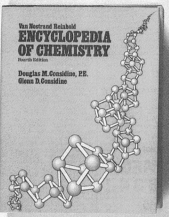

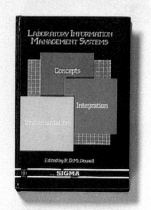

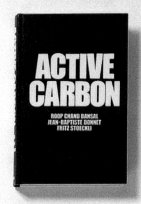

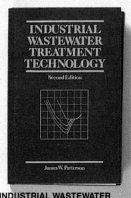

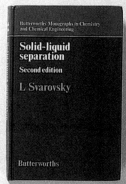

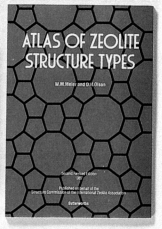

**HANDBOOK OF COATINGS
ADDITIVES**
Calbo
MARCEL DEKKER
ISBN 0-8247-7561-9
ORDER NO. CH-4004 **$149.75**

**LABORATORY INFORMATION
MANAGEMENT SYSTEMS**
McDowall
WILEY
ISBN 0-470-20947-X
ORDER NO. CS-1123 **$59.95**

**BIOMEMBRANES, MOLECULAR
STRUCTURE AND FUNCTION**
Gennis
SPRINGER-VERLAG
ISBN 0-387-96760-5
ORDER NO. **$59.00**

ACTIVE CARBON
Bansal, Donnet, Stoeckli
MARCEL DEKKER
ISBN 0-8247-7842-1
ORDER NO. CH-4001 **$125.00**

**EPOXY RESINS, CHEMISTRY AND
TECHNOLOGY, 2ND ED.**
May
MARCEL DEKKER
ISBN 0-8247-7690-9
ORDER NO. CH-4003 **$79.75**

**INDUSTRIAL WASTEWATER
TREATMENT TECHNOLOGY, 2ND ED.**
Patterson
BUTTERWORTHS
ISBN 0-409-90002-8
ORDER NO. CM-4012 **$64.95**

**HANDBOOK OF ORGANIC
CHEMISTRY**
Dean
MCGRAW-HILL
ISBN 0-07-016193-3
ORDER NO. CH-4023 **$78.00**

SOLID-LIQUID SEPARATION, 2ND ED.
Svarovsky
BUTTERWORTHS
ISBN 0-408-70943-X
ORDER NO. CM-4013 **$105.00**

**VAN NOSTRAND REINHOLD
ENCYCLOPEDIA OF CHEMISTRY
4TH, ED.**
Considine, Considine
ISBN 0-442-22572-5
ORDER NO. CM-0160 **$107.95**

**ATLAS OF ZEOLITE STRUCTURE
TYPES**
Meier, Olson
BUTTERWORTHS
ISBN 0-408-02740-1
ORDER NO. CH-4011 **$36.00**

ΩE OMEGA Recommended

Chemistry/Chemical Engineering

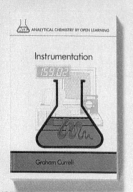

INSTRUMENTATION
Currell
WILEY
ISBN 0-471-91369-3
ORDER NO. GE-0451 **$32.95**

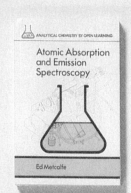

ATOMIC ABSORPTION AND EMISSION SPECTROSCOPY
Metcalfe
WILEY
ISBN 0-471-91385-5
ORDER NO. CM-0513 **$27.95**

HIGH PERFORMANCE LIQUID CHROMATOGRAPHY
Lindsay
WILEY
ISBN 0-471-91373-1
ORDER NO. CM-0502 **$24.95**

SAMPLE PRETREATMENT AND SEPARATION
Anderson
WILEY
ISBN 0-471-91361-8
ORDER NO. CH-4016 **$41.95**

MEASUREMENT, STATISTICS AND COMPUTATION
McCormick, Roach
WILEY
ISBN 0-471-91367-7
ORDER NO. MA-1119 **$42.95**

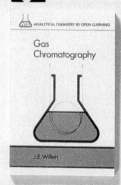

GAS CHROMATOGRAPHY
Willet
WILEY
ISBN 0-471-91332-4
ORDER NO. CM-0499 **$24.95**

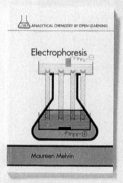

ELECTROPHORESIS
Melvin
WILEY
ISBN 0-471-91375-8
ORDER NO. EE-1084 **$24.95**

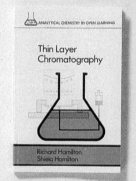

THIN LAYER CHROMATOGRAPHY
Hamilton, Hamilton
WILEY
ISBN 0-471-91377-4
ORDER NO. CH-4020 **$24.95**

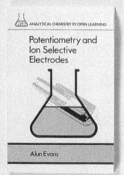

POTENTIOMETRY AND ION SELECTIVE ELECTRODES
Evans
WILEY
ISBN 0-471-91393-6
ORDER NO. EE-1086 **$27.95**

MASS SPECTROMETRY
Davis, Frearson
WILEY
ISBN 0-471-91389-8
ORDER NO. CH-4015 **39.95**

To Order, Call Toll-Free
Book Hot Line (to Order Books Only)
1-800-222-BooK™
1-800-222-2665

For Instruments and Books
1-800-TC-OMEGA
1-800-82 6 6342

In CT Dial (203) 359-1660

ΩΕ OMEGA Recommended

Y-13

Civil Engineering

ENVIRONMENTAL ENGINEERING
esilind, Peirce, Weiner
UTTERWORTHS
BN 0-409-90050-8
ORDER NO. CE-0652 **$39.95**

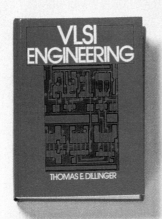

VLSI ENGINEERING
Dillinger
PRENTICE HALL
ISBN 0-13-942731-7
ORDER NO. CS-1232 **$56.00**

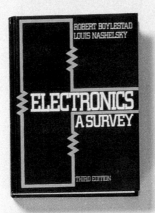

ELECTRONICS, A SURVEY, 3RD ED.
Boylestad, Nashelsky
PRENTICE HALL
ISBN 0-13-252438-4
ORDER NO. EE-1099 **$43.00**

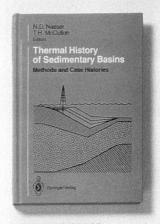

**THERMAL HISTORY OF
SEDIMENTARY BASINS**
Naeser, McColloh
SPRINGER-VERLAG
ISBN 0-387-96702-8
ORDER NO. CE-0659 **$64.00**

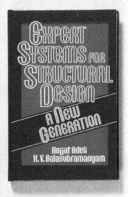

**XPERT SYSTEMS FOR
TRUCTURAL DESIGN**
deli, Balasubramanyam
RENTICE HALL
BN 0-13-295643-8
ORDER NO. CE-0655 **$48.00**

**TREATMENT AND REUSE OF
WASTEWATER**
Biswas, Arar
BUTTERWORTHS
ISBN 0-408-02335-X
ORDER NO. GE-0654 **$90.00**

**BUILDING STRUCTURAL DESIGN
HANDBOOK**
White, Salmon
WILEY
ISBN 0-471-08150-7
ORDER NO. CE-0603 **$84.95**

CONCRETE TECHNOLOGY
Neville, Brooks
WILEY
ISBN 0-470-20716-7
ORDER NO. CE-0601 **$39.95**

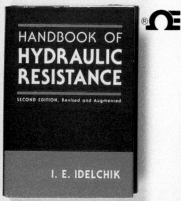

**ANDBOOK OF HYDRAULIC
ESISTANCE**
elchik
EMISPHERE
BN 0-89116-284-4
RDER NO. ME-0614 **$89.95**

**HANDBOOK OF VENTILATION FOR
CONTAMINANT CONTROL**
McDermott
BUTTERWORTHS
ISBN 0-250-40641-1
ORDER NO. CE-0653 **$45.00**

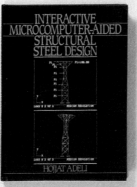

**INTERACTIVE MICROCOMPUTER-
AIDED STRUCTURAL DESIGN**
Adeli
PRENTICE HALL
ISBN 0-13-469982-3
ORDER NO. CE-0658 **$48.00**

ΩE OMEGA Recommended

APPLIED RELIABILITY
Tobiad, Trindade
VAN NOSTRAND REINHOLD
ISBN 0-442-28310-5
ORDER NO. MS-0902   **$36.95**

QUALITY CONTROL FOR PROFIT
Lister, Enrick, Mottley
MARCEL DEKKER
ISBN 0-8247-7424-8
ORDER NO. GE-0509   **$65.00**

PROJECT COST DATABANKS
Miller
BUTTERWORTHS
ISBN 0-408-02630-8
ORDER NO. GE-0517   **$59.95**

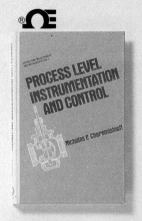

**PROCESS LEVEL
INSTRUMENTATION AND CONTROL**
Cheremisinoff
MARCEL DEKKER
ISBN 0-8247-1212-9
ORDER NO. GE-0508   **$69.75**

**THE ART AND SCIENCE OF
GEOTECHNICAL ENGINEERING**
Cording, Hall, Haltiwanger, Hendron,
Mesri
PRENTICE HALL
ISBN 0-13-047655-2
ORDER NO. MS-0925   **$48.00**

**PROGRAMMABLE CONTROLLERS
FOR FACTORY AUTOMATION**
Johnson
MARCEL DEKKER
ISBN 0-8247-7674-7
ORDER NO. EE-1110   **$69.75**

STATISTICAL PROCESS CONTROL
Oakland
WILEY
ISBN 0-470-20360-9
ORDER NO. CM-0459   **$54.95**

**MANAGING TECHNOLOGY IN THE
DECENTRALIZED FIRM**
Rubenstein
WILEY
ISBN 0-471-61024-0
ORDER NO. GE-0542   **$49.95**

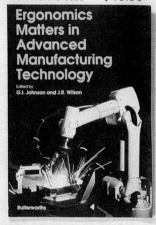

**ERGONOMICS MATTERS IN
ADVANCED MANUFACTURING
TECHNOLOGY**
Johnson, Wilson
BUTTERWORTHS
ISBN 0-408-02422-4
ORDER NO. GE-0513   **$45.00**

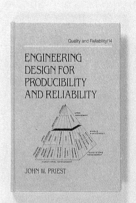

**ENGINEERING DESIGN FOR
PRODUCTIVITY AND RELIABILITY**
Priest
MARCEL DEKKER
ISBN 0-8247-7708-5
ORDER NO. GE-0506   **$79.75**

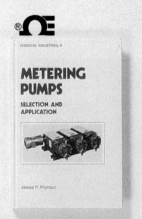

METERING PUMPS
Poynton
MARCEL DEKKER
ISBN 0-8247-1759-7
ORDER NO. MS-0919   **$59.75**

**PROJECT MANAGEMENT; A
SYSTEMS APPROACH TO
PLANNING, SCHEDULING AND
CONTROLLING, 3RD ED.**
Kerzner
VAN NOSTRAND REINHOLD
ISBN 0-442-20751-4
ORDER NO. GE-0210   **$44.95**

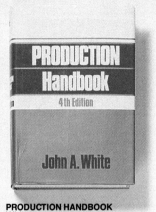

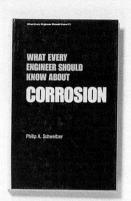

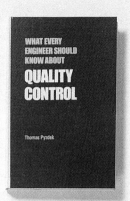

PRODUCTION HANDBOOK
White
WILEY
ISBN 0-471-86347-5
ORDER NO. MS-0912 **$82.95**

WHAT EVERY ENGINEER SHOULD KNOW ABOUT CORROSION
Schweitzer
MARCEL DEKKER
ISBN 0-8247-7755-7
ORDER NO. MM-0801 **$35.00**

WHAT EVERY ENGINEER SHOULD KNOW ABOUT QUALITY CONTROL
Pyzdek
MARCEL DEKKER
ISBN 0-8247-7966-5
ORDER NO. GE-0512 **$49.75**

HANDBOOK OF INDUSTRIAL ENGINEERING
Salvendy
WILEY
ISBN 0-471-05841-6
ORDER NO. MS-0178 **$105.00**

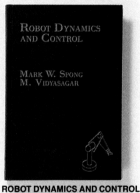

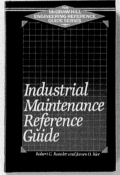

MANAGING ENGINEERING AND CONSTRUCTION OF SMALL PROJECTS
Westney
MARCEL DEKKER
ISBN 0-8247-7417-5
ORDER NO. GE-0507 **$55.00**

STATISTICAL QUALITY CONTROL FOR MANUFACTURING MANAGERS
Messina
WILEY
ISBN 0-471-85774-2
ORDER NO. MS-0901 **$49.95**

ROBOT DYNAMICS AND CONTROL
Spong, Vidyasagar
WILEY
ISBN 0-471-61243-X
ORDER NO. ME-0841 **$59.95**

INDUSTRIAL MAINTENANCE REFERENCE GUIDE
Rosaler, Rice
MCGRAW-HILL
ISBN 0-07-052162-X
ORDER NO. MS-0914 **$39.50**

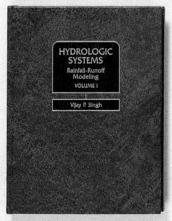

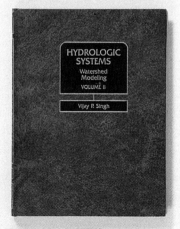

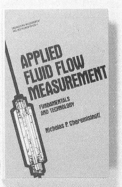

HYDROLOGIC SYSTEMS RAINFALL-RUNOFF MODELING VOL 1
Singh
PRENTICE HALL
ISBN 0-13-448051-1
ORDER NO. CE-0656 **$57.00**

HYDROLOGIC SYSTEMS WATERSHED MODELING VOL 2
Singh
PRENTICE HALL
ISBN 0-13-448028-7
ORDER NO. CE-0657 **$54.00**

APPLIED FLUID FLOW MEASUREMENT
Cheremisinoff
MARCEL DEKKER
ISBN 0-8247-6871-X
ORDER NO. MS-0915 **$69.75**

STATISTICAL PROCESS CONTROL IN AUTOMATED MANUFACTURING
Keats, Huble
MARCEL DEKKER
ISBN 0-8247-7889-8
ORDER NO. ST-0608 **$69.75**

Mechanical Engineering

**VIBRATION WITH CONTROL,
MEASUREMENT AND STABILITY**
Inman
PRENTICE HALL
ISBN 0-130942798-8
ORDER NO. ME-0832 **$48.00**

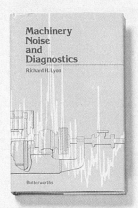

**MACHINERY NOISE AND
DIAGNOSTICS**
Lyon
BUTTERWORTHS
ISBN 0-409-90101-6
ORDER NO. ME-0809 **$42.95**

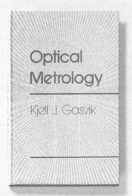

OPTICAL METROLOGY
Gasvik
WILEY
ISBN 0-471-91246-8
ORDER NO. ME-0733 **$54.95**

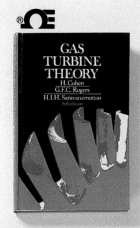

GAS TURBINE THEORY
Cohen, Rogers
WILEY
ISBN 0-470-20705-1
ORDER NO. ME-0709 **$49.95**

**MECHANICAL ENGINEERS'
HANDBOOK**
Kutz
WILEY
ISBN 0-471-08817-X
ORDER NO. ME-0013 **$89.95**

**FIBER-REINFORCED COMPOSITES
MATERIALS, MANUFACTURING,
AND DESIGN**
Mallick
MARCEL DEKKER
ISBN 0-8247-7796-4
ORDER NO. MM-0961 **$65.00**

ON-LINE PROCESS ANALYZERS
Nichols
WILEY
ISBN 0-471-86608-3
ORDER NO. ME-0481 **$54.91**

**HANDBOOK OF MECHANICS,
MATERIALS, AND STRUCTURES**
Blake
WILEY
ISBN 0-471-86239-8
ORDER NO. ME-0003 **$72.95**

**STRESS CONCENTRATION
FACTORS**
Peterson
WILEY
ISBN 0-471-68329-9
ORDER NO. ME-0090 **$64.95**

MECHANICAL RELIABILITY
Carter
WILEY
ISBN 0-470-20694-2
ORDER NO. ME-0718 **$69.95**

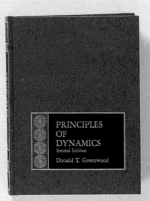

PRINCIPLES OF DYNAMICS
Greenwood
PRENTICE HALL
ISBN 0-13-709981-9
ORDER NO. ME-0830 **$58.00**

**THEORY OF VIBRATION WITH
APPLICATIONS**
Thomson
PRENTICE HALL
ISBN 0-13-914532-X
ORDER NO. ME-0831 **$53.00**

Mechanical Engineering

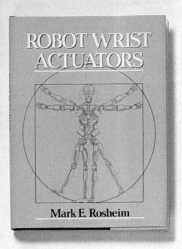

ROBOT WRIST ACTUATORS
Rosheim
WILEY
ISBN 0-471-61595-1
ORDER NO. MS-0933 **$54.95**

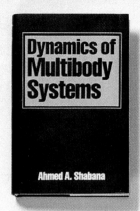

DYNAMICS OF MULTIBODY SYSTEMS
Shabana
WILEY
ISBN 0-471-61494-7
ORDER NO. GE-0556 **$54.95**

ADVANCED COMPOSITE MOLD MAKING
Morena
VAN NOSTRAND REINHOLD
ISBN 0-442-26414-3
ORDER NO. ME-0823 **$53.95**

PRESSURE VESSEL DESIGN HANDBOOK
Bednar
VAN NOSTRAND REINHOLD
ISBN 0-422-21385-9
ORDER NO. ME-0370 **$51.95**

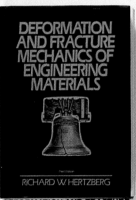

DEFORMATION AND FRACTURE MECHANICS OF ENGINEERING MATERIALS
Hertzberg
WILEY
ISBN 0-471-63589-8
ORDER NO. MM-0013 **$52.50**

FLUID MECHANICS FOR ENGINEERING TECHNOLOGY
Granet
PRENTICE HALL
ISBN 0-13-322876-2
ORDER NO. ME-0828 **$44.00**

MARKS' STANDARD HANDBOOK FOR MECHANICAL ENGINEERS
Avallone, Baumeister
MCGRAW-HILL
ISBN 0-07-004127-X
ORDER NO. ME-0301 **$92.00**

COMBUSTION
Classman
ACADEMIC PRESS
ISBN 0-12-285851-4
ORDER NO. ME-0708 **$49.50**

DESIGN FOR ASSEMBLY
Swift
SPRINGER-VERLAG
ISBN 0-387-18929-7
ORDER NO. GE-0547 **$79.00**

SOLVING PROBLEMS IN SOLID MECHANICS VOL 1
Urry, Turner
WILEY
ISBN 0-470-20686-1
ORDER NO. ME-0732 **$26.95**

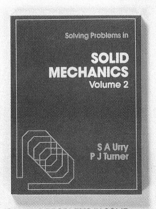

SOLVING PROBLEMS IN SOLID MECHANICS VOL 2
Urry, Turner
WILEY
ISBN 0-470-20687-X
ORDER NO. ME-0735 **$27.95**

PRESSURE GAUGE HANDBOOK
Harland
MARCEL DEKKER
ISBN 0-8247-7433-7
ORDER NO. CH-4051 **$55.00**

Mechanical Engineering

MCGRAW-HILL DICTIONARY OF MECHANICAL AND DESIGN ENGINEERING
Parker
MCGRAW-HILL
ISBN 0-07-045414-0
ORDER NO. ME-396 **$21.95**

STRUCTURAL ANALYSIS AND DESIGN OF PROCESS EQUIPMENT
Jawas, Farr
WILEY
ISBN 0-471-62471-3
ORDER NO. GE-0533 **$67.95**

WHAT EVERY ENGINEER SHOULD KNOW ABOUT FINITE ELEMENT ANALYSIS
Frauer
MARCEL DEKKER
ISBN 0-8247-7832-4
ORDER NO. MS-0920 **$39.75**

SELF-TUNING CONTROL 1
Gawthorp
WILEY
ISBN 0-471-91417-7
ORDER NO. ME-0835 **$82.95**

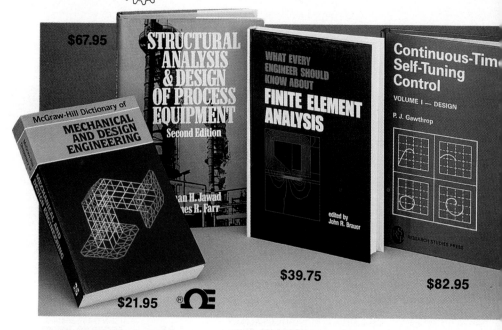

$67.95

$39.75

$82.95

$21.95

FRACTURE AT HIGH TEMPERATURES
Riedel
SPRINGER-VERLAG
ISBN 0-387-17271-8
ORDER NO. MM-0637 **$77.00**

RESIDUAL STRESS
Noyan
SPRINGER-VERLAG
ISBN 0-387-96378-2
ORDER NO. MM-0639 **$57.50**

INTRODUCTION TO RELIABILITY ENGINEERING
Lewis
WILEY
ISBN 0-471-81199-8
ORDER NO. ME-0734 **$63.50**

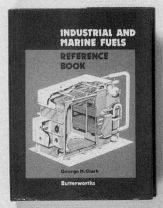

INDUSTRIAL AND MARINE FUELS REFERENCE BOOK
Clark
BUTTERWORTHS
ISBN 0-408-01488-1
ORDER NO. ME-0808 **$150.00**

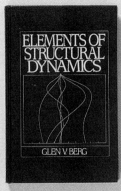

ELEMENTS OF STRUCTURAL DYNAMICS
Berg
PRENTICE HALL
ISBN 0-13-272493-6
ORDER NO. ME-0826 **$40.00**

APPLIED THERMODYNAMICS
Eastop, McConkey
WILEY
ISBN 0-470-20666-7
ORDER NO. ME-0737 **$36.95**

To Order, Call Toll-Free
Book Hot Line (to Order Books Only)
1-800-222-BOOK™
1-800-222-2665

For Instruments and Books
1-800-TC-OMEGA
1-800-82 6 6 342

In CT Dial (203) 359-1660

ΩE OMEGA Recommended

Mechanical Engineering

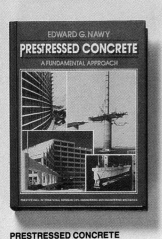

PRESTRESSED CONCRETE
Nawy
PRENTICE HALL
ISBN 0-13-698375-8
ORDER NO. ME-0829   **$58.00**

HEAT EXCHANGER DESIGN, 2ND ED
Fraas
WILEY
ISBN 0-471-62868-9
ORDER NO. ME-0208   **$59.95**

**TRANSPORT PROCESSES IN
CHEMICALLY REACTING FLOW
SYSTEMS**
Rosner
BUTTERWORTHS
ISBN 0-409-95178-1
ORDER NO. ME-0810   **$54.95**

**FUNDAMENTALS OF
TEMPERATURE, PRESSURE, AND
FLOW MEASUREMENTS**
Benedict
WILEY
ISBN 0-471-89383-8
ORDER NO. OP-6   **$69.95**

FLEXIBLE MANUFACTURING
Lenz
MARCEL DEKKER
ISBN 0-8247-7683-6
ORDER NO. MS-0917   **$79.95**

**FLOW MEASUREMENT FOR
ENGINEERS AND SCIENTISTS**
Cheremisinoff, Cheremisinoff
MARCEL DEKKER
ISBN 0-8247-7831-6
ORDER NO. MS-0918   **$99.75**

**ENGINEERING MECHANICS STATICS
AND DYNAMICS**
Sandor
PRENTICE HALL
ISBN 0-13-279092-0
ORDER NO. ME-0827   **$62.00**

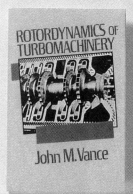

**ROTOR DYNAMICS OF
TURBOMACHINERY**
Vance
WILEY
ISBN 0-471-80258-1
ORDER NO. ME-0842   **$59.95**

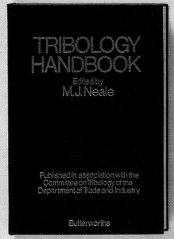

TRIBOLOGY HANDBOOK
Neale
BUTTERWORTHS
ISBN 0-408-00082-1
ORDER NO. ME-0811   **$125.00**

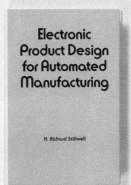

**ELECTRONIC PRODUCT DESIGN
FOR AUTOMATED MANUFACTURING**
Stillwell
MARCEL DEKKER
ISBN 0-8247-7937-1
ORDER NO. EE-1057   **$89.75**

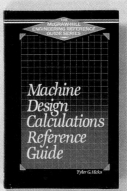

**MACHINE DESIGN CALCULATIONS
REFERENCE GUIDE**
Hicks
MCGRAW-HILL
ISBN 0-07-028799-6
ORDER NO. ME-0713   **$32.50**

**DESIGN OF REINFORCED
CONCRETE STRUCTURES**
Cowan
PRENTICE HALL
ISBN 0-13-201443-2
ORDER NO. ME-0825   **$42.00**

ΩE OMEGA Recommended

Mechanical Engineering

HANDBOOK OF ENGINEERING DESIGN
Cullum
BUTTERWORTHS
ISBN 0-408-00558-0
ORDER NO. ME-0807 **$85.00**

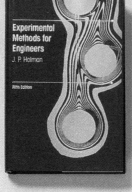

EXPERIMENTAL METHODS FOR ENGINEERS
Holman
MCGRAW-HILL
ISBN 0-07-029622-7
ORDER NO. ME-0822 **$44.95**

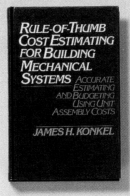

RULE-OF-THUMB COST ESTIMATING FOR BUILDING MECHANICAL SYSTEMS
Konkel
MCGRAW-HILL
ISBN 0-07-044957-0
ORDER NO. ME-0712 **$44.50**

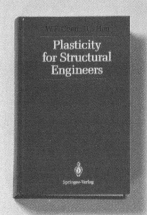

PLASTICITY FOR STRUCTURAL ENGINEERS
Chen, Han
SPRINGER-VERLAG
ISBN 0-387-96711-7
ORDER NO. MM-0638 **$59.00**

FUNDAMENTALS OF GEAR DESIGN
Drago
BUTTERWORTHS
ISBN 0-409-90127-X
ORDER NO. ME-0803 **$69.95**

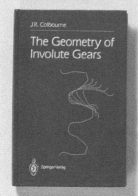

THE GEOMETRY OF INVOLUTE GEARS
Colbourne
SPRINGER-VERLAG
ISBN 0-387-96522-X
ORDER NO. MA-1113 **$60.00**

WELDING METALLURGY OF STAINLESS STEELS
Folkhard
SPRINGER-VERLAG
ISBN 0-387-82043-4
ORDER NO. MM-0640 **$50.00**

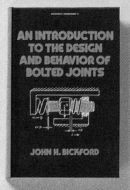

AN INTRODUCTION TO THE DESIGN AND BEHAVIOR OF BOLTED JOINTS
Bickford
MARCEL DEKKER
ISBN 0-8247-1508-X
ORDER NO. ME-0804 **$69.75**

SOLVING PROBLEMS IN FLUID MECHANICS VOL 1
Douglas
WILEY
ISBN 0-470-20775-2
ORDER NO. ME-0729 **$19.95**

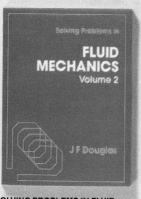

SOLVING PROBLEMS IN FLUID MECHANICS VOL 2
Douglas
WILEY
ISBN 0-470-20776-0
ORDER NO. ME-0731 **$19.95**

DESIGN OF MECHANICAL JOINTS
Blake
MARCEL DEKKER
ISBN 0-8247-7351-9
ORDER NO. CH-4050 **$85.00**

To Order, Call Toll-Free
Book Hot Line (to Order Books Only)
1-800-222-Book ™
1-800-222-2665

For Instruments and Books
1-800-TC-OMEGA
1-800-82 66342

In CT Dial (203) 359-1660

ΩE OMEGA Recommended

Electrical Engineering ⎯⋀⋀⋀⎯

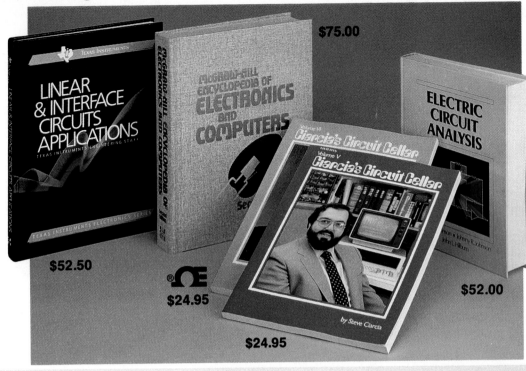

LINEAR & INTERFACE CIRCUITS APPLICATIONS
Texas Instr. Staff
MCGRAW-HILL
ISBN 0-07-063762-8
ORDER NO. EE-0441 **$52.50**

MCGRAW-HILL ENCYCLOPEDIA OF ELECTRONICS AND COMPUTERS
Parker
MCGRAW-HILL
ISBN 0-07-045499-X
ORDER NO. EE-0409 **$75.00**

CIARCIA'S CIRCUIT CELLAR VOL V
Ciarcia
MCGRAW-HILL
ISBN 0-07-010967-2
ORDER NO. CS-0225 **$24.95**

CIARCIA'S CIRCUIT CELLAR VOL VI
Ciarcia
MCGRAW-HILL
ISBN 0-07-010968-0
ORDER NO. EE-1050 **$24.95**

ELECTRIC CIRUIT ANALYSIS
Johnson, Johnson, Hilburn
PRENTICE HALL
ISBN 0-13-247776-9
ORDER NO. EE-1092 **$52.00**

$75.00

$52.50

$24.95

$24.95

$52.00

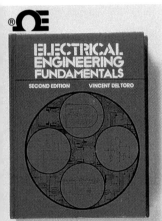

ELECTRICAL ENGINEERING FUNDAMENTALS, 2ND ED.
Del Toro
PRENTICE HALL
ISBN 0-13-2471313-0
ORDER NO. EE-1100 **$55.00**

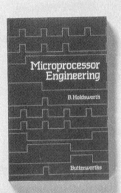

ELECTRONICS AND ELECTRONIC SYSTEMS
Olsen
BUTTERWORTHS
ISBN 0-408-01369-9
ORDER NO. EE-1070 **$54.95**

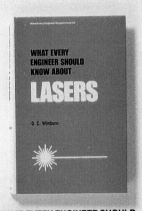

MICROPROCESSOR ENGINEERING
Holdsworth
BUTTERWORTHS
ISBN 0-408-01361-3
ORDER NO. EE-1072 **$39.95**

WHAT EVERY ENGINEER SHOULD KNOW ABOUT LASERS
Winburn
MARCEL DEKKER
ISBN 0-8247-7748-4
ORDER NO. EE-1065 **$35.00**

PRODUCTIVITY AND QUALITY IMPROVEMENT IN ELECTRONICS ASSEMBLY
Edosomwan, Ballakur
MCGRAW-HILL
ISBN 0-07-019026-7
ORDER NO. EE-1076 **$49.50**

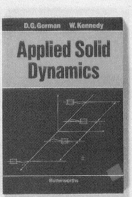

APPLIED SOLID DYNAMICS
Gorman, Kennedy
BUTTERWORTHS
ISBN 0-408-02309-0
ORDER NO. EE-1067 **$44.95**

LASERS IN MANUFACTURING
Luxon, Parker, Plotkowski
SPRINGER-VERLAG
ISBN 0-387-17427-3
ORDER NO. GE-0549 **$59.00**

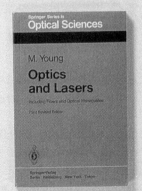

OPTICS AND LASERS
Young
SPRINGER-VERLAG
ISBN 0-387-16127-9
ORDER NO. GE-0550 **$38.00**

Ω**E OMEGA Recommended**

Electrical Engineering ─⋏⋏⋏─

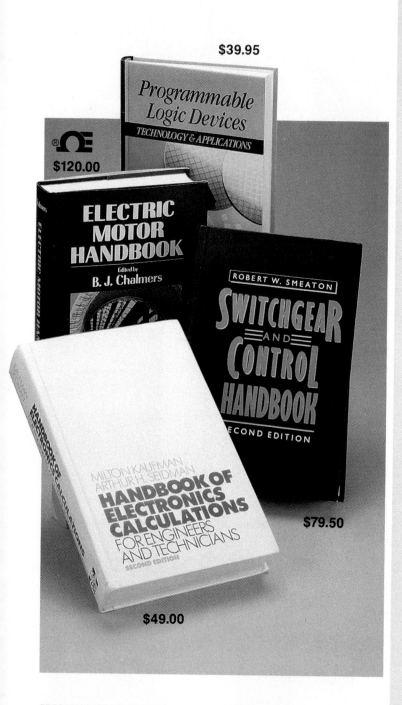

$39.95

$120.00

$79.50

$49.00

PROGRAMMABLE LOGIC DEVICES
Bostock
MCGRAW-HILL
ISBN 0-07-006611-6
ORDER NO. EE-1056 $39.95

ELECTRIC MOTOR HANDBOOK
Chalmers
BUTTERWORTHS
ISBN 0-408-00707-9
ORDER NO. EE-1069 $120.00

SWITCHGEAR AND CONTROL HANDBOOK
Smeaton
MCGRAW-HILL
ISBN 0-07-058449-4
ORDER NO. EE-1010 $79.50

HANDBOOK OF ELECTRONICS CALCULATIONS FOR ENGINEERS & TECHNICAL
Kaufman, Seidman
MCGRAW-HILL
ISBN 0-07-033528-1
ORDER NO. EE-0407 $49.00

PRINCIPLES OF FEEDBACK CONTROL FEEDBACK SYSTEM DESIGN VOL 1
Biernson
WILEY
ISBN 0-471-82167-5
ORDER NO. EE-1089 $69.95

PRINCIPLES OF FEEDBACK CONTROL ADVANCED CONTROL TOPICS VOL 2
Bierson
WILEY
ISBN 0-471-50120-4
ORDER NO. EE-1088 $59.

ELECTRONIC TRANSFORMERS AND CIRCUITS
Lee, Wilson, Carter
WILEY
ISBN 0-471-81976-X
ORDER NO. EE-1083 $54.95

ENGINEERING OPTICS
Lizuka
SPRINGER-VERLAG
ISBN 0-387-17131-2
ORDER NO. GE-0548 $44.

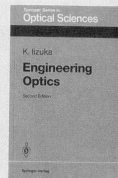

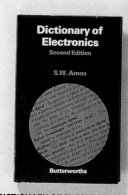

J & P TRANSFORMER BOOK
Franklin, Franklin
BUTTERWORTHS
ISBN 0-408-00494-0
ORDER NO. EE-1071 $120.00

DICTIONARY OF ELECTRONICS
Amos
BUTTERWORTHS
ISBN 0-408-02750-9
ORDER NO. EE-1068 $34.

ΩE OMEGA Recommended

Electrical Engineering

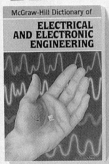

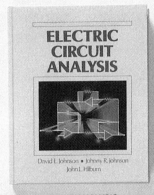

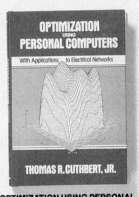

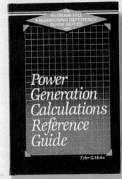

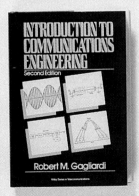

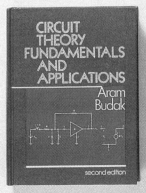

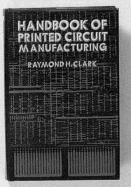

**PRINTED CIRCUIT ASSEMBLY
MANUFACTURING**
Kear
MARCEL DEKKER
ISBN 0-8247-7675-5
ORDER NO. EE-1059   **$89.75**

**NON-LINEAR AND PARAMETRIC
CIRCUITS**
Kouril, Vrba
WILEY
ISBN 0-470-20014-6
ORDER NO. EE-1093   **$135.00**

DIGITAL DESIGN FUNDAMENTALS
Breeding
PRENTICE HALL
ISBN 0-13-212721-0
ORDER NO. EE-1091   **$46.00**

PRINTED CIRCUIT ENGINEERING
Clark
VAN NOSTRAND REINHOLD
ISBN 0-442-21115-5
ORDER NO. EE-1080   **$50.95**

**MCGRAW-HILL DICTIONARY OF
ELECTRICAL AND ELECTRONIC
ENGINEERING**
Parker
MCGRAW-HILL
ISBN 0-07-045413-2
ORDER NO. GE-0124   **$42.00**

ELECTRIC CIRCUIT ANALYSIS
Johnson, Johnson Hilburn
PRENTICE HALL
ISBN 0-13-247776-9
ORDER NO. EE-1092   **$52.00**

**OPTIMIZATION USING PERSONAL
COMPUTERS**
Cuthbert
WILEY
ISBN 0-471-81863-1
ORDER NO. EE-1040   **$49.95**

**POWER GENERATION
CALCULATIONS REFERENCE GUIDE**
Hicks
MCGRAW-HILL
ISBN 0-07-028800-3
ORDER NO. EE-1012   **$36.50**

**INTRODUCTION TO
COMMUNICATIONS ENGINEERING**
Gagliardi
WILEY
ISBN 0-471-85644-4
ORDER NO. EE-0082   **$49.95**

**CIRCUIT THEORY FUNDAMENTALS
AND APPLICATIONS, 2ND ED.**
Budak
PRENTICE HALL
ISBN 0-13-134057-3
ORDER NO. EE-1206   **$55.00**

**HANDBOOK OF PRINTED CIRCUIT
MANUFACTURING**
Clark
VAN NOSTRAND REINHOLD
ISBN 0-442-21610-6
ORDER NO. EE-0608   **$62.95**

**THE ELECTRONIC BUSINESS
INFORMATION SOURCEBOOK**
Wasik
WILEY
ISBN 0-471-62464-0
ORDER NO. EE-1089   **$27.95**

ΩE OMEGA Recommended

MICROCOMPUTER BUS STRUCTURES AND BUS INTERFACE DESIGN
Dexter
MARCEL DEKKER
ISBN 0-8247-7435-3
ORDER NO. EE-1058   **$69.75**

BASIC CIRCUIT THEORY, 2ND ED
Huelsman
PRENTICE HALL
ISBN 0-13-057711-1
ORDER NO. EE-1101   **$55.00**

TRANSDUCERS IN MECHANICAL AND ELECTRONIC DESIGN
Trietley
MARCEL DEKKER
ISBN 0-8247-7598-8
ORDER NO. EE-1063   **$69.75**

HIGH-FREQUENCY SWITCHING POWER SUPPLIES THEORY & DESIGN
Chryssis
MCGRAW-HILL
ISBN 0-07-010951-6
ORDER NO. MS-0328   **$39.95**

THYRISTOR DESIGN AND REALIZATION
Taylor
WILEY
ISBN 0-471-91178-X
ORDER NO. EE-1008   **$59.95**

CIRCUIT DESIGN FOR ELECTRONIC INSTRUMENTATION
Wobschall
MCGRAW-HILL
ISBN 0-07-071231-X
ORDER NO. MS-0335   **$49.50**

VIBRATION ANALYSIS FOR ELECTRONIC EQUIPMENT
Steinberg
WILEY
ISBN 0-471-63301-1
ORDER NO. EE-1090   **$61.95**

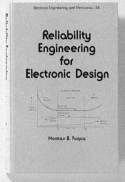

RELIABILITY ENGINEERING FOR ELECTRONIC DESIGN
Fuqua
MARCEL DEKKER
ISBN 0-8247-7571-6
ORDER NO. EE-1061   **$83.50**

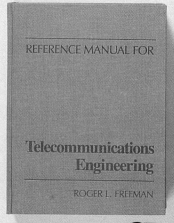

REFERENCE MANUAL FOR TELECOMMUNICATIONS ENGINEERING
Freeman
WILEY
ISBN 0-471-86753-5
ORDER NO. EE-0077   **$95.00**

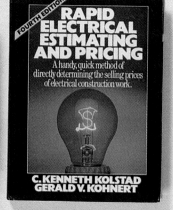

RAPID ELECTRICAL ESTIMATING AND PRICING
Kolstad, Kohnert
MCGRAW-HILL
ISBN 0-07-035131-7
ORDER NO. EE-0523   **$49.75**

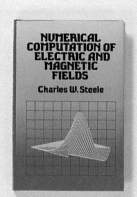

NUMERICAL COMPUTATION OF ELECTRIC AND MAGNETIC FIELDS
Steele
VAN NOSTRAND REINHOLD
ISBN 0-442-27841-1
ORDER NO. EE-1005   **$44.95**

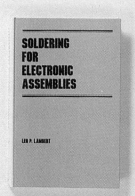

SOLDERING FOR ELECTRONIC ASSEMBLIES
Lambert
MARCEL DEKKER
ISBN 0-8247-7681-X
ORDER NO. EE-1062   **$69.75**

ΩE OMEGA Recommended

Electrical Engineering ─\/\/\/─

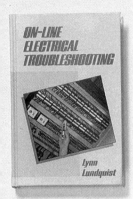

**ON-LINE ELECTRICAL
TROUBLESHOOTING**
Lundquist
MCGRAW-HILL
ISBN 0-07-039110-6
ORDER NO. EE-1075   **$34.50**

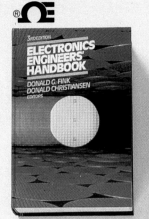

**3RD ELECTRONICS ENGINEERS'
HANDBOOK**
Fink, Christiansen
MCGRAW-HILL
ISBN 0-07-020982-0
ORDER NO. EE-0515   **$89.50**

**AUTOMATED CONTROL
ENGINEERING**
Raven
MCGRAW-HILL
ISBN 0-07-051233-7
ORDER NO. ME-0714   **$44.95**

**MICROELECTRONICS PACKAGING
HANDBOOK**
Tummala, Rymaszewski
VAN NOSTRAND REINHOLD
ISBN 0-442-20578-3
ORDER NO. EE-1079   **$94.95**

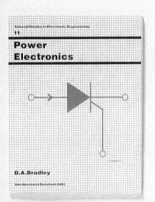

POWER ELECTRONICS
Bradely
VAN NOSTRAND REINHOLD
ISBN 0-442-31778-6
ORDER NO. EE-1031   **$18.95**

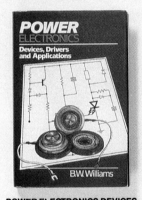

**POWER ELECTRONICS DEVICES,
DRIVERS AND APPLICATIONS**
Williams
WILEY
ISBN 0-470-20696-9
ORDER NO. EE-1009   **$51.95**

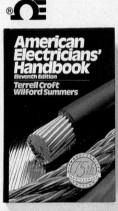

**AMERICAN ELECTRICIANS'
HANDBOOK 11TH EDIT**
Croft, Summers
MCGRAW-HILL
ISBN 0-07-013932-6
ORDER NO. EE-0682   **$69.50**

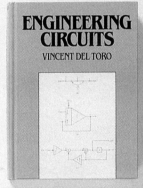

ENGINEERING CIRCUITS
Del Toro
PRENTICE HALL
ISBN 0-13-277922-6
ORDER NO. EE-1102   **$55.00**

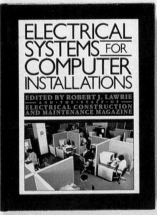

**ELECTRICAL SYSTEMS FOR
COMPUTER INSTALLATIONS**
Lawrie
MCGRAW-HILL
ISBN 0-07-036729-9
ORDER NO. EE-1074   **$33.25**

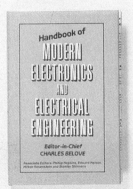

**HANDBOOK OF MODERN
ELECTRONICS AND ELCTRICAL
ENGINEERING**
Belove
WILEY
ISBN 0-471-09754-3
ORDER NO. EE-0170   **$95.00**

**COMMUNICATIONS SATELLITE
HANDBOOK**
Gordon, Morgan
WILEY
ISBN 0-471-31603-2
ORDER NO. EE-1082   **$69.95**

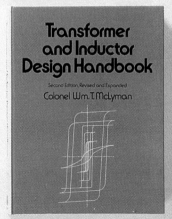

**TRANSFORMER AND INDUCTOR
DESIGN HANDBOOK**
McLyman
MARCEL DEKKER
ISBN 0-8247-7828-6
ORDER NO. EE-1064   **$55.00**

ΩE OMEGA Recommended   Y-26

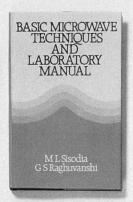

ANTENNA HANDBOOK
Lo, Lee
VAN NOSTRAND REINHOLD
ISBN 0-442-25843-7
ORDER NO. EE-1078 **$140.00**

**BASIC MICROWAVE TECHNIQUES
AND LABORATORY MANUAL**
Sisodia, Raghuvanshi
WILEY
ISBN 0-470-20265-3
ORDER NO. EE-1081 **$19.95**

**HANDBOOK OF SURFACE MOUNT
TECHNOLOGY**
Hinch
WILEY
ISBN 0-470-21094-X
ORDER NO. EE-1085 **$74.95**

**WHAT EVERY ENGINEER SHOULD
KNOW ABOUT DATA
COMMUNICATIONS**
Clilfton
MARCEL DEKKER
ISBN 0-8247-7566-X
ORDER NO. EE-1066 **$35.00**

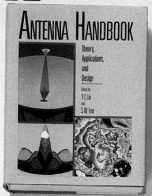

**X.25 EXPLAINED PROTOCOLS FOR
PACKET SWITCHING NETWORKS**
Deasington
WILEY
ISBN 0-470-20731-0
ORDER NO. CS-0072 **$29.95**

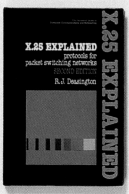

**NOISE REDUCTION TECHNIQUES IN
ELECTRONIC SYSTEMS**
Ott
WILEY
ISBN 0-471-85068-3
ORDER NO. EE-0242 **$39.95**

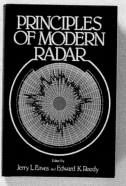

PRINCIPLES OF MODERN RADAR
Eaves, Reedy
VAN NOSTRAND REINHOLD
ISBN 0-442-22104-5
ORDER NO. EE-1025 **$59.95**

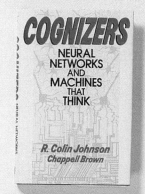

**COGNIZERS NEURAL NETWORKS &
MACHINES THAT THINK**
Johnson, Brown
WILEY
ISBN 0-471-61161-1
ORDER NO. CS-1211 **$22.95**

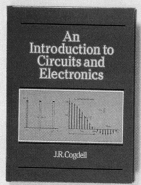

**AN INTRODUCTION TO CIRCUITS
AND ELECTRONICS**
Cogdell
PRENTICE HALL
ISBN 0-13-277922-3
ORDER NO. EE-1105 **$49.00**

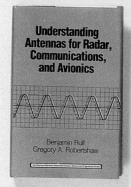

**UNDERSTANDING ANTENNAS FOR
RADAR, COMMUNICATIONS, AND
AVIONICS**
Rulf, Robertshaw
VAN NOSTRAND REINHOLD
ISBN 0-442-27772-5
ORDER NO. EE-1026 **$55.95**

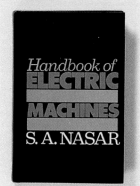

**HANDBOOK OF ELECTRIC
MACHINES**
Nasar
MCGRAW-HILL
ISBN 0-07-045888-X
ORDER NO. EE-1201 **$59.00**

**ELECTRONICS OF MEASURING
SYSTEMS**
Lang
WILEY
ISBN 0-471-91157-7
ORDER NO. EE-1020 **$64.95**

ΩE OMEGA Recommended

Safety ✚

EMERGENCY RESPONSE TO CHEMICAL ACCIDENTS
O'Reilly
MCGRAW-HILL
ISBN 0-07-047758-2
ORDER NO. MS-0907 **$39.50**

MODERN ACCIDENT INVESTIGATION AND ANALYSIS
Ferry
WILEY
ISBN 0-471-62481-0
ORDER NO. MS-0142 **$49.95**

MAJOR CHEMICAL HAZARDS
Marshall
WILEY
ISBN 0-470-20813-9
ORDER NO. CE-0621 **$112.00**

HEALTH HAZARD CONTROL IN THE CHEMICAL PROCESS INDUSTRY
Lipton, Lynch
WILEY
ISBN 0-471-84478-0
ORDER NO. CM-0501 **$70.00**

ENGINEERING DESIGN FOR THE CONTROL OF WORKPLACE HAZARDS
Wadden, Scheff
MCGRAW-HILL
ISBN 0-07-067664-X
ORDER NO. MS-0905 **$69.50**

DANGEROUS PROPERTIES OF INDUSTRIAL MATERIALS
Sax, Lewis
VAN NOSTRAND REINHOLD
ISBN 0-442-31810-3
ORDER NO. MS-0388 **$395.00**

THE SAFE HANDLING OF CHEMICALS IN INDUSTRY
VOL 1 VOL 2
Carson, Mumford
WILEY
ISBN 0-470-20886-4
ORDER NO. CH-4019 **$150.00**

$39.50

$49.95 $69.50 $395.00 $112.00

SAFETY AT WORK
Ridley
BUTTERWORTHS
ISBN 0-408-00840-7
ORDER NO. GE-0518 **$110.00**

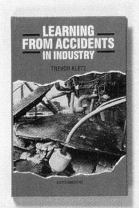

LEARNING FROM ACCIDENTS IN INDUSTRY
Kletz
BUTTERWORTHS
ISBN 0-408-02696-0
ORDER NO. GE-0516 **$29.95**

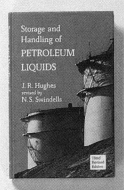

STORAGE AND HANDLING OF PETROLEUM LIQUIDS
Hughes Swindells
WILEY
ISBN 0-471-62966-9
ORDER NO. CM-0510 **$60.00**

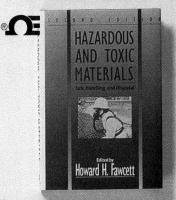

HAZARDOUS AND TOXIC MATERIALS
Fawcett
WILEY
ISBN 0-471-62729-1
ORDER NO. CH-0333 **$59.95**

INTRODUCTION TO SAFETY SCIENCE
Kuhlmann
SPRINGER-VERLAG
ISBN 0-387-96192-5
ORDER NO. MS-0930 **$98.00**

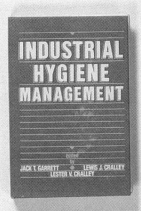

INDUSTRIAL HYGIENE MANAGEMENT
Garrett, Cralley, Cralley
WILEY
ISBN 0-471-85128-0
ORDER NO. MS-0962 **$65.00**

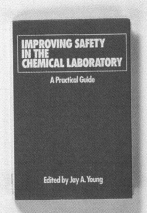

IMPROVING SAFETY IN THE CHEMICAL LABORATORY
Young
WILEY
ISBN 0-471-84693-7
ORDER NO. CM-0503 **$47.95**

HEALTH, SAFETY AND ERGONOMICS
Nicholson, Ridd
BUTTERWORTHS
ISBN 0-408-02386-4
ORDER NO. GE-0514 **$34.95**

Ω **OMEGA Recommended**

Y-28

Self Help

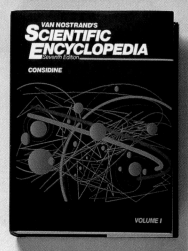

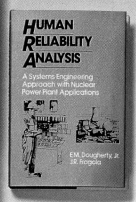

**VAN NOSTRAND'S SCIENTIFIC
ENCYCLOPEDIA, 7TH ED.**
Considine
ISBN 0-442-31814-6
ORDER NO. GE-0181 **$195.00**

HUMAN RELIABILITY ANALYSIS
Dougherty, Fragola
WILEY
ISBN 0-471-60614-6
ORDER NO. GE-0545 **$75.00**

**INSTRUMENTATION REFERENCE
BOOK**
Noltingk
BUTTERWORTHS
ISBN 0-408-01562-4
ORDER NO. GE-0500 **$220.00**

**HANDBOOK OF ADVANCED
SEMICONDUCTOR TECHNOLOGY
AND COMPUTER SYSTEMS**
Rabbat
VAN NOSTRAND REINHOLD
ISBN 0-442-27688-5
ORDER NO. CS-1204 **$70.95**

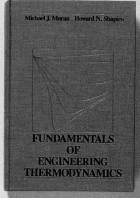

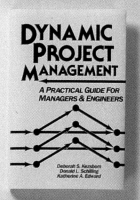

**COPPER OXIDE
SUPERCONDUCTORS**
Poole, Datta, Farach
WILEY
ISBN 0-471-62342-3
ORDER NO. MM-0634 **$35.00**

**FUNDAMENTALS OF
ENGINEERING
THERMODYNAMICS**
Moran, Shapiro
WILEY
ISBN 0-471-89576-8
ORDER NO. GE-0528 **$57.50**

**THE BEST RESUMES FOR
SCIENTISTS AND ENGINEERS**
Lewis
WILEY
ISBN 0-471-62769-0
ORDER NO. CS-1117 **$22.95**

DYNAMIC PROJECT MANAGEMENT
Kezsbom, Schilling, Edward
WILEY
ISBN 0-471-85248-1
ORDER NO. MS-0924 **$39.95**

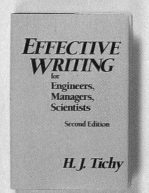

**Effective WRITING FOR ENGINEERS,
MANAGERS, SCIENTISTS**
Tichy
WILEY
ISBN 0-471-80708-7
ORDER NO. GE-0527 **$29.95**

**HOW TO SUCCEED AS AN
INDEPENDENT CONSULTANT**
Holtz
WILEY
ISBN 0-471-84729-1
ORDER NO. CS-1246 **$22.95**

**HOW TO WRITE WINNING
PROPOSALS FOR YOUR COMPANY
OF CLIENT**
Tepper
WILEY
ISBN 0-471-60932-3
ORDER NO. CS-1245 **$39.95**

**SUCCEEDING AT BUSINESS
TECHNICAL PRESENTATIONS**
Meuse
WILEY
ISBN 0-471-62486-1
ORDER NO. CS-1244 **$29.95**

Computers

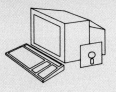

MASTERING 1-2-3
Jorgensen
SYBEX
ISBN 0-89588-528-X
ORDER NO. CS-1167 **$22.95**

THE ABC'S OF 1-2-3
Gilbert, Williams
SYBEX
ISBN 0-89588-355-4
ORDER NO. CS-1183 **$18.95**

1-2-3 FOR SCIENTISTS & ENGINEERS
Orvis
SYBEX
ISBN 0-89588-407-0
ORDER NO. CS-1160 **$24.95**

MASTERING SYMPHONY
Cobb
SYBEX
ISBN 0-89588-494-1
ORDER NO. CS-1176 **$26.95**

LOTUS 1-2-3 DESKTOP COMPANION
Harvey
SYBEX
ISBN 0-89588-501-8
ORDER NO. CS-1165 **$24.95**

ADVANCED TECHNIQUES IN LOTUS 1-2-3
Lunsford, Antoniak
SYBEX
ISBN 0-89588-556-5
ORDER NO. CS-1162 **$21.95**

LOTUS 1-2-3 TIPS AND TRICKS
Weisskipf
SYBEX
ISBN 0-89588-454-2
ORDER NO. CS-1166 **$21.95**

ADVANCED TOPICS IN SIGNAL PROCESSING
Lim, Oppenheim
PRENTICE HALL
ISBN 0-13-013129-6
ORDER NO. CS-1217 **$50.00**

ENCYCLOPEDIA OF COMPUTER SCIENCE AND ENGINEERING, 2ND ED.
Ralston, Reilly
VAN NOSTRAND REINHOLD
ISBN 0-442-24496-7
ORDER NO. CS-0407 **$101.75**

DISCRETE-TIME SIGNAL PROCESSING
Oppenheim, Schafer
PRENTICE HALL
ISBN 0-13-216292-X
ORDER NO. CS-1222 **$49.00**

DIGITAL SIGNAL PROCESSING
Oppenheim, Schafer
PRENTICE HALL
ISBN 0-13-214635-5
ORDER NO. CS-1221 **$52.00**

ENGINEERING WORKSTATIONS, TECHNOLOGY AND APPLICATION TRENDS
Bowerman, Fertig
VAN NOSTRAND REINHOLD
ISBN 0-442-22628-4
ORDER NO. GE-0504 **$42.95**

ΩE OMEGA Recommended

Computers

NUMERICAL ALGORITHMS FOR MODERN PARALLEL COMPUTER ARCHITECTURE
Schultz
SPRINGER-VERLAG
ISBN 0-387-96733-8
ORDER NO. MA-1110 **$25.00**

REDUCE SOFTWARE FOR ALGEBRAIC COMPUTATION
Rayna
SPRINGER-VERLAG
ISBN 0-387-96598-X
ORDER NO. CS-1243 **$34.00**

A GUIDE TO SPSS/PC+
Frude
SPRINGER-VERLAG
ISBN 0-387-91312-2
ORDER NO. CS-1233 **$32.00**

THE FAST FOURIER TRANSFORM AND ITS APPLICATIONS
Brigham
PRENTICE HALL
ISBN 0-13-307505-2
ORDER NO. CS-1231 **$50.00**

PERSONAL COMPUTERS IN INDUSTRIAL CONTROL
Giorgi
BUTTERWORTHS
ISBN 0-408-03297-9
ORDER NO. CS-1202 **$69.95**

$25.00 $32.00 $50.00 $69.95 $34.00

DOS USER'S DESKTOP COMPANION
Robbins
SYBEX
ISBN 0-89588-505-0
ORDER NO. CS-1164 **$24.95**

MASTERING DOS
Robbins
SYBEX
ISBN 0-89588-555-7
ORDER NO. CS-1170 **$24.95**

UNDERSTANDING HARD DISK MANAGEMENT ON THE PC
Kamin
SYBEX
ISBN 0-89588-561-1
ORDER NO. CS-1194 **$22.95**

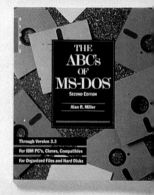

THE ABC'S OF MS-DOS
Miller
SYBEX
ISBN 0-89588-493-3
ORDER NO. CS-1186 **$18.95**

WRITING A UNIX DEVICE DRIVER
Egan, Teixeira
WILEY
ISBN 0-471-62811-5
ORDER NO. CS-1216 **$34.95**

NUMERICAL METHODS AND SOFTWARE
Kahaner, Moler, Nash
PRENTICE HALL
ISBN 0-13-627258-4
ORDER NO. CS-1227 **$50.00**

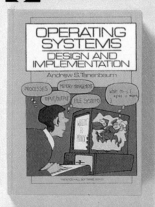

OPERATING SYSTEMS DESIGN AND IMPLEMENTATION
Tanenbaum
PRENTICE HALL
ISBN 0-13-637406-9
ORDER NO. CS-1228 **$46.00**

KNOWLEDGE ACQUISITION, PRINCIPLES AND GUIDELINES
McGraw, Briggs
PRENTICE HALL
ISBN 0-13-516436-2
ORDER NO. CS-1226 **$29.95**

ΩE OMEGA Recommended

Computers

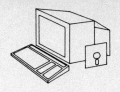

MASTERING TURBO PASCAL 5
Hergert
SYBEX
ISBN 0-89588-529-8
ORDER NO. CS-1178 **$22.95**

TURBO PASCAL TOOLBOX
Dutton
SYBEX
ISBN 0-89588-602-2
ORDER NO. CS-1191 **$21.95**

TURBO PASCAL PROGRAMS FOR SCIENTISTS & ENGINEERS
Miller
SYBEX
ISBN 0-89588-424-0
ORDER NO. CS-1190 **$19.95**

PROGRAMMING WITH MACINTOSH PASCAL
Rink, Wisebaker, Vance
PRENTICE HALL
ISBN 0-13-730540-0
ORDER NO. CS-1229 **$33.00**

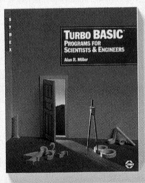

TURBO BAXIC PROGRAMS FOR SCIENTISTS & ENGINEERS
Miller
SYBEX
ISBN 0-89588-429-1
ORDER NO. CS-1189 **$19.95**

MASTERING TURBO C
Kelly-Bootle
SYBEX
ISBN 0-89588-462-3
ORDER NO. CS-1177 **$24.95**

STRUCTURED PROGRAMMING USING PASCAL
Crawley, McArther
PRENTICE HALL
ISBN 0-13-854035-7
ORDER NO. CS-1230 **$34.00**

CRAFTING KNOWLEDGE-BASED SYSTEMS
Walters, Nielsen
WILEY
ISBN 0-471-62479-9
ORDER NO. CS-1115 **$29.95**

PROGRAMMING IN MODULA-2
Wirth
SPRINGER-VERLAG
ISBN 0-387-50150-9
ORDER NO. CS-1241 **$29.95**

FORTRAN TOOLS FOR VAX/VMS AND MS-DOS
Jones, Crabtree
WILEY
ISBN 0-471-61976-0
ORDER NO. CS-1212 **$29.95**

PROGRAMMING IN PROLOG
Clocksin, Mellish
SPRINGER-VERLAG
ISBN 0-387-17539-3
ORDER NO. CS-1242 **$19.95**

WHAT EVERY ENGINEER SHOULD KNOW ABOUT MICRO-COMPUTERS
Bennett, Evert
DEKKER
ISBN 0-8247-6909-0
ORDER NO. CS-1198 **$35.00**

ΩE OMEGA Recommended

Computers

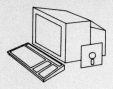

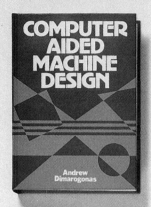

COMPUTER AIDED MACHINE DESIGN
Dimarogonas
PRENTICE HALL
ISBN 0-13-166497-2
ORDER NO. CS-1218 **$45.00**

THE ENGINEERING DATABASE
Chorafas, Legg
BUTTERWORTHS
ISBN 0-408-02280-9
ORDER NO. CS-1203 **$34.95**

ENGINEERING PRODUCTIVITY THROUGH CAD/CAM
Chorafas
BUTTERWORTHS
ISBN 0-408-01588-8
ORDER NO. CS-1201 **$45.00**

SSADM STRUCTURED SYSTEMS ANALYSIS AND DESIGN METHODOLOGY
Cutts
VAN NOSTRAND REINHOLD
ISBN 0-442-31827-8
ORDER NO. CS-1209 **$53.95**

MASTERING AUTOCAD
Omura
SYBEX
ISBN 0-89588-574-3
ORDER NO. CS-1169 **$29.95**

ADVANCED TECHNIQUES IN AUTOCAD
Thomas
SYBEX
ISBN 0-89588-593-X
ORDER NO. CS-1161 **$26.95**

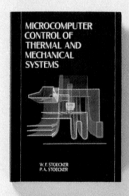

MICROCOMPUTER CONTROL OF THERMAL AND MECHANICAL SYSTEMS
Stoecker, Stoecker
VAN NOSTRAND REINHOLD
ISBN 0-442-20648-8
ORDER NO. CS-1206 **$53.95**

PUTTING EXPERT SYSTEMS INTO PRACTICE
Bower, Glover
VAN NOSTRAND REINHOLD
ISBN 0-442-20842-1
ORDER NO. CS-1208 **$42.95**

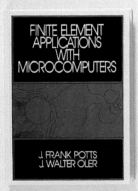

FINITE ELEMENT APPLICATIONS WITH MICROCOMPUTERS
Potts, Oler
PRENTICE HALL
ISBN 0-13-317439-5
ORDER NO. CS-1223 **$46.00**

COMPUTER-CONTROLLED SYSTEMS
Astro, Wittenmark
PRENTICE HALL
ISBN 0-13-164319-3
ORDER NO. CS-1219 **$56.00**

COMPUTER-INTEGRATED MANUFACTURING
Weatherall
BUTTERWORTHS
ISBN 0-408-00733-8
ORDER NO. CS-1200 **$95.00**

IMPLEMENTING CIM
Kochan, Cowan
SPRINGER-VERLAG
ISBN 0-387-16352-2
ORDER NO. CS-1239 **$38.00**

ΩΕ OMEGA Recommended

Computers

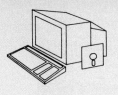

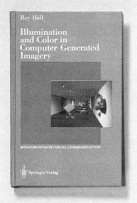

ILLUMINATION AND COLOR IN COMPUTER GENERATED IMAGERY
Hall
SPRINGER-VERLAG
ISBN 0-387-96774-5
ORDER NO. CS-1238   **$49.80**

VISUAL PROGRAMMING
Shu
VAN NOSTRAND REINHOLD
ISBN 0-442-28014-9
ORDER NO. CS-1210   **$39.95**

MICROPROGRAMMING AND FIRMWARE ENGINEERING METHODS
Habib
VAN NOSTRAND REINHOLD
ISBN 0-442-23554-2
ORDER NO. CS-1207   **$48.95**

CGM AND CGI
Arnold, Bono
SPRINGER-VERLAG
ISBN 0-387-18950-5
ORDER NO. CS-1235   **$39.50**

PROGRAMMING THE 80286
Viellefond
SYBEX
ISBN 0-89588-277-9
ORDER NO. CS-1181   **$22.95**

PROGRAMMING THE 80386
Crawford, Gelsinger
SYBEX
ISBN 0-89588-381-3
ORDER NO. CS-1182   **$26.95**

UNDERSTANDING POSTSCRIPT PROGRAMMING
Molzgang
SYBEX
ISBN 0-89588-566-2
ORDER NO. CS-1195   **$24.95**

CD-ROM FUNDAMENTALS TO APPLICATIONS
Oppenheim
BUTTERWORTHS
ISBN 0-408-00746-X
ORDER NO. CS-1199   **$95.00**

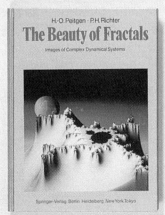

THE BEAUTY OF FRACTALS
Peitgen, Richter
SPRINGER-VERLAG
ISBN 0-387-15851-0
ORDER NO. MA-1112   **$39.00**

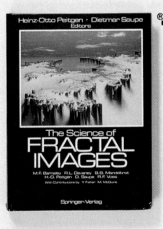

THE SCIENCE OF FRACTAL IMAGES
Peitgen, Saupe
SPRINGER-VERLAG
ISBN 0-387-96608-0
ORDER NO. MA-1116   **$34.00**

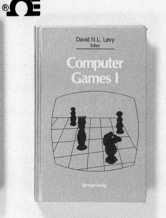

COMPUTER GAMES I
Levy
SPRINGER-VERLAG
ISBN 0-387-96496-7
ORDER NO. CS-1236   **$45.00**

COMPUTER GAMES II
Levy
SPRINGER-VERLAG
ISBN 0-387-96609-9
ORDER NO. CS-1237   **$59.00**

$50.00

$39.95

$46.00

$50.00

$49.95

OPERATING SYSTEM DESIGN THE
XINU APPROACH
Comer
PRENTICE HALL
ISBN 0-13-637539-1
ORDER NO. CS-1152 **$50.00**

FRACTALS EVERYWHERE
Barnsley
ACADEMIC PRESS
ISBN 0-12-079062-9
ORDER NO. MA-1100 **$39.95**

OPERATING SYSTEM DESIGN VOL 1
THE XINU APPROACH
Comer, Fossum
PRENTICE HALL
ISBN 0-13-638180-4
ORDER NO. CS-1151 **$46.00**

OPERATING SYSTEM DESIGN VOL II
INTERNETWORKING WITH XINU
Comer
PRENTICE HALL
ISBN 0-13-637414-X
ORDER NO. CS-1150 **$50.00**

THE THEORY AND PRACTICE OF
MODEM DESIGN
Bingham
WILEY
ISBN 0-471-85108-6
ORDER NO. CS-1215 **$49.95**

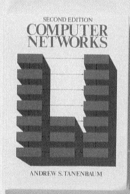

ISDN THE INTEGRATED SERVICES
DIGITAL NETWORK
Bocker
SPRINGER-VERLAG
ISBN 0-387-17446-X
ORDER NO. CS-1240 **$64.50**

COMPUTER NETWORKS
Tanenbaum
PRENTICE HALL
ISBN 0-13-162959-X
ORDER NO. CS-1220 **$50.00**

INTERNETWORKING WITH TCP/IP
Comer
PRENTICE HALL
ISBN 0-13-470154-2
ORDER NO. CS-1225 **$38.00**

THE INTEGRATED SERVICES
DIGITAL NETWORK: FROM
CONCEPT TO APPL.
Ronayne
WILEY
ISBN 0-470-21025-7
ORDER NO. CS-1214 **$34.95**

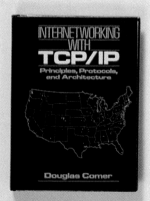

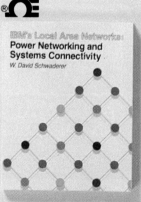

AN INTRODUCTION TO TCP/IP
Davidson
SPRINGER-VERLAG
ISBN 0-387-96651-X
ORDER NO. CS-1234 **$24.95**

MASTERING SERIAL
COMMUNICATIONS
Grofton
SYBEX
ISBN 0-89588-180-2
ORDER NO. CS-1175 **$19.95**

IBM'S LOCAL AREA NETWORKS:
POWER NETWORKING AND
SYSTEMS CONNE
Schwaderer
VAN NOSTRAND REINHOLD
ISBN 0-442-20713-1
ORDER NO.CS-1205 **$32.95**

THE RS-232 SOLUTION
Campbell
SYBEX
ISBN 0-89588-140-3
ORDER NO. CS-1188 **$21.95**

®**ΩE OMEGA Recommended**

Computers

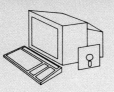

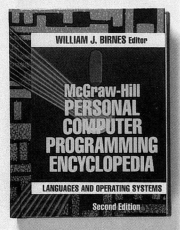

THE ABC'S OF dBASE III PLUS
Cowart
SYBEX
ISBN 0-89588-379-1
ORDER NO. CS-1184 **$18.95**

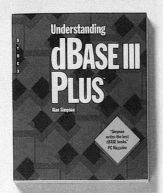

UNDERSTANDING dBASE III PLUS
Simpson
SYBEX
ISBN 0-89588-349-X
ORDER NO. CS-1192 **$22.95**

dBASE III PLUS PROGRAMMER'S REFERENCE/GUIDE
Simpson
SYBEX
ISBN 0-89588-508-5
ORDER NO. CS-1163 **$26.95**

UNDERSTANDING R:BASE
Simpson, Watters
SYBEX
ISBN 0-89588-503-4
ORDER NO. CS-1196 **$24.95**

MCGRAW-HILL PERSONAL/COMPUTER PROGRAMMING ENCY
Birnes
MCGRAW
ISBN 0-07-005393-6
ORDER NO. CS-0210 **$95.00**

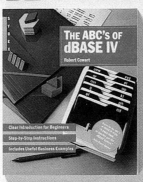

THE ABC'S OF dBASE IV
Cowart
SYBEX
ISBN 0-89588-531-X
ORDER NO. CS-1185 **$18.95**

UNDERSTANDING dBASE IV
Simpson
SYBEX
ISBN 0-89588-509-3
ORDER NO. CS-1193 **$24.95**

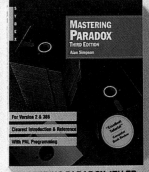

MASTERING PARADOX 4TH ED.
Simpson
SYBEX
ISBN 0-89588-490-9
ORDER NO. CS-1174 **$24.95**

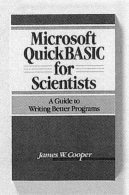

MICROSOFT QUICKBASIC FOR SCIENTISTS
Cooper
WILEY
ISBN 0471-61301-0
ORDER NO. CS-1213 **$29.95**

Ω **OMEGA Recommended**

Computers

THE ABC'S OF WORDPERFECT 5
Neibauer
SYBEX
ISBN 0-89588-504-2
ORDER NO. CS-1187 **$18.95**

MASTERING WORDPERFECT 5
Kelly
SYBEX
ISBN 0-89588-500-X
ORDER NO. CS-1180 **$24.95**

WORDPERFECT 5 DESKTOP COMPANTION
Harvey and Nelson
SYBEX
IBSN 0-89588-522-0
ORDER NO. CS-1197 **$24.95**

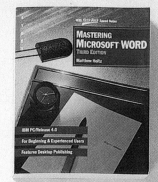

MASTERING MICROSOFT WORD 3RD EDIT
Holtz
SYBEX
ISBN 0-89588-524-7
ORDER NO. CS-1171 **$21.95**

MASTERING ADOBE ILLUSTRATOR
Holzgang
SYBEX
ISBN 0-89588-463-1
ORDER NO. CS-1168 **$22.95**

MASTERING MULTIMATE ADVANTAGE II
Ackerman
SYBEX
ISBN 0-89588-482-8
ORDER NO. CS-1172 **$22.95**

MASTERING VENTURA 2ND ED.
Holts
SYBEX
ISBN 0-89588-427-5
ORDER NO. CS-1179 **$24.95**

MASTERING PAGEMAKER ON THE IBM PC 2ND EDIT
Jolles
SYBEX
ISBN 0-89588-521-2
ORDER NO. CS-1173 **$22.95**

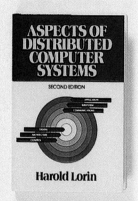

ASPECTS OF DISTRIBUTED COMPUTER SYSTEMS
Lorin
WILEY
ISBN 0471-62589-2
ORDER NO. CS-1250 **$42.95**

NEURAL AND MASSIVELY PARALLEL COMPUTER
Soucek
WILEY
ISBN 0427-63533-2
ORDER NO. CS-1251 **$49.95**

To Order, Call Toll-Free
Book Hot Line (to Order Books Only)
1-800-222-BooK™
1-800-222-2665

For Instruments and Books
1-800-TC-OMEGA
1-800-82 66342
In CT Dial (203) 359-1660

®Œ OMEGA Recommended

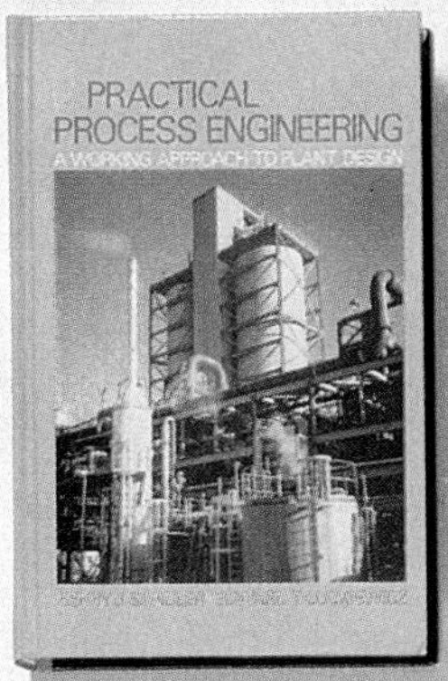

PRACTICAL PROCESS ENGINEERING
Sandler, Luckiewicz
MCGRAW-HILL
ISBN 0-07-078595-3
ORDER NO. CM-0461 **$54.50**

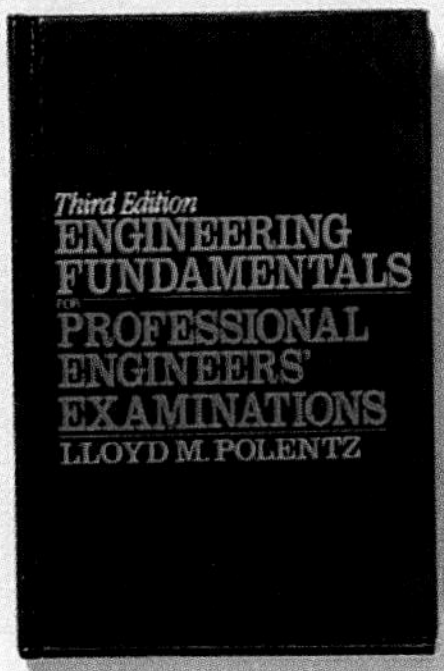

ENGINEERING FUNDAMENTALS FOR PROFESSIONAL ENGINEERS' EXAMINATIONS 3RD ED.
Polentz
MCGRAW-HILL
ISBN 0-07-050393-1
ORDER NO. GE-0400 **$36.50**

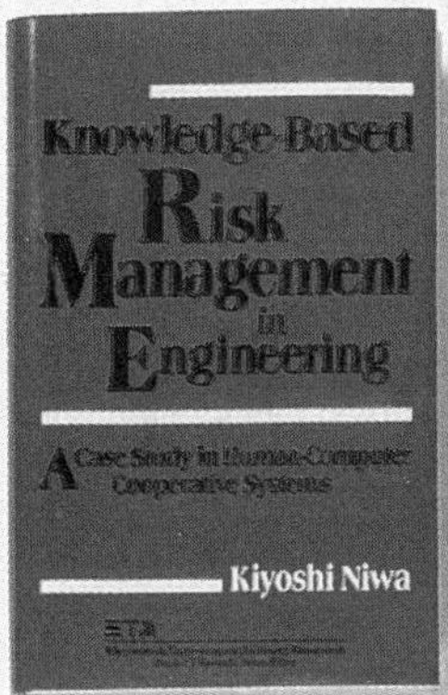

KNOWLEDGE-BASED RISK MANAGEMENT IN ENGINEERING
Niwa
WILEY
ISBN 0-471-62893-X
ORDER NO. GE-0554 **$29.95**

INFORMATION SOURCES IN ENERGY TECHNOLOGY
Anthony
BUTTERWORTHS
ISBN 0-408-03050-X
ORDER NO. GE-0515 **$105.00**

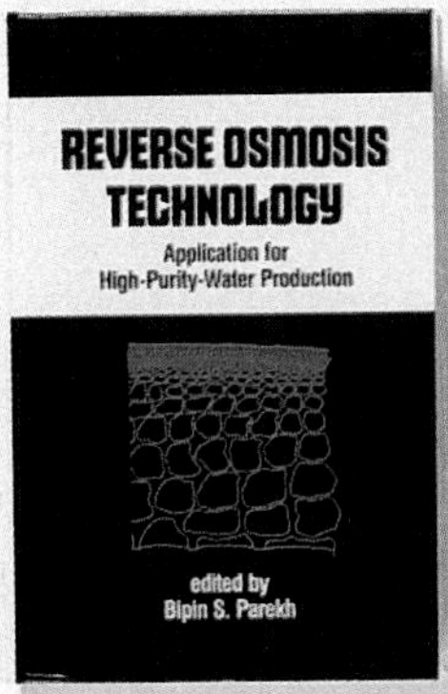

REVERSE OSMOSIS TECHNOLOGY
Parekh
MARCEL DEKKER
ISBN 0-8247-7985-1
ORDER NO. CH-4010 **$99.75**

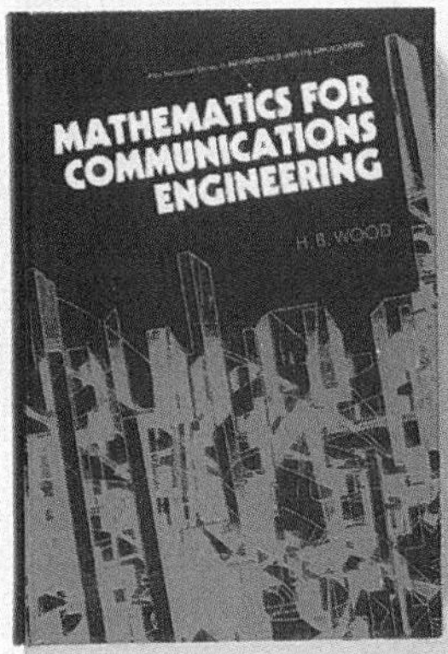

MATHEMATICS FOR COMMUNICATIONS ENGINEERING
Wood
WILEY
ISBN 0-470-21245-4
ORDER NO. GE-0543 **$74.95**

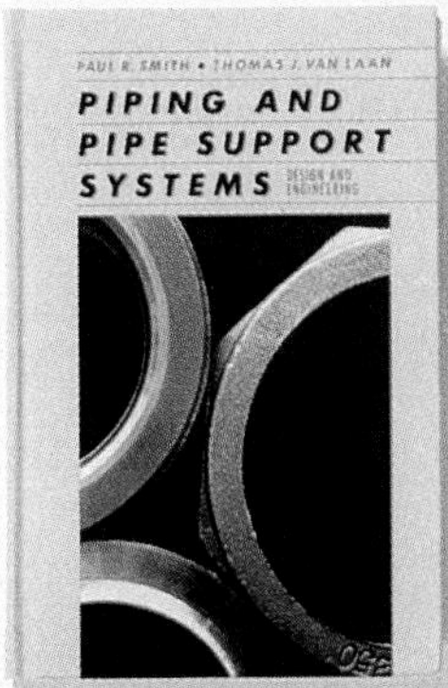

PIPING AND PIPE SUPPORT SYSTEMS
Smith, Laan
MCGRAW-HILL
ISBN 0-07-058931-3
ORDER NO. ME-0715 **$44.95**

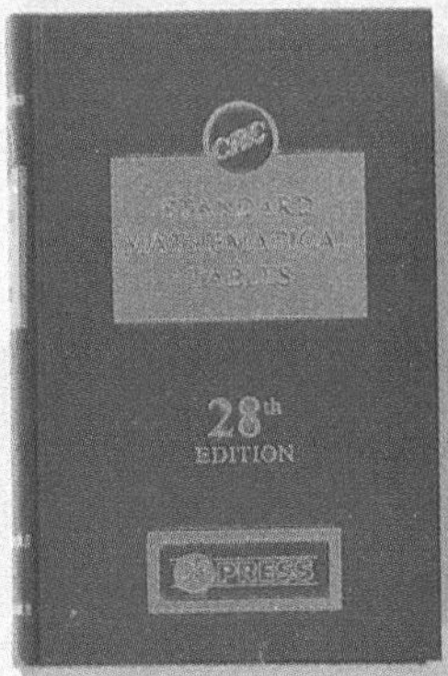

STANDARD MATHEMATICAL TABLES, 28TH ED.
Beyer
CRC PRESS
ISBN 0-8493-0628-0
ORDER NO.SD-0502 **$29.95**

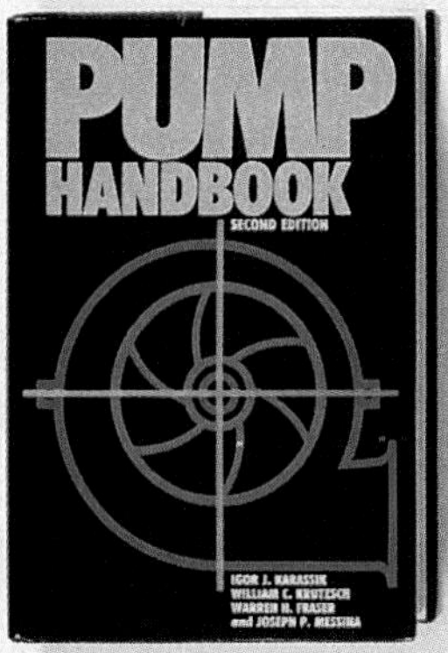

PUMP HANDBOOK, 2ND ED.
Karassik, Krutzsch, Fraser, Messina
MCGRAW-HILL
ISBN 0-07-033302-5
ORDER NO. ME-0341 **$96.00**

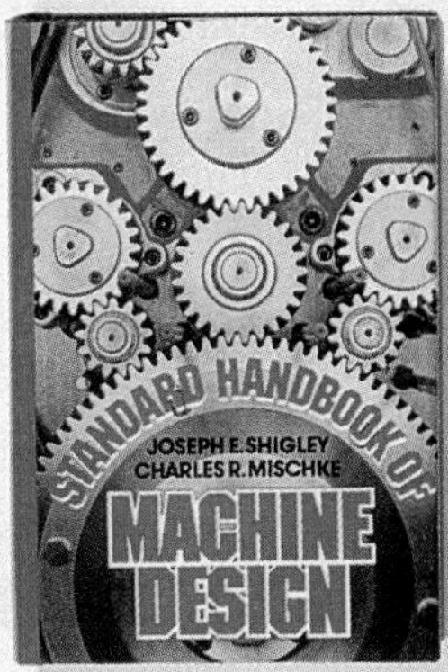

STANDARD HANDBOOK OF MACHINE DESIGN
Shigley, Mischke
MCGRAW-HILL
ISBN 0-07-056892-8
ORDER NO. GE-0135 **$108.00**

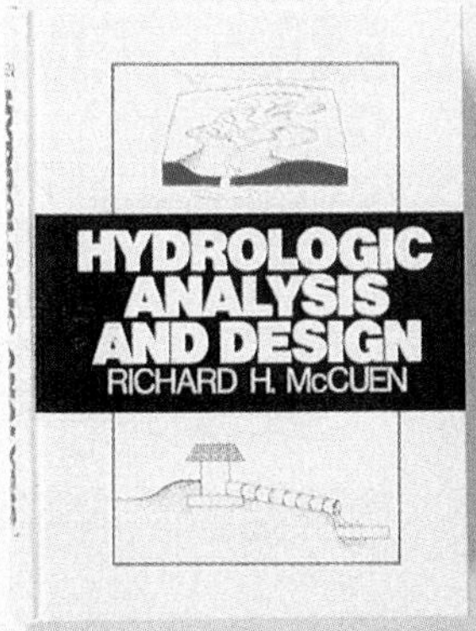

HYDROLOGIC ANALYSIS AND DESIGN
McCuen
PRENTICE HALL
ISBN 0-13-447954-8
ORDER NO. GE-0538 **$60.00**

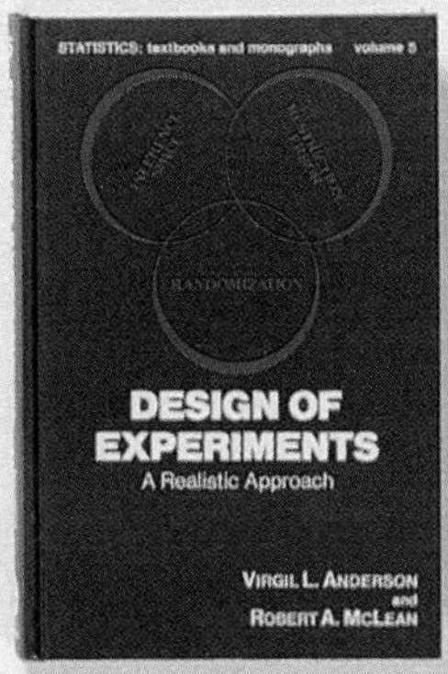

DESIGN OF EXPERIMENTS, A REALISTIC APPROACH
Anderson, McLean
MARCEL DEKKER
ISBN 0-8247-6131-6
ORDER NO. MS-0916 **$45.00**

General Engineering

PROCESS INSTRUMENTS AND CONTROLS HANDBOOK
Considine
MCGRAW-HALL
ISBN 0-07-012436-1
ORDER NO. MS-0333 **$102.00**

MCGRAW-HILL DICTIONARY OF ENGINEERING
Parker
MCGRAW-HILL
ISBN 0-07-045412-4
ORDER NO. GE-0124 **$42.00**

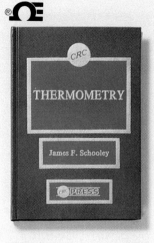

THERMOMETRY
Schooley
CRC PRESS
ISBN 0-8493-5833-7
ORDER NO. SD-0501 **$139.00**

MATERIALS HANDBOOK 12TH EDITION
Brady, Clauser
MCGRAW-HILL
ISBN 0-07-007071-7
ORDER NO. MM-0200 **$66.50**

MAINTENANCE ENGINEERING HANDBOOK
Higgins
MCGRAW-HILL
ISBN 0-07-028766-X
ORDER NO. MS-0345 **$79.50**

THEORY & PRACTICE OF RADIATION THERMOMETRY
Dewitt, Nutter
WILEY
ISBN 0-471-61018-6
ORDER NO. GE-0534 **$84.95**

OPERATIONAL AMPLIFIERS
Barna, Porat
WILEY
ISBN 0-471-84715-1
ORDER NO. GE-0532 **$36.95**

HANDBOOK OF TRANSDUCERS
Norton
PRENTICE HALL
ISBN 0-13-382599-X
ORDER NO. EE-1103 **$44.00**

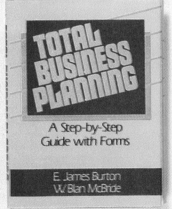

TOTAL BUSINESS PLANNING
Burton, McBride
WILEY
ISBN 0-471-82379-1
ORDER NO. GE-0535 **$49.95**

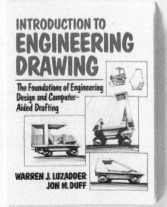

INTRODUCTION TO ENGINEERING DRAWING
Luzadder, Duff
PRENTICE HALL
ISBN 0-13-482373-7
ORDER NO. GE-0539 **$25.00**

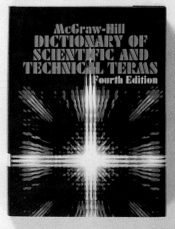

MCGRAW-HILL DICTIONARY OF SCIENCE & TECHNICAL TERMS
Parker
MCGRAW-HILL
ISBN 0-07-045270-9
ORDER NO. GE-0126 **$95.00**

OMEGA Recommended

General Engineering

**HANDBOOK OF SEPARATION
PROCESS TECHNOLOGY**
Rousseau
WILEY
ISBN 0-471-89558-X
ORDER NO. CM-0457 **$69.95**

**HANDBOOK OF EFFECTIVE
TECHNICAL COMMUNICATIONS**
Hicks, Valorie
MCGRAW-HILL
ISBN 0-07-028781-3
ORDER NO. GE-0523 **$49.50**

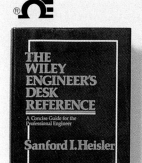

**THE WILEY ENGINEERS DESK
REFERENCE**
Heisler
WILEY
ISBN 0-471-86332-6
ORDER NO. GE-0009 **$44.95**

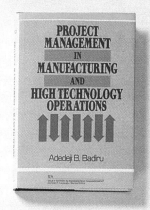

**PROJECT MANAGEMENT IN
MANUFACTURING & HIGH
TECHNOLOGY OPERATING**
Baidiru
WILEY
ISBN 0-471-62892-1
ORDER NO. ME-0802 **$44.95**

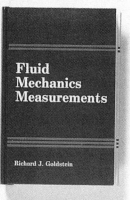

**FLUID MECHANICS
MEASUREMENTS**
Goldstein
HEMISPHERE
ISBN 0-540-12501-9
ORDER NO. ME-0611 **$55.00**

**WHAT EVERY ENGINEER SHOULD
KNOW ABOUT PROJECT
MANAGEMENT**
Ruskin, Estes
MARCEL DEKKER
ISBN 0-8247-1718-X
ORDER NO. GE-0511 **$35.00**

**EXCAVATION PLANNING
REFERENCE GUIDE**
Church
MCGRAW-HILL
ISBN 0-07-010904-4
ORDER NO. GE-0522 **$39.50**

ENGINEERING FORMULAS
Gieck
MCGRAW-HILL
ISBN 0-07-023231-8
ORDER NO. GE-0106 **$22.95**

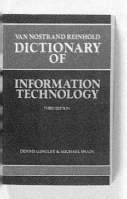

**VAN NOSTRAND REINHOLD
DICTIONARY OF INFORMATION
TECHNOLOGY, 3RD ED.**
Longley, Shain
VAN NOSTRAND REINHOLD
ISBN 0-44-223685-9
ORDER NO. CS-1248 **$22.95**

**FLOW MEASUREMENT
ENGINEERING HANDBOOK**
Miller
MCGRAW-HILL
ISBN 0-07-042045-9
ORDER NO. OP-9 **$83.00**

**INTRODUCTION TO THE THEORY OF
TRAFFIC FLOW**
Leutzbach
SPRINGER-VERLAG
ISBN 0-387-17113-4
ORDER NO. CE-0660 **$43.50**

ΩE OMEGA Recommended

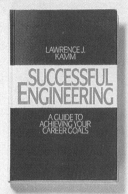

FINITE ELEMENTS IN FLUIDS
Gallagher, Glowinski, Oden, Gresho,
Zienkiezicz
WILEY
ISBN 0-471-91804-0
ORDER NO. ME-0824 **$112.00**

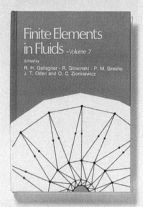

SUCCESSFUL ENGINEERING
Kamm
MCGRAW-HILL
ISBN 0-07-033267-3
ORDER NO. GE-0526 **$39.95**

**STATISTICAL QUALITY CONTROL
METHODS**
Burr
MARCEL DEKKER
ISBN 0-8247-6344-0
ORDER NO. ST-0609 **$49.75**

**JURAN'S QUALITY CONTROL
HANDBOOK**
Juran
MCGRAW-HILL
ISBN 0-07-033175-8
ORDER NO. GE-0142 **$85.00**

**MCGRAW-HILL CONCISE
ENCYCLOPEDIA OF SCIENCE &
TECHNOLOGY**
Parker
MCGRAW-HILL
ISBN 0-07-045482-5
ORDER NO. GS-0002 **$99.50**

FINITE ELEMENT HANDBOOK
Kardestuncer
MCGRAW-HILL
ISBN 0-07-033305-X
ORDER NO. GE-0429 **$105.00**

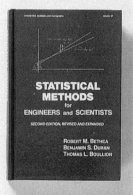

**STATISTICAL METHODS FOR
ENGINEERS AND SCIENTISTS**
Bethea, Duran, Boullion
MARCEL DEKKER
ISBN 0-8247-7227-X
ORDER NO. ST-0606 **$45.00**

**ANALYTICAL ASPECTS OF DRUG
TESTING**
Deutsch
WILEY
ISBN 0-471-85309-7
ORDER NO. GE-0555 **$75.00**

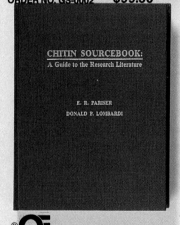

**CHITIN SOURCEBOOK: A GUIDE TO
THE RESEARCH LITERATURE**
Pariser, Lombardi
WILEY
ISBN 0-471-62423-3
ORDER NO. MS-0931 **$150.00**

STATISTICAL COMPUTING
Kennedy, Gentle
MARCEL DEKKER
ISBN 0-8247-6898-1
ORDER NO. ST-0605 **$45.00**

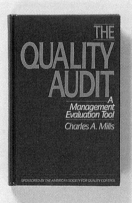

THE QUALITY AUDIT
Mills
MCGRAW-HILL
ISBN 0-07-042428-4
ORDER NO. MS-0921 **$42.50**

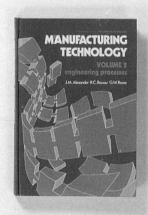

MANUFACTURING TECHNOLOGY
Alexander Brewer, Rowe
WILEY
ISBN 0-470-20960-7
ORDER NO. ME-0801 **$64.95**

ΩE OMEGA Recommended

$44.80

$90.00

$95.00

®ΩΕ

$62.50

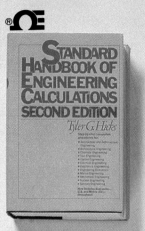

**STANDARD HANDBOOK OF
ENGINEERING CALCULATIONS, 2ND
ED.**
Hicks
MCGRAW-HILL
ISBN 0-07-028735-X
ORDER NO. GE-0113   **$75.00**

**WHAT EVERY ENGINEER SHOULD
KNOW ABOUT PATENTS, 2ND ED.**
Konold, Tittel, Frei, Stallard
MARCEL DEKKER
ISBN 0-8247-8010-8
ORDER NO. GE-0510   **$39.75**

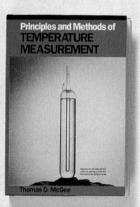

**PRINCIPLES AND METHODS OF
TEMPERATURE MEASUREMENT**
McGee
WILEY
ISBN 0-471-62767-4
ORDER NO. ME-0750   **$54.95**

**ADSORPTION EQUILIBRIUM DATA
HANDBOOK**
Valenzuela, Myers
PRENTICE HALL
ISBN 0-13-008815-3
ORDER NO. GE-0536   **$40.00**

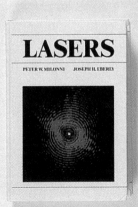

LASERS
Milonni, Eberly
WILEY
ISBN 0-471-62731-3
ORDER NO. GE-0531   **$49.95**

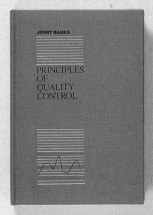

**MCGRAW-HILL DICTIONARY OF
ENGINEERING**
Parker
ISBN 0-07-045412-4
ORDER NO. GE-0124   **$42.00**

ENGINEERING GRAPHICS
Groft, Meyers, Boyer, Miller, Demel
WILEY
ISBN 0-471-85788-2
ORDER NO.   **MS-0928 $44.80**

**HANDBOOK OF NUMERICAL HEAT
TRANSFER**
Minkowycz, Sparrow, Schneider,
Pletcher
WILEY
ISBN 0-471-83093-3
ORDER NO. GE-0529   **$90.00**

**HANDBOOK OF SINGLE-PHASE
CONVECTIVE HEAT TRANSFER**
Kakac, Shah, Aung
WILEY
ISBN 0-471-81702-3
ORDER NO. GE-0530   **$95.00**

**ROARK'S FORMULAS FOR STRESS
& STRAIN**
Young
MCGRAW-HILL
ISBN 0-07-072541-1
ORDER NO. GE-0524   **$62.50**

®ΩΕ OMEGA Recommended

General Engineering

Complete Set **$700.00**

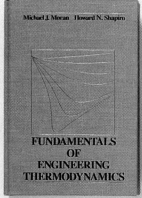

THE WILEY/NBS REGISTRY OF
MASS SPECTRAL DATA 7 VOLUME
SET
ISBN 0-471-62886-7
ORDER NO. MA-1117   **$700.00**

FUNDAMENTALS OF ENGINEERING
THERMODYNAMICS
Moran, Shapiro
WILEY
ISBN 0-471-89576-8
ORDER NO. GE-0528   **$57.50**

COPPER OXIDE
SUPERCONDUCTORS
Poole, Datta, Farach
WILEY
ISBN 0-471-62342-3
ORDER NO. MM-0634   **$35.00**

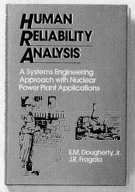

HUMAN RELIABILITY ANALYSIS
Dougherty, Fragola
WILEY
ISBN 0-471-60614-6
ORDER NO. GE-0545   **$75.00**

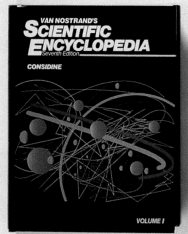

VAN NOSTRAND'S SCIENTIFIC
ENCYCLOPEDIA, 7TH ED.
Considine
ISBN 0-442-31814-6
ORDER NO. GE-0181   **$195.00**

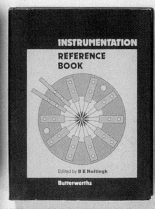

INSTRUMENTATION REFERENCE
BOOK
Noltingk
BUTTERWORTHS
ISBN 0-408-01562-4
ORDER NO. GE-0500   **$220.00**

HANDBOOK OF ADVANCED
SEMICONDUCTOR TECHNOLOGY
AND COMPUTER SYSTEMS
Rabbat
VAN NOSTRAND REINHOLD
ISBN 0-442-27688-5
ORDER NO. CS-1204   **$70.95**

ΩE OMEGA Recommended   Y-43

Math π $\sqrt{}$ e^x $\log$

Michael A. Arbib
Brains, Machines, and Mathematics
Second Edition
$29.50

NONLINEAR REGRESSION ANALYSIS & ITS APPLICATIONS
$39.95

Paul R. Halmos
I WANT TO BE A MATHEMATICIAN
An Automathography
$46.00

STATISTICAL METHODS FOR QUALITY IMPROVEMENT
THOMAS P. RYAN
$49.95

K A STROUD
ENGINEERING MATHEMATICS
PROGRAMMES AND PROBLEMS
SECOND EDITION
Springer-Verlag New York
$36.00

ΩE

BRAINS, MACHINES AND MATHEMATICS
Arbib
SPRINGER-VERLAG
ISBN 0-387-96539-4
ORDER NO. MA-1160 **$29.50**

NONLINEAR REGRESSION ANALYSIS & ITS APPLICATIONS
Bates, Watts
WILEY
ISBN 0-471-81643-4
ORDER NO. MA-1103 **$39.95**

I WANT TO BE A MATHEMATICIAN
Halmos
SPRINGER-VERLAG
ISBN 0-387-96078-3
ORDER NO. MA-1115 **$46.00**

STATISTICAL METHODS FOR QUALITY IMPROVEMENT
Ryan
WILEY
ISBN 0-471-84337-7
ORDER NO. ST-0610 **$49.95**

ENGINEERING MATHEMATICS
Stroud
SPRINGER-VERLAG
ISBN 0-387-91218-5
ORDER NO. MA-1161 **$36.00**

ΩE OMEGA Recommended

ΩE

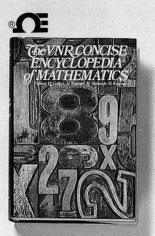

THE VNR CONCISE ENCYCLOPEDIA OF MATHEMATICS
Editors: Gellert, Kustner Hellwich, Kastner
VAN NOSTRAND REINHOLD
ISBN 0-442-22646-2
ORDER NO. MA-0434 **$31.95**

LEARNING DISCRETE MATHEMATICS WITH ISETL
Baxter, Dubinsky, Levin
SPRINGER-VERLAG
ISBN 0-387-96898-9
ORDER NO. MA-1162 **$45.00**

SOLVING ELLIPTIC PROBLEMS WITH ELLPACK
Rics, Boisvert
SPRINGER-VERLAG
ISBN 0-387-90910-9
ORDER NO. MA-1111 **$47.00**

DYNAMIC SYSTEMS CONTROL
Skelton
WILEY
ISBN 0-471-83779-2
ORDER NO. MM-0635 **$57.50**

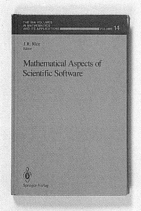

MATHEMATICAL ASPECTS OF SCIENTIFIC SOFTWARE
Weinberger, Miller
SPRINGER-VERLAG
ISBN 0-387-96706-0
ORDER NO. MA-1163 **$21.00**

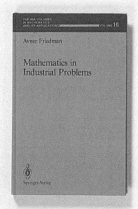

MATHEMATICS IN INDUSTRIAL PROBLEMS
Friedman
SPRINGER-VERLAG
ISBN 0-387-96860-1
ORDER NO. MA-1109 **$19.80**

Math π √ e log

**ENCYCLOPEDIA OF STATISTICAL
SCIENCES VOL 1-9**
Kotz, Johnson
WILEY
ISBN 0-471-05544-1
ORDER NO. ST-0133   **$775.00**

®Ω̄E

Complete Set $775.00

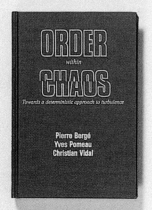

ORDER WITHIN CHAOS
Berge, Pomeau, Vidal
WILEY
ISBN 0-471-84967-7
ORDER NO. MS-0927   **$54.95**

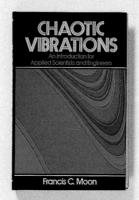

CHAOTIC VIBRATIONS
Moon
WILEY
ISBN 0-471-85685-1
ORDER NO. GE-0540   **$41.95**

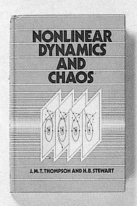

**NONLINEAR DYNAMICS AND
CHAOS**
Thompson, Stewart
WILEY
ISBN 0-471-90960-2
ORDER NO. MA-0189   **$49.95**

®Ω̄E

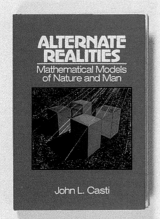

ALTERNATE REALITIES
Casti
WILEY
ISBN 0-471-61842-X
ORDER NO. MS-0923   **$34.95**

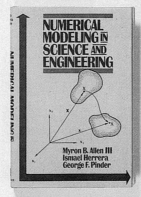

**NUMERICAL MODELING IN SCIENCE
AND ENGINEERING**
Allen, Herrera, Pinder
WILEY
ISBN 0-471-80635-8
ORDER NO. MM-1150   **$39.95**

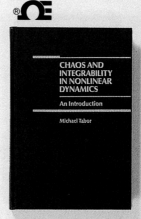

**CHAOS AND INTEGRABILITY IN
NONLINEAR DYNAMICS**
Tabor
WILEY
ISBN 0-471-82728-2
ORDER NO. MA-1101   **$55.00**

®Ω̄E **OMEGA Recommended**

...a society for materials

OMEGA Is proud to offer a wide ranging selection of technical books from ASM INTERNATIONAL. If you or your colleagues are members of this respected organization, you'll be pleased to hear that we are offering these texts to ASM members at MEMBERSHIP PRICES.

ASM INTERNATIONAL is one of the world's largest technical societies a not for profit organization dedicated to the advancement of technology for engineered materials—metals, plastics, composites, ceramics, and electronic materials.

ASM has more than 53,000 members worldwide. The basic mission of ASM and the focus of all its activities is the gathering, processing, and disseminating of useful, reliable technical information on engineered materials. ASM is a leading publisher of technical books with more than 150 titles now in print. These authoritative books are used as texts in engineering schools and universities worldwide and as working information sources throughout industry.

The following pages list more than 80 of these informative engineering texts, to order please call the convenient toll-free number listed below.

Why You Should Order From Book of Books®

- ✔ **No Shipping Charges on Pre-Paid Orders**
- ✔ **No Handling Charges Ever**
- ✔ **One Source for All Your Technical and Scientific Books**
- ✔ **Order by Calling Toll-Free in the USA**

To Order, Call Toll-Free

Book Hot Line (to Order Books Only)

1-800-222-BooK™
1-800-222-2665

For Instruments and Books

1-800-TC-OMEGA
1-800-82 66342

In CT Dial (203) 359-1660

ASM Books

EXTRUSION
Lane;Stenger
ISBN 087170-094-8
ASM MEMBER: $106.00
ORDER NO. MM-0649 **$133.00**

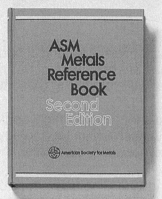

ASM METALS REFERENCE BOOK, 2ND ED.
ISBN 087170-156-1
ASM MEMBER: $65.60
ORDER NO. MM-0642 **82.00**

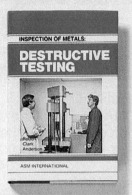

INSPECTION OF METALS VOLUME 2: DESTRUCTIVE TESTING
Anderson
ISBN 087170-348-3
ASM MEMBER: $68.00
ORDER NO. MM-0645 **$85.00**

INSPECTION OF METALS VOLUME 1: VISUAL EXAMINATION
Anderson
ISBN 087170-159-6
ASM MEMBER: $47.20
ORDER NO. MM-0646 **$59.00**

ELECTRONIC PACKAGING: MATERIALS AND PROCESSES
Edited by J.A. Sartell
ISBN 087170-257-6
ASM MEMBER: $60.80
ORDER NO. EE-1095 **$76.00**

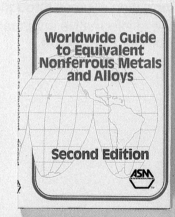

WORLDWIDE GUIDE TO EQUIVALENT NONFERROUS METALS AND ALLOYS, 2ND ED.
ISBN 087170-306-8
ASM MEMBER: $102.00
ORDER NO. MM-0648 **$128.00**

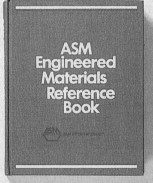

ASM ENGINEERED MATERIALS REFERENCE BOOK
ISBN 087170-350-5
ASM MEMBER: $65.60
ORDER NO. MM-0641 **$82.00**

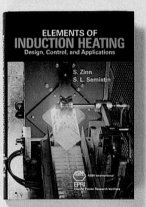

ELEMENTS OF INDUCTION HEATING: DESIGN, CONTROL, AND APPLICATIONS
Zinn;Semiatin
ISBN 087170-308-4
ASM MEMBER: $78.40
ORDER NO. MS-0932 **$98.00**

WORLDWIDE GUIDE TO EQUIVALENT IRONS AND STEELS, 2ND ED.
ISBN 087170-305-X
ASM MEMBER: $102.00
ORDER NO. MM-0647 **$128.00**

MACHINING SOURCE BOOK
Edited by M. Schwartz
ISBN 087170-323-8
ASM MEMBER: $47.20
ORDER NO. ME-0837 **$59.00**

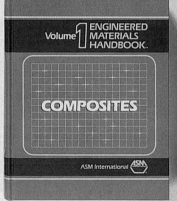

COMPOSITES, ENGINEERED MATERIALS HANDBOOK, VOLUME 1
ISBN 087170-279-7
ASM MEMBER: $88.00
ORDER NO. MM-0644 **$111.00**

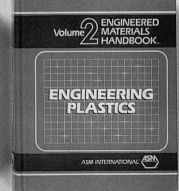

ENGINEERING PLASTICS, ENGINEERED MATERIALS HANDBOOK, VOLUME 2
ISBN 087170-280-0
ASM MEMBER: $88.00
ORDER NO. MM-0643 **$111.00**

$138.00

$117.00

$128.00

$126.00

$76.00

ASM Books

HYDROGEN EMBRITTLEMENT AND STRESS CORROSION CRACKING
Edited by Gibala;Hehemann
ISBN 087170-185-5
ASM MEMBER:$93.60
ORDER NO. MM-0657 **$117.00**

ATLAS OF FATIGUE CURVES
Edited by Boyer
ISBN 087170-214-2
ASM MEMBER: $110.00
ORDER NO. PH-1314 **$138.00**

SURFACE ALLOYING BY ION, ELECTRON, AND LASER BEAMS
Edited by Rehn; Picraux; Wiedersich
ISBN 087170-274-6
ASM MEMBER: $102.00
ORDER NO. MM-0655 **$128.00**

SYSTEMATIC ANALYSIS OF GEAR FAILURES
Alban
ISBN 087170-200-2
ASM MEMBER: $60.80
ORDER NO. ME-0838 **$76.00**

TOOL STEELS, 4TH ED.
Roberts,Cary
ISBN 087170-096-4
ASM MEMBER: $101.00
ORDER NO. MM-0653 **$126.00**

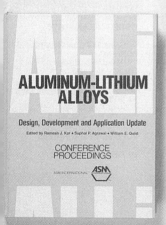

CASE HARDENING OF STEEL
ISBN 087170-265-7
ASM MEMBER: $60.00
ORDER NO. MM-0656 **$75.00**

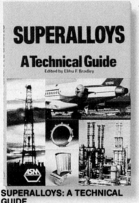

SUPERALLOYS: A TECHNICAL GUIDE
Edited by F. Bradley
ISBN 087170-327-0
ASM MEMBER: $55.20
ORDER NO. MM-0650 **$69.00**

SEM: A USER'S MANUAL FOR MATERIALS SCIENCE
Gabriel
ISBN 087170-202-9
ASM MEMBER: $56.80
ORDER NO. MM-0659 **$71.00**

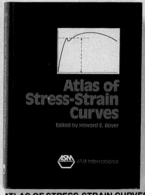

ATLAS OF STRESS-STRAIN CURVES
Edited by Boyer
ISBN 087170-240-1
ASM MEMBER: $110.00
ORDER NO. ME-0839 **$138.00**

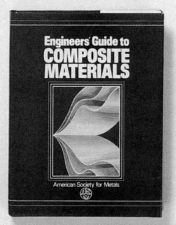

ALUMINUM-LITHIUM ALLOYS
Edited by Karr; Agrawal;Quist
ISBN 087170-325-4
ASM MEMBER: $66.40
ORDER NO. MM-0654 **$83.00**

ENGINEERS' GUIDE TO COMPOSITE MATERIALS
Edited by J Weeton
ISBN 087170-226-6
ASM MEMBER: $82.40
ORDER NO. MM-0652 **$103.00**

ADVANCED CASTING TECHNOLOGY
Edited by J. Easwaran
ISBN 087170-277-0
ASM MEMBER: $60.80
ORDER NO. MM-0651 **$76.00**

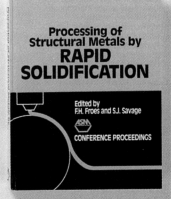

PROCESSING OF STRUCTURAL METALS BY RAPID SOLIDIFICATION
Edited by Froes; Savage
ISBN 087170-292-4
ASM MEMBER: $66.40
ORDER NO. MM-0658 **$83.00**

ΩE OMEGA Recommended

ASM Books

Complete 16 Volume Set
ORDER NO. MM-0662
$1595 Set Price
$1276 Member Set Price

Now—Put the world of metals and Materials at your fingertips!

METALS HANDBOOK, NINTH EDITION
This 16-volume set offers you concise, easy-to-use information on engineering analysis, concepts, methods, techniques, applications and markets. To ensure usefulness and technical reliability, these volumes have been prepared and reviewed by technical experts from industry and academia. The quick-reference format allows you to scan a section to readily obtain only the needed information, including data displayed in easy-to-read diagrams, tables, graphs, charts and specifications.
ORDER NO. FOR 16-VOLUME SET MM-0662
*PRICE: $111.00 EACH VOLUME, ASM MEMBER: $88.80 EACH VOLUME

NOW PRICED AS A SET!
INCLUDES VOLUMES 1-16
Price if purchased
separately:........$1776.00
Set Price:..........$1595.00
You Save:..........$ 181.00
Special Member
Price:................$1276.00
Members Save: $ 500.00

METALS HANDBOOK
COMPREHENSIVE INDEX, 2ND ED.
ISBN 087170-298-3
ASM MEMBER: $88.80
ORDER NO. MM-0663 **$110.00**

VOLUME 1: PROPERTIES AND SELECTION: IRONS AND STEELS
ISBN 087170-007-7
ORDER NO. MM-0664

VOLUME 2: PROPERTIES AND SELECTION: NONFERROUS ALLOYS AND PURE METALS
ISBN 087170-008-5
ORDER NO. MM-0665

VOLUME 3: PROPERTIES AND SELECTION: STAINLESS STEELS, TOOL MATERIALS AND SPECIAL PURPOSE METALS
ISBN 087170-009-3
ORDER NO. MM-0717

VOLUME 4: HEAT TREATING
ISBN 087170-019-7
ORDER NO. MM-0666

VOLUME 5: SURFACE CLEANING, FINISHING AND COATING
ISBN 087170-011-5
ORDER NO. MM-0667

VOLUME 6: WELDING, BRAZING, AND SOLDERING
ISBN 087170-012-3
ORDER NO. MM-0668

VOLUME 7: POWER METALLURGY
ISBN 087170-013-1
ORDER NO. MM-0669

VOLUME 8: MECHANICAL TESTING
ISBN 087170-014-X
ORDER NO. MM-0670

VOLUME 9: METALLOGRAPHY AND MICROSTRUCTURES
ISBN 087170-015-8
ORDER NO. MM-0671

VOLUME 10: MATERIALS CHARACTERIZATION
ISBN 087170-016-6
ORDER NO. MM-0672

VOLUME 11: FAILURE ANALYSIS AND PREVENTION
ISBN 087170-017-4
ORDER NO. MM-0673

VOLUME 12: FRACTOGRAPHY
ISBN 087170-018-2
ORDER NO. MM-0674

VOLUME 13: CORROSION
ISBN 087170-019-0
ORDER NO. MM-0675

VOLUME 14 FORMING AND FORGING
ISBN 0-87170-020-4
ORDER NO. MM-0676

VOLUME 15: CASTING METALS HANDBOOK
ISBN 087170-021-2
ORDER NO. MM-0800

VOLUME 16: MACHINING
ISBN 087170-022-0
ORDER NO. MM-0678

ASM Books

TECHNICAL WRITER'S HANDBOOK
Chandler
ISBN 087170-151-0
ASM MEMBER: $46.40
ORDER NO. GE-0551   **$58.00**

METAL FORMING: FUNDAMENTALS AND APPLICATIONS
Altan; Oh; Gegel
ISBN 087170-167-7
ASM MEMBER: $84.80
ORDER NO. MM-0661   **$106.00**

STAINLESS STEEL
Lula
ISBN 087170-208-8
ASM MEMBER: $46.00
ORDER NO. MM-0660   **$58.00**

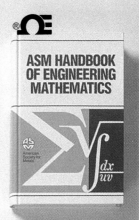

HANDBOOK OF ENGINEERING MATHEMATICS
Edited by Belding
ISBN 087170-15HX
ASM MEMBER: $84.80
ORDER NO. MA-1118   **$106.00**

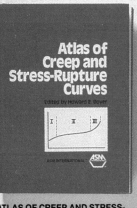

ATLAS OF CREEP AND STRESS-RUPTURE CURVES
Edited by Boyer
ISBN 087170-322-X
ASM MEMBER: $102.00
ORDER NO. ME-0840   **$128.00**

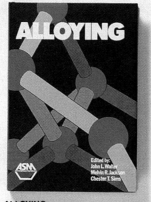

ALLOYING
Edited by Walter;Jackson;Sims
SBN 087170-326-2
ASM MEMBER: $81.60
ORDER NO. MM-0679   **$102.00**

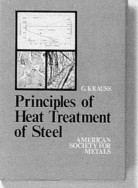

PRINCIPLES OF HEAT TREATMENT OF STEEL
Krauss
ISBN 087170-100-6
ASM MEMBER: $74.40
ORDER NO. MM-0681   **$93.00**

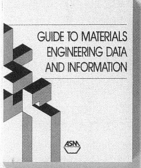

GUIDE TO MATERIALS ENGINEERING DATA AND INFORMATION
ISBN 087170-322-X
ASM MEMBER: $60.00
ORDER NO. MM-0680   **$75.00**

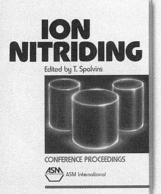

ION NITRIDING
Edited by Spalvins
ISBN 087170-315-7
ASM MEMBER: $56.80
ORDER NO. CH-4021   **$71.00**

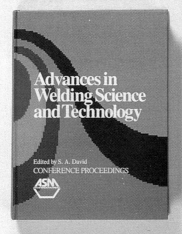

ADVANCES IN WELDING SCIENCE AND TECHNOLOGY
Edited David
ISBN 087170-245-2
ASM MEMBER: $73.60
ORDER NO. MM-0682   **$92.00**

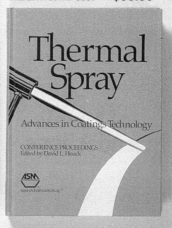

THERMAL SPRAY: ADVANCES IN COATING TECHNOLOGY
Edited Houck
ISBN 087170-320-3
ASM MEMBER: $66.40
ORDER NO. CM-0511   **$83.00**

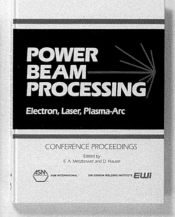

POWER BEAM PROCESSING: ELECTRON, LASER, AND PLASMA-ARC
Edited by Metzbower;Hauser
ISBN 087170-324-6
ASM MEMBER: $62.40
ORDER NO. EE-1096   **$78.00**

ASM Books

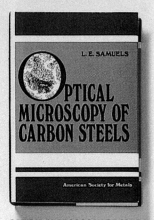

OPTICAL MICROSCOPY OF CARBON STEELS
Samuels
ISBN 087170-082-4
ASM MEMBER: $102.00
ORDER NO. MM-0686 **$128.00**

TRIBOLOGY IN METALWORKING FRICTION, LUBRICATION AND WEAR
Schey
ISBN 087170-155-3
ASM MEMBER $98.00
ORDER NO. MM-0693 **$123.00**

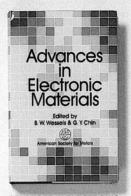

ADVANCES IN ELECTRONIC MATERIALS
Edited By Wessels;Chin
ISBN 087170-252-5
ASM MEMBER $103.00
ORDER NO. EE-1098 **$129.00**

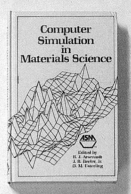

COMPUTER SIMULATION IN MATERIALS SCIENCE
Edited by Arsenault;Beeler;Esterling
ISBN 087170-296-7
ASM MEMBER: $102.00
ORDER NO. CS-1247 **$128.00**

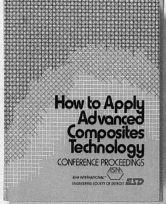

HOW TO APPLY ADVANCED COMPOSITES TECHNOLOGY
ISBN 087170-347-5
ASM MEMBER: $69.60
ORDER NO. MM-0689 **$87.00**

ADVANCED COMPOSITES III: EXPANDING THE TECHNOLOGY
ISBN 087170-307-6
ASM MEMBER: $63.20
ORDER NO. MM-0690 **$79.00**

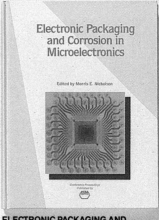

ELECTRONIC PACKAGING AND CORROSION IN MICROELECTRONICS
Edited by Nicholson
ISBN 087170-291-6
ASM MEMBER $63.20
ORDER NO. EE-1097 **$79.00**

HIGH INTEGRITY CASTINGS
Edited by White;Eylon;Foes
ISBN 087170-344-0
ASM MEMBER: $51.20
ORDER NO. MM-0692 **$64.00**

HEAT TREATMENT AND SURFACE ENGINEERING: NEW TECHNOLOGY AND PRACTICAL APPLICATIONS
Edited by Krauss
ISBN 087170-334-3
ASM MEMBER: $64.80
ORDER NO. MM-0685 **$81.00**

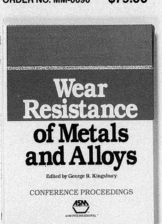

WEAR RESISTANCE OF METALS AND ALLOYS
Edited by Kingsbury
ISBN 087170-336-X
ASM MEMBER: $55.20
ORDER NO. MM-0691 **$69.00**

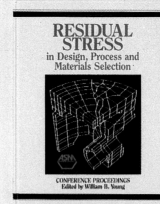

RESIDUAL STRESS IN DESIGN, PROCESS AND MATERIALS SELECTION
Edited by Young
ISBN 087170-304-1
ASM MEMBER: $60.00
ORDER NO. MM-0687 **$75.00**

ENGINEERED MATERIALS FOR ADVANCED FRICTION AND WEAR APPLICATIONS
Edited by Smidt
ISBN 087170-331-9
ASM MEMBER: $64.00
ORDER NO. MM-0688 **$80.00**

ASM Books

HSLA STEELS: METALLURGY AND APPLICATIONS
Edited by
Gray;Ko;Shouhua;Baorong;Xishan
ISBN 087170-299-0
ASM MEMBER: $75.20
ORDER NO. MM-0697 **$94.00**

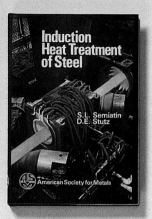

INDUCTION HEAT TREATMENT OF STEEL
Semiatin;Stutz
ISBN 087170-211-8
ASM MEMBER: 78.40
ORDER NO. MM-0703 **$98.00**

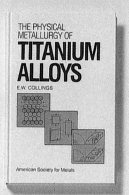

THE PHYSICAL METALLURGY OF TITANIUM ALLOYS
Collings
ISBN 087170-181-2
ASM MEMBER: $76.00
ORDER NO. MM-0704 **$95.00**

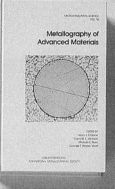

METALLOGRAPHY OF ADVANCED MATERIALS
Edited by Cialone; Johnson;Blum; Voort
ISBN 087170-349-1
ASM MEMBER: $61.60
ORDER NO. MM-0696 **$77.00**

THE MECHANISM OF FRACTURE
Edited by Goel
ISBN 087170-273-8
ASM MEMBER: $68.80
ORDER NO. MM-0701 **$86.00**

FATIGUE LIFE: ANALYSIS AND PREDICTION
Edited by Goel
ISBN 087170-271-1
ASM MEMBER: $62.40
ORDER NO. MM-0699 **$78.00**

ANALYZING FAILURES: THE PROBLEMS AND THE SOLUTIONS
Edited by Goel
ISBN 087170-270-3
ASM MEMBER: $60.00
ORDER NO. MM-0702 **$75.00**

CORROSION CRACKING
Edited by Goel
ISBN 087170-272-X
ASM MEMBER: $60.80
ORDER NO. MM-0802 **$76.00**

TOOL MATERIALS FOR HIGH-SPEED MACHINING
Edited Loush
ISBN 087170-297-5
ASM MEMBER: $55.20
ORDER NO. MM-0695 **$69.00**

THE HEAT TREATING SOURCE BOOK
Edited by Gupton
ISBN 087170-225-8
ASM MEMBER: $47.20
ORDER NO. MM-0694 **$59.00**

ΩE OMEGA **Recommended**

ASM Books

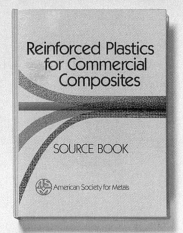

**REINFORCED PLASTICS FOR
COMMERCIAL COMPOSITES,
SOURCE BOOK**
Edited by Shook
ISBN 087170-259-2
ASM MEMBER: $47.20
ORDER NO. MM-0707   **$59.00**

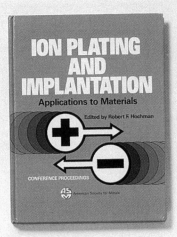

FORGING HANDBOOK
Edited by Byrer
ISBN 087170-194-4
ASM MEMBER: $58.40
ORDER NO. GE-0552   **$73.00**

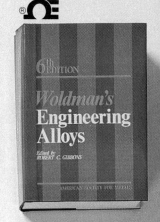

**ION PLATING AND IMPLANTATION
APPLICATIONS TO MATERIALS**
Edited by Hochman
ISBN 087170-269-X
ASM MEMBER: $58.40
ORDER NO. MM-0711   **$73.00**

**WOLDMAN'S ENGINEERING
ALLOYS**
Edited by Gibbons
ISBN 087170-086-7
ASM MEMBER: $96.00
ORDER NO. MM-0706   **$120.00**

**WELDING, FAILURE ANALYSIS, AND
METALLOGRAPHY**
Edited by Louthan;Lemay;Voort
ISBN 087170-237-1
ASM MEMBER: $56.00
ORDER NO. MM-0705   **$70.00**

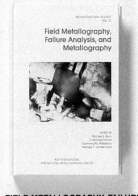

**FIELD METALLOGRAPHY, FAILURE
ANALYSIS, AND METALLOGRAPHY**
Edited by
Blum;French;Middeton;Voort
ISBN 087170-299-1
ASM MEMBER $60.00
ORDER NO. MM-0712   **$75.00**

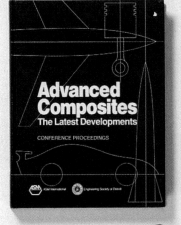

**ADVANCED COMPOSITES: THE
LATEST DEVELOPMENTS**
ISBN 087170-241-X
ASM MEMBER: $56.00
ORDER NO. MM-0709   **$70.00**

**METALLOGRAPHIC POLISHING BY
MECHANICAL METHODS**
Samuels
ISBN 087170-135-9
ASM MEMBER: $90.40
ORDER NO. MM-0708   **$113.00**

**QUENCHING AND CONTROL OF
DISTORTION**
Edited by Boyer;Cary
ISBN 087170-346-7
ASM MEMBER $51.20
ORDER NO. MM-0713   **$64.00**

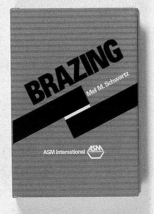

BRAZING
Schwartz
ISBN 087170-246-0
ASM MEMBER $77.60
ORDER NO. MM-0714   **$97.00**

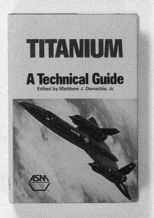

TITANIUM: A TECHNICAL GUIDE
Edited by Donachie
ISBN 087170-309-2
ASM MEMBER: $58.40
ORDER NO. MM-0715   **$73.00**

**MATERIALS AT LOW
TEMPERATURES**
Edited by Reed;Clark
ISBN 087170-146-4
ASM MEMBER: $110.00
ORDER NO. MM-0710   **$138.00**

ΩE OMEGA Recommended

INDEX

Books are Arranged Alphabetically by Title, Followed by Author and Page Number

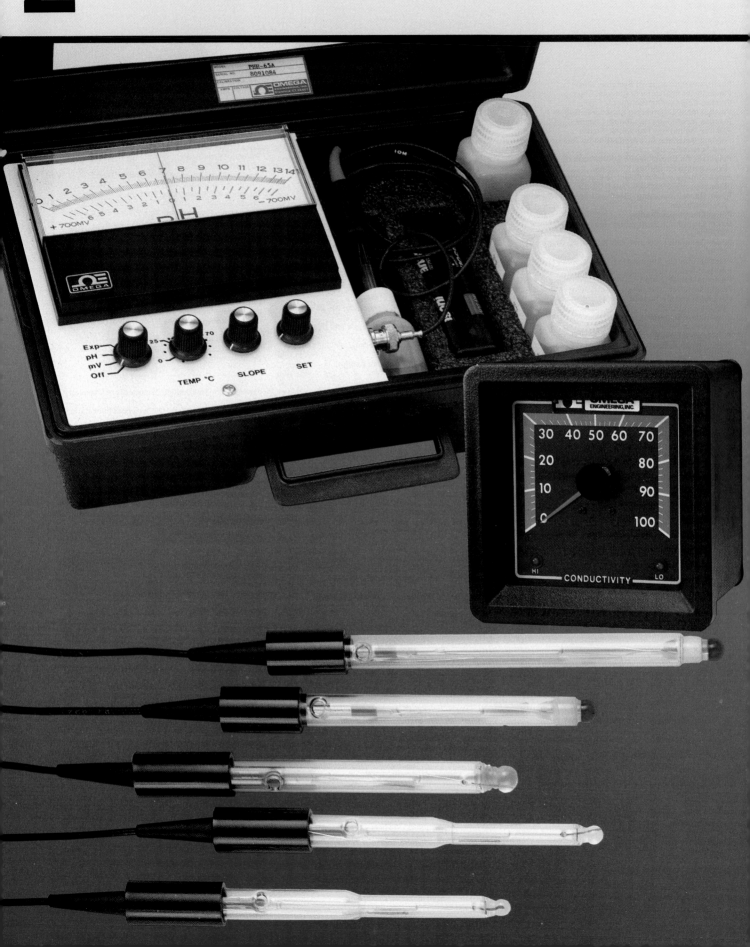

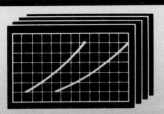

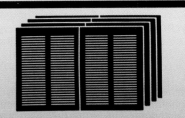

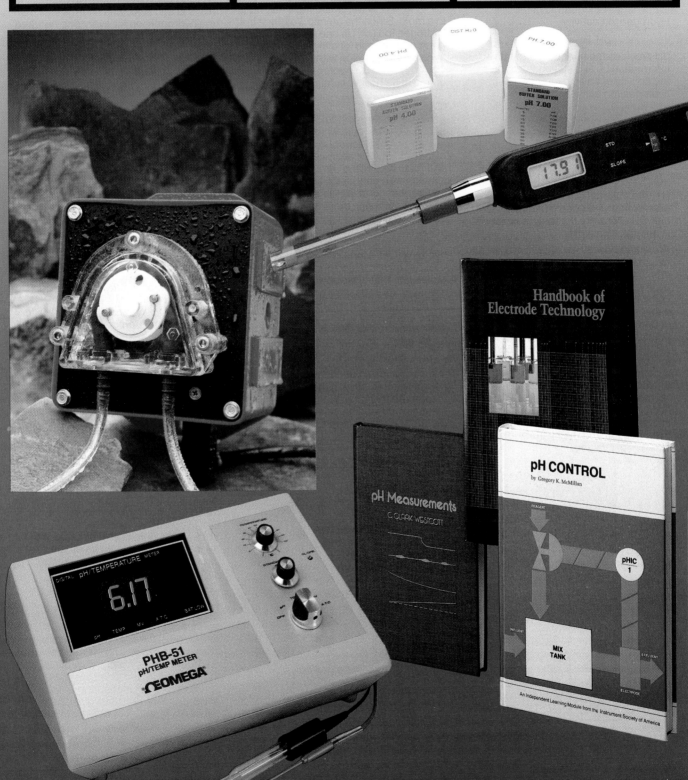

Z TECHNICAL REFERENCE

Introduction to pH

INTRODUCTION

pH is a unit of measure which describes the degree of acidity or alkalinity of a solution. It is measured on a scale of 0 to 14. The term pH is derived from "p", the mathematical symbol of the negative logarithm, and "H", the chemical symbol of Hydrogen. The formal definition of pH is the negative logarithm of the Hydrogen ion activity.

$$pH = -\log[H+]$$

pH provides the needed quantitative information by expressing the degree of the activity of an acid or base in terms of hydrogen ion activity.

The pH value of a substance is directly related to the ratio of the hydrogen ion [H+] and the hydroxyl ion [OH−] concentrations. If the H+ concentration is greater than OH−, the material is acidic; i.e., the pH value is less than 7. If the OH− concentration is greater than H+, the material is basic, with a pH value greater than 7. If equal amounts of H+ and OH− ions are present, the material is neutral, with a pH of 7.

Acids and bases have free hydrogen and hydroxyl ions, respectively. Since the relationship between hydrogen ions and hydroxyl ions in a given solution is constant for a given set of conditions, either one can be determined by knowing the other. Thus, pH is a measurement of both acidity and alkalinity, even though by definition it is a selective measurement of hydrogen ion activity. Since pH is a logarithmic function, a change of one pH unit represents a ten-fold change in hydrogen ion concentration. Table 1 shows the concentration of both the hydrogen ion and the hydroxyl ion at different pH values.

THE MOLAR CONCEPT

A mole of a compound is defined as Avogadro's number of molecules (6.02×10^{23} molecules), which has a mass approximately equal to the molecular weight, expressed in grams. For example, sodium hydroxide, NaOH, which has a molecular weight of $23 + 16 + 1 = 40$, would have 40 grams in a mole. Since the atomic weight of the hydrogen ion (H+) is one (1), there is one gram of hydrogen ions in a mole of hydrogen. A solution with a pH of 10 has 1×10^{-10} moles of hydrogen ions, or 10^{-10} grams in a one liter solution.

IONIZATION

An ion is a charged particle, created by an atom or molecule which has either gained or lost electron(s). The presence of ions in solution allows electrical energy to be passed through the solution as a conductor. Different compounds form ions in solution in different amounts, depending on the ability of the atoms to gain or lose electrons. They will dissociate (or ionize) in solution to form hydrogen (H+) or hydroxyl (OH−) ions in the solution.

Molecules that dissociate easily will form strong acids or bases when in aqueous solution (water solvent). Examples of these are hydrochloric acid (HCl) or sodium hydroxide (NaOH):

$$HCl + H_2O \longrightarrow H_3O^+ + Cl^-$$
$$NaOH \longrightarrow Na^+ + OH^-$$

In an aqueous solution, hydrogen ions normally combine with the water solvent to form the hydronium ion (H_3O^+). pH measurements of these solutions are therefore measurements of the hydronium ion concentration. Normally, the terms "hydronium ion" and "hydrogen ion" are used interchangeably in pH measurement applications.

Some compounds form weak acids or bases; only a very small percentage of the compounds dissociates into its constituent ions, so very few hydrogen or hydroxyl ions are formed. An example of this is acetic acid, which forms less than one hydrogen ion for every one hundred molecules:

$$H_2O + CH_3COOH \longrightarrow H_3O^+ + CH_3COO^-$$

Pure water also dissociates weakly, with 10^{-7} hydrogen and 10^{-7} hydroxyl ions formed for every water molecule at 25°C:

$$2H_2O \longrightarrow H_3O^+ + OH^-$$

The addition of acid to water increases the concentration of hydrogen ions and reduces the concentration of hydroxyl ions. A base added to water has the opposite effect, increasing the concentration of hydroxyl ions and reducing the concentration of hydrogen ions:

$$H_2O + HCl \longrightarrow H_3O^+ + Cl^-$$
$$H_2O + NaOH \longrightarrow Na^+ + H_2O + OH^-$$

There is a wide variety of applications for pH measurement. For example, pH measurement and control is the key to the successful purification of drinking water, the manufacture of sugar, sewage treatment, food processing, electroplating, and the effectiveness and safety of medicines, cosmetics, etc. Plants require the soil to be within a certain pH range in order to grow properly, and animals can sicken or die if their blood pH level is not within the correct limits. Figure 1 gives pH values for some common industrial and household products.

pH MEASUREMENT

A rough indication of pH can be obtained using pH papers or indicators, which change color as the pH level varies. These indicators have limitations on their accuracy, and can be difficult to interpret correctly in colored or murky samples.

More accurate pH measurements are obtained with a pH meter. A pH measurement system consists of three parts: a pH measuring electrode, a reference electrode, and a high input impedance meter. The pH electrode can be thought of as a battery, with a voltage that varies with the pH of the measured solution. The pH measuring electrode is a hydrogen ion sensitive glass bulb, with a millivolt output that varies with the changes in the relative hydrogen ion concentration inside and outside of the

HYDROGEN ION CONCENTRATION IN MOLES/LITER AT 25°C		
pH	H+	OH−
0	(10^0) 1	0.00000000000001 (10^{-14})
1	(10^{-1}) 0.1	0.0000000000001 (10^{-13})
2	(10^{-2}) 0.01	0.000000000001 (10^{-12})
3	(10^{-3}) 0.001	0.00000000001 (10^{-11})
4	(10^{-4}) 0.0001	0.0000000001 (10^{-10})
5	(10^{-5}) 0.00001	0.000000001 (10^{-9})
6	(10^{-6}) 0.000001	0.00000001 (10^{-8})
7	(10^{-7}) 0.0000001	0.0000001 (10^{-7})
8	(10^{-8}) 0.00000001	0.000001 (10^{-6})
9	(10^{-9}) 0.000000001	0.00001 (10^{-5})
10	(10^{-10}) 0.0000000001	0.0001 (10^{-4})
11	(10^{-11}) 0.00000000001	0.001 (10^{-3})
12	(10^{-12}) 0.000000000001	0.01 (10^{-2})
13	(10^{-13}) 0.0000000000001	0.1 (10^{-1})
14	(10^{-14}) 0.00000000000001	1 (10^0)

Table 1

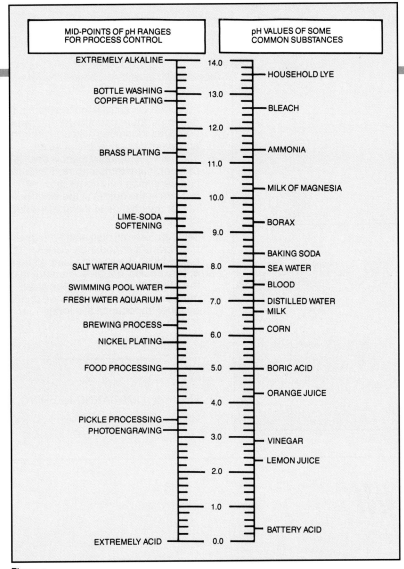

Figure 1

MID-POINTS OF pH RANGES FOR PROCESS CONTROL	pH VALUES OF SOME COMMON SUBSTANCES

Left scale (MID-POINTS OF pH RANGES FOR PROCESS CONTROL):
- EXTREMELY ALKALINE — 14.0
- BOTTLE WASHING / COPPER PLATING — 13.0
- BRASS PLATING — 11.0
- LIME-SODA SOFTENING — 9.0
- SALT WATER AQUARIUM — 8.0
- SWIMMING POOL WATER / FRESH WATER AQUARIUM — 7.0
- BREWING PROCESS / NICKEL PLATING — 6.0
- FOOD PROCESSING — 5.0
- PICKLE PROCESSING / PHOTOENGRAVING — 3.0
- EXTREMELY ACID — 0.0

Right scale (pH VALUES OF SOME COMMON SUBSTANCES):
- HOUSEHOLD LYE
- BLEACH
- AMMONIA
- MILK OF MAGNESIA
- BORAX
- BAKING SODA
- SEA WATER
- BLOOD
- DISTILLED WATER / MILK
- CORN
- BORIC ACID
- ORANGE JUICE
- VINEGAR
- LEMON JUICE
- BATTERY ACID

bulb. The reference electrode output does not vary with the activity of the hydrogen ion. The pH electrode has very high internal resistance, making the voltage change with pH difficult to measure. The input impedance of the pH meter and leakage resistances are therefore important factors. The pH meter is basically a high impedance amplifier that accurately measures the minute electrode voltages and displays the results directly in pH units on either an analog or digital display. In some cases, voltages can also be read for special applications or for use with ion-select or Oxidation-Reduction Potential (ORP) electrodes.

TEMPERATURE COMPENSATION

Temperature compensation is contained within the instrument, because pH electrodes and measurements are temperature sensitive. The temperature compensation may be either manual or automatic. With manual compensation, a separate temperature measurement is required, and the pH meter manual compensation control can be set with

the approximate temperature value. With automatic temperature compensation (ATC), the signal from a separate temperature probe is fed into the pH meter, so that it can accurately determine pH value of the sample at that temperature.

BUFFER SOLUTIONS

Buffers are solutions that have constant pH values and the ability to resist changes in that pH level. They are used to calibrate the pH measurement system (electrode and meter). There can be small differences between the output of one electrode and another, as well as changes in the output of electrodes over time. Therefore, the system must be periodically calibrated. Buffers are available with a wide range of pH values, and they come in both premixed liquid form or as convenient dry powder capsules. Most pH meters require calibration at several specific pH values. One calibration is usually performed near the isopotential point (the signal produced by an electrode at pH 7 is 0 mV at 25°C), and a second is typically

performed at either pH 4 or pH 10. It is best to select a buffer as close as possible to the actual pH value of the sample to be measured.

TEMPERATURE EFFECTS

As previously stated, the pH electrode is temperature dependent, and may be compensated for in the pH meter circuitry. The circuitry of the pH meter utilizes the Nernst equation, which is a general mathematical description of electrode behavior.

$$E = E_x + \frac{2.3RT_K}{nF} \log (a_i)$$

where:

E_x = constant depending upon reference electrode
R = constant
T_K = absolute temperature (Kelvin)
n = charge of the ion (including sign)
F = constant
a_i = activity of the ion

For pH measurement, we are interested in the hydrogen ion for H^+:

$$\frac{2.3RT_K}{nF} = 59.16 \text{ mV}$$

where: $n = 1$ and $T = 25°C$. This term is commonly known as the Nernst coefficient. Since pH is defined as the negative logarithm of the hydrogen ion activity, the general equation at any temperature can be expressed as:

$$E = E_x - 1.98 \, T_K \, pH$$

Changes in temperature of a solution will vary the millivolt output of the glass pH electrode in accordance with the Nernst equation. Its variation in the electrode sensitivity versus temperature is a linear function, and most pH meters have circuitry designed to compensate for this effect (refer to *Temperature Compensation*). Figure 2 shows the effect on the glass pH electrode signal at various temperatures.

In figure 2, all three slopes intersect at the point of 0 mV and pH 7.0; this implies no millivolt change with temperature at this, the isopotential point. Also, it can be seen that when working near 7.0 pH, temperature compensation is not a significant factor. However, when working at pH levels of 3.0 or 11.0, a temperature change of 15°C can result in an error of 0.2 pH. Since the temperature effect on the electrode has been shown to be linear, the temperature dependence of pH can then be expressed as:

$$0.03 \text{ pH error/pH unit/10°C}$$

The actual pH of the sample can change with temperature due to a change in the hydrogen ion activity in the solution, because ionization of compounds and

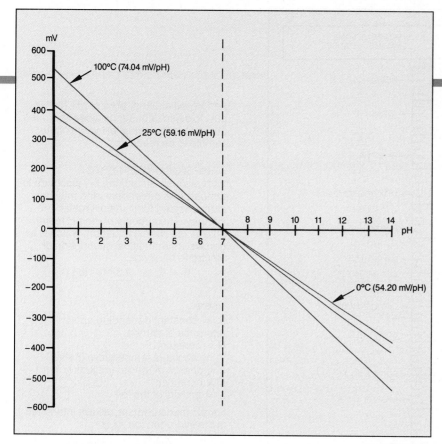

Figure 2

hydrogen ion activity in the solution may be temperature dependent. Temperature compensation does not correct for this, and is not desirable, because an accurate pH measurement is desired at that particular temperature. Temperature compensation only corrects for the change in the output of the electrode, not for the change in the actual solution pH.

Temperature will also affect the glass membrane's impedance. For each 8° below 25°C, the specified impedance approximately doubles. Depending on the original impedance of the glass membrane, the meter will have to handle a higher impedance at a lower temperature. ΩE

Written by: OMEGA ENGINEERING, INC.

Measurement of pH

The measurement of pH is one of the most common analytical techniques used in chemistry laboratories today. Nonetheless, pH measurements often suffer from the effects of incorrect materials or incorrect maintenance. The purpose of this paper is to help simplify the choice of materials, methods, and maintenance protocols for pH measurements.

pH MEASUREMENT SYSTEM

A pH measurement system always consists of four parts: a pH sensing electrode, an amplifier that translates the signal into something the user can read, a reference electrode, and the sample being measured. Each part of the system plays a critical role in the measurement process.

A glass electrode is actually a small battery (technically, a transducer). This battery displays a varying voltage, depending upon the pH of the solution in which it is immersed. A reasonable representation of that voltage is given in Figure 1. The potential of the glass electrode is a function of the activity of the free-hydrogen ions and a value E_0 which is supposed to be the 0 or rest

potential of the system. This is actually the voltage of the system when the pH is 0.

The reference electrode is also a battery; however, unlike the pH electrode, its voltage does not vary with the activity of hydrogen ion or any other ion solution, but is a function only of the value E_0 or the rest potential.

There are nine actual voltages in the system. Inside the body of the electrode is a wire — normally a silver wire coated with silver chloride. On that wire is some matrix that should present a constant voltage to the wire. At the interface of the wire and solution is a voltage which we can call E_1. Between the wire and the inner surface of the glass is another voltage, on the inner surface of the glass is a voltage (E_3), and across the glass membrane there is a voltage (E_4), which is called the asymmetry potential. There is a voltage on the outer surface of the electrode, a voltage between the pH electrode and the reference electrode; another voltage, referred to as the liquid junction potential or streaming potential, at the point where the filling solution of the reference electrode contacts the

sample (E_7); a voltage between the inner surface of the reference electrode and the metal wire that connects the inner filling solution of the reference electrode to the lead wire, and, of course, another voltage on the surface of the connecting wire (E_9).

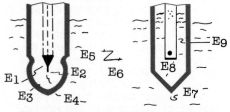

E_5 — Potential of ion of interest
E_7 — Liquid-junction potential

Figure 1. *Flow chart of selection process for reference electrodes.*

When making a pH measurement, one assumes that all of those voltages remain constant except the voltage on the outer surface of the pH electrode. If that assumption is correct, legitimate pH measurements can be made; if not, then incorrect pH measurements will certainly result. In other words, it is assumed that the pH electrode delivers a varying voltage to the pH meter, while the reference electrode delivers a constant voltage to the meter.

THE REFERENCE ELECTRODE

The reference electrode is the most complicated part of a pH measurement system. When application problems arise, they normally devolve to the reference electrode. When difficulties in pH measurements are encountered, the source of the problem is typically the reference electrode. In our experience the reference electrode accounts for 70% of the problems that arise in the pH measuring process.

A reference electrode consists of three principal parts: an internal element, which is normally either a silver wire coated with silver chloride or a platinum wire covered with a mixture of calomel (Hg_2Cl_2), some filling solution, and a permeable junction through which the filling solution escapes the electrode (called the fluid junction or liquid junction). The liquid junction can come in several forms, but its principal function is to allow small quantities of the reference electrode's filling solution to slowly leak or migrate into the sample being measured. There are three common forms of this junction: 1) ceramic or other frit material, 2) a fibrous material (the best of which is quartz fiber) or 3) a sleeve junction.

Fritted materials are usually white and are composed of small particles pressed closely together. The filling solution leaks through the open cells between these particles. Since the cells vary considerably in size, the flow rate across the surface is quite variable. In some areas, there is almost no net outward flow of filling solution. At those points the junction is considered to be a "diffusion junction." In the areas where the net outward migration of filling solution is rapid, the electrode is considered to have a flowing junction.

Fiber references come in two types: woven fibers and straight fibers. Woven fibers, such as asbestos fiber, have cells of varying size because of the structure of the woven material. Some of these cells are very small and tightly packed together; at those points there is a diffusion junction. Where the fibers are loosely packed, the flow rate is high and a flowing junction exists.

The quartz fiber reference electrode consists of straight fibers of quartz laid next to each other with straight channels of filling solution passing between them. This junction generally is considered to have no diffusion properties and to be strictly a flowing junction.

The sleeve junction reference electrode is constructed by putting a hole in the side of a glass or plastic tube, grinding the surface around that tube, and covering it with a tapered glass or plastic sleeve. Such a junction is similar in its overall function to a frit junction in that certain areas are pressed tightly and other areas are not, so that both diffusion and flowing junctions exist. A sleeve junction electrode is much faster flowing and much easier to clean than the others.

Reference electrodes are available in a variety of types to accommodate many types of samples. Certain samples require reference electrodes that flow very slowly, whereas other samples require reference electrodes that are easy to clean. The flow chart in Figure 2 should serve as a guide in selecting the reference electrode most appropriate for the application.

The best way to understand the purpose of a reference electrode is to imagine measuring the voltage on a battery with a voltmeter. A voltage measurement cannot be made if only one end of the battery is connected to the meter. If, however, two leads are plugged into the voltmeter and both ends of the battery are touched, a reading is possible.

A pH electrode can be compared to the battery in this example. The wire inside the pH electrode serves the same purpose as the first lead from the voltmeter. The reference electrode can be compared to the second lead, which completes the circuit and enables the measurement of the voltage, or voltage changes, at the pH electrode.

In reality, the pH and reference electrodes are immersed in the same solution with the filling solution of the reference electrode flowing into the sample and completing the circuit with the pH electrode. If the reference electrode is not immersed in the sample, a legitimate measurement is not possible. If the reference electrode immersed in the sample is completely dry, no reading would be forthcoming. If it were filled with filling solution but completely occluded, then it would not establish good consistent electrical connection with the sample, and the readings would vary. A reference electrode that is partially plugged up allows the sample ions to migrate into the junction of the electrode and set up new potentials: voltages that are measured by the system and interpreted as changing pH readings. This is the most common source of problems in a pH measuring system.

The first indication of difficulty in the reference electrode usually is a very long stabilization time. This can be caused by changes in temperature, by reactions taking place in the solution, or by pickup of CO_2 from the atmosphere. Generally, however, a long stabilization time is caused by either the incompatibility of the reference electrode with the sample being measured or by a faulty reference electrode.

It is usually possible to differentiate between drift caused by a faulty electrode and drift caused by other factors (incompatibility between electrode and sample, temperature changes, or reaction within the sample) by moving a hand quickly toward and then away from the electrode. If the reading on the pH meter changes significantly in response to the hand movement, and if the change in the meter reading reverses when retracting the hand, then it would be very safe to assume that the reference electrode is either plugged up or otherwise defective. If the drift continues undisturbed by the movement of the hand toward and away from the electrode, then the problem is probably in the sample. Although this is not a foolproof method, it works most of the time.

There are other ways to check for improperly functioning reference electrodes. The most positive checks are performed using a magnetic stirrer.

• If stirring a sample seems to cause an unstable reading, turn the stirrer off. If the reading changes significantly (by one or two tenths of a pH unit), then there is a reference electrode problem.

• If, while stirring, there is a fair amount of noise (variation in the reading), and turning the stirring motor down to a slower speed reduces the amount of noise, it is safe to assume that there is a reference electrode problem.

If the reference electrode is so dirty that it is completely occluded, it may be just like an open circuit. If this is the case, it exhibits the typical slow, never-ending drift. There are a number of other sources of this same problem (including the electrode's not being plugged in to the meter!), such as: broken wires within the pH or reference electrode; a broken lead wire from the pH or reference electrode; or an open circuit within the meter. A quick way to check whether the problem is in the electrodes or the meter is to substitute new electrodes or, using a wire, paper clip, or shorting plug, short between the reference electrode input and the pH electrode input on the meter. If shorting the electrode inputs does

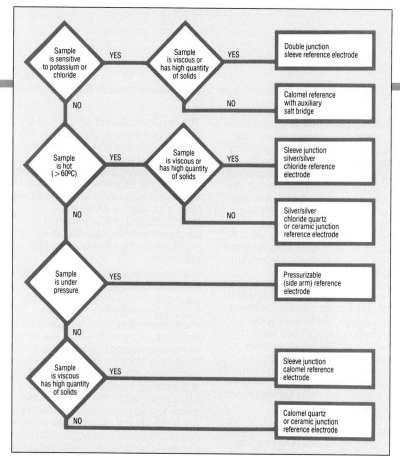

Figure 2. *Flow chart of selection process for reference electrodes.*

eliminate the drift, then a substitution of the pH, and subsequently, the reference electrode, should determine which electrode is the open circuit. If the reference electrode exhibits an open circuit, then follow a cleaning procedure to see if the situation improves.

Another way to determine if a reference electrode is serviceable is to attach the reference electrode in question to the pH meter through the reference electrode input and, through an adapter, connect a good reference electrode to the glass electrode input of the meter. This pair of electrodes is then immersed in either a buffer near pH 4 or near pH 10 (*not* pH 7 buffer). If the electrodes are of the same type (both calomel or both silver chloride) and are functioning properly, the meter reading should be steady and should not exceed 2 to 3 mV. If the reading does exceed 3 mV or varies by more than 1 mV, it is safe to assume that the reference electrode needs rejuvenation.

Restoring an electrode to proper function depends upon the type of reference electrode and the severity of the problem. Most rejuvenation procedures that can be used on combination pH electrodes are also appropriate for separate reference electrodes. Following are the rejuvenation procedures, arranged in increasing order of the ''severity'' of the procedure.

1. *Soaking the junction.* Problems can often be eliminated by dissolving crystals from the end of the electrode. To perform this cleaning, make a solution of 10% saturated potassium chloride, 90% distilled or deionized water. Fill the reference electrode with its filling solution and place it in a large beaker. Warm the soaking mixture until it is tepid, but be careful not to get it too hot to touch. Pour the mixture into the beaker until the electrodes are immersed about 2 in. Allow this to stand for 20 min to 2 or 3 hr. Test the electrodes.

2. *Ammonia soak.* The junction of electrodes which employ silver chloride reference elements often become clogged with silver chloride. An excellent way to remove silver chloride from a junction is with concentrated ammonium hydroxide (concentrated ammonia). Follow these steps:

a) Empty the filling solution from the reference electrode.

b) Immerse only the end of the electrode in concentrated ammonia (do not put ammonia inside the electrode).

c) Soak the electrode in this solution for 10 to 20 min. Do *not* leave the electrode immersed in ammonia overnight or for periods of longer than ½ hr. Ammonia is volatile; once inside the reference electrode, it can condense on the silver element and dissolve all the silver chloride. This will permanently damage the reference electrode.

d) After soaking the electrode in ammonia for 10 to 20 min, thoroughly rinse both the outside and inside with deionized or distilled water. Empty the electrode and replace the filling solution, and retest.

This rejuvenation procedure is also very good for pH-sensitive glass. The result should be a very fast responding, very stable electrode.

3. *Urea soak.* When protein coats the glass of a pH electrode or penetrates the junction of a reference electrode, it can be very difficult to remove. One of the best ways to eliminate protein is by soaking in 8 M urea for about 2 hr. After soaking in urea, rinse the electrode well, empty and rinse the filling solution, and refill with fresh filling solution.

4. *Vacuum.* A separate reference electrode often can be cleaned by applying vacuum to the junction. The easiest way is to use an aspirator. Place some flexible tubing on the aspirator, cover the end of the reference electrode with this tubing, and turn on the water. The vacuum should be sufficient to draw some filling solution through the reference junction and remove any mechanical obstructions. Most reference electrodes will not be damaged by such a procedure, but note that it is possible to dislodge the material of the reference junction. At this stage the electrode may not have been salvageable otherwise, so it is certainly worth trying.

5. *Boiling the junction.* Boiling the junction sometimes removes obstructions that cannot be removed by the previous steps, but the procedure can ruin the electrode. (Note: do *not* boil a calomel reference electrode. Calomel breaks down at about 67°C [some sources say 80°C], and this permanently damages the electrode.)

An Ag/AgCl reference can be boiled without fear of damage to the reference half-cell. If this stage is reached with a calomel type electrode, and the electrode is still unserviceable, the junction should be immersed in boiling water for no more than 10 to 15 sec. Remove the electrode and allow to cool to room temperature before boiling again. A silver electrode can be immersed safely in boiling water for 20 to 30 sec. For a silver chloride reference, the only danger in this procedure is that the glass may break because of thermal stress.

6. *Sanding the junction.* When all else has failed, try sanding the junction of the electrode. The reason this step is left until last is that it is possible to drive the grit of the sandpaper into the junction,

where it will lodge permanently. If the electrode were going to be discarded as unserviceable, this procedure would not make it more unserviceable and might possibly remove a stubborn clog from the end of the electrode.

Since it is far easier to prevent a problem than to solve it, a great deal of attention should be paid to the handling and storage of pH and reference electrodes. This is an area of considerable diversity of opinion.

REFERENCE ELECTRODE MAINTENANCE

Ag/AgCl

The silver chloride electrode should not be used in solutions containing proteins, S^{-2}, Br^-, I^- or any other solutions that would precipitate with the silver found in the filling solution of an Ag/AgCl type reference electrode. Strong reducing agents also should be avoided because they can reduce the silver ions to silver metal, thus silverplating the junction.

The proclivity of silver to precipitate in the junction of an Ag/AgCl reference electrode also dictates special storage procedures. Probably the best storage solution for an Ag/AgCl reference electrode is saturated KCl. The KCl tends to prevent precipitation of silver chloride in the junction of the electrode and maintains that junction in operable condition.

Calomel and double junction

Both calomel and double junction reference electrodes may be stored in a 1 to 10 dilution of their filling solutions. These electrodes generally can be used in any type of sample without damage to the electrode. One exception is solutions containing high concentrations of silver. These solutions should be measured using a reference electrode containing no chloride, such as a double-junction reference electrode, the outer body of which is filled with something that does not precipitate with silver, such as Na_2SO_4 or KNO_3.

Most separate reference electrodes contain a reference half-cell consisting of a glass tube sealed at the top around a piece of wire. This wire, usually silver or platinum, is immersed in a mixture of crystals. In a silver chloride reference electrode, the crystals are silver chloride; in a calomel reference electrode, the crystals are Hg_2Cl_2. The end of the glass tube usually is plugged with a wad of cotton, glass wool or a frit. The crystals must be wet in order to provide electrical continuity. At the factory the glass tube and the body are filled with a potassium chloride solution.

The electrode is then sealed at the filling hole and the junction before shipment.

If the body is allowed to dry out completely, the fluid in the half-cell tube leaks out through the porous junction at the end of that tube. This happens particularly quickly if the electrode is on its side and is either dry or three quarters empty. When the fluid has leaked out of the inner glass tube, there is no continuity through the crystals. If the electrode is refilled, an air bubble remains in the glass tube, since there is no way for it to escape. This air bubble causes an open circuit condition.

To rectify the problem, fill the electrode with filling solution, plug the junction, and evacuate, using a laboratory aspirator. Keep vacuum on the electrode body until no more bubbles emerge from the end of the inner glass tube. (This may be difficult to determine, because the filling solution will be out-gassing while under vacuum.) When there is no more air in the inner glass tube, slowly release the vacuum; the filling solution will now be drawn up into the tube and will saturate the crystals.

pH ELECTRODE MAINTENANCE

In the early days of pH measurements, it was necessary to keep the pH electrode immersed in an aqueous solution to maintain proper function, because the glass was most repeatable and stable when there was a hydrated layer on the surface. In the earlier glass formulations, that hydrated layer could dry out quite easily. Newer formulations (used in most pH electrodes today) do not require immersion in an aqueous solution. However, it is important that the electrode and the sample be in intimate contact and that there be no surface contamination to provide a barrier between the ions in solution and the surface of the glass. To prevent airborne contaminants from depositing on the sensitive glass surface, the electrode should be either covered or immersed in a liquid. When soaking a pH electrode, make the solution somewhat acidic, so that contaminants in the pH glass are exchanged out of the glass for hydrogen ions, keeping the electrode more sensitive to pH.

Combination pH electrode maintenance

Combination pH electrodes are almost invariably based on an Ag/AgCl reference half-cell. Thus, the electrodes should not be soaked in any solution that might cause precipitation of the silver in the junction of the electrode. Silver chloride is more soluble in very high concentrations of chloride than it is in low concentrations. (This can be shown

by putting a few drops of combination electrode filling solution, KCl saturated with AgCl, into deionized water. An "opalescent" cloud, a silver chloride precipitate, forms.) Therefore, it is not good to cover the filling hole of a combination pH electrode and store it in solutions of low chloride concentration.

Solutions very high in sodium chloride or potassium chloride represent a problem for the pH-sensitive glass. Because the glass is an ion exchange surface, it will exchange the hydrogen ions in the glass for the potassium ions in the solution, thus reducing the electrode sensitivity to hydrogen ion. Because a combination pH electrode should be stored neither in solutions of low potassium chloride concentration nor in solutions of high potassium chloride concentration, it is best to store these electrodes for long periods of time (overnight or over a weekend) in air with the protective cap on the end of the electrode and the filling hole covered (to retain the filling solution in the electrode). For very long-term storage, it is best to keep the electrode completely dry; that is, remove the filling solution from the reference portion of the electrode, rinse with deionized water, and put the electrode in a safe place.

Gel-filled combination electrodes

There is very little that can be done to rejuvenate a gel-filled electrode, but one method that is effective for certain designs is to heat a saturated potassium chloride solution to about 50°C, immerse the electrode deeply in this solution, and allow solution and electrode to cool. This sometimes forces contaminants out of the junction of the electrode and draws potassium chloride into that junction to bring it back to life.

If an electrode is treated well, stored properly, and occasionally rejuvenated, it should provide several years of relatively trouble-free service. **ΩE**

OMEGA ENGINEERING, INC. gratefully acknowledges American Laboratory for permission to reprint the article "Measurement of pH".

Trademarks	
Omega Engineering, Inc.	Dialtemp™ White Box®
Apple Computer, Inc.	Apple®
E.I. DuPont de Nemours & Co.	Teflon® Viton® KEL-F®
General Electric Co.	Noryl®
International Business Machines, Inc.	IBM®
Laboratory Technologies Corp.	Labtech®
Lotus Development Corp.	1-2-3® Symphony®
Orion Research, Inc.	Ross®
Pennwalt Corp.	Kynar®

Oxidation-Reduction Potential (ORP) Measurements

Oxidation-reduction potential (ORP) measurements are used to monitor chemical reactions, quantify ion activity or determine the oxidizing or reducing properties of solutions. While ORP measurements are somewhat similar to those of pH, the potential value must be interpreted carefully for meaningful results.

An ORP measurement is made using the millivolt mode of a pH meter. By substituting a metallic electrode for the pH glass electrode, many other ions beside the hydrogen ion can be detected with the same pH meter.

In many chemical reactions, electrons are transferred from one substance to another. By definition a substance gains electrons in an oxidation reaction. Oxidation and reduction reactions occur together. The available electrons from an oxidized substance are taken up by the reduced substance until an equilibrium condition is reached.

The relative tendency of different substances to gain electrons (relative reduction potentials) varies depending on the number of electrons in the outer shell and the size of the atom or ion. Accordingly, these substances can be tabulated in descending order with those substances which gain electrons most easily at the top.

Since it is impossible to measure absolute potentials, an arbitrary standard, the hydrogen electrode is chosen. Oxidation-reduction potentials are defined relative to this standard. The electrode reaction:

$$2H^+ + 2e^- = H_2$$

is assigned a potential 0.00 volts when the hydrogen ion activity is 1.0M and the partial pressure is one atmosphere.

When reactions are written as oxidations (for example, $Na^+ = Na + e^-$), potentials have the opposite polarity.

The standard potential, E, of any oxidation-reduction reaction is referred to the standard hydrogen electrode and refers to conditions of the oxidation-reduction reaction where temperature is 25°C, ion activities are unity and gases are at 1 atm pressure. Table 1 shows the standard potential, E, associated with various reactions.

The oxidation-reduction potential (ORP) is characteristic of reactions involving both oxidation and reduction. ORP varies as a function of : (a) the standard potential E associated with each reaction, (b) relative ion concentrations, (c) temperature, (d) the number of electrons transferred in the reactions.

COMMON ORP POTENTIAL VALUES

Oxidation-reduction potentials are usually displayed as millivolts (mV). When measured with a pH meter (which is set to read in millivolts), this oxidation potential is generally the EMF difference developed between the ORP metallic indicating electrode and a constant voltage reference electrode, (for example, saturated calomel instead of a normal hydrogen electrode) that is immersed in the test solution. Any of three different types of metallic electrodes may be used. The nature of the test solution and the method to be used will determine the choice of electrode.

MAKING ORP MEASUREMENTS

There are three types of metallic electrodes used in ORP measurements which differ in construction, but all are based on the same principle that an oxidized and a reduced state must always be present.

The first type of metallic electrode to be considered consists of a metal in contact with a solution of its own ions. The metal electrode is in the reduced state and its ions are in the oxidized state. An

example of this type is silver in a silver nitrate solution. It is used for the direct measurement and potentiometric titration of a solution containing the anions of the sparingly soluble salt forming the coating of the electrode.

The second type of metallic electrode consists of a metal coated with a sparingly soluble salt of this metal in contact with a solution of a soluble salt with the same anion; for example, silver-silver chloride in a solution of potassium chloride. Electrodes fo this type can be used for direct determination by potentiometric titration of a solution containing the anions of the sparingly soluble salt forming the coating of the electrode.

The third type of metallic electrode consists of an inert metal in contact with a solution containing both the oxidized and reduced states of an oxidation-reduction system. The particular metal used is relatively unimportant as long as it is sufficiently noble. Platinum and gold are the most common ORP electrodes. An example is platinum in contact with a solution of ferric-ferrous ions. Electrodes of this type are used for potentiometric oxidation-reduction titrations, and for the direct measurement of the oxidizing or reducing intensity of solutions.

EQUIPMENT FOR MEASUREMENT

Equipment for ORP measurement compares closely to that for pH measurement. The reference electrodes can be identical, but a noble metal electrode replaces the glass pH electrode. The potential is measured in millivolts. Temperature compensation is not used. The signal from the electrodes must be fed into an amplifier with high input impedance.

The sleeve junction calomel reference electrode is recommended for many applications since it provides an easily cleaned junction with fast response.

WHEN ORP BECOMES pH DEPENDENT

If one or both of the half reactions involve hydrogen ions, the ORP measurement becomes pH dependent.

In industrial plants ORP is rarely applied to nice clean reactions where the potentials can be estimated easily. In sewage and paper pulp, for example, solutions contain a host of constituents that the reagent oxidizes and reduces simultaneously. ORP relates to the concentration and activities of all participating reactions. It frequently becomes necessary to determine the control point experimentally. Temperature compensation is not used because the compensation would be

Table 1

Electrode Reaction	EO Volts
$Na^+ + e^- = Na$	− 2.714
$CNO^- + H_2O + 2e^- = CN^- + 20H^-$	− 0.97
$Zn^{+2} + 2e^- = Zn$	− 0.763
$2H^+ + 2e^- = H_2$	0.0
$SO_4^{-2} + 4H^+ + 2e^- = H_2SO_3 + H_2O$	+ 0.17
Ag/AgCl electrode, 4N KCl	+ 0.199
Calomel electrode, Saturated KCl	+ 0.244
$Ag^+ + e^- = Ag$	+ 0.8
$Cr_2O_7^{-2} + 14H^+ + 6e^- = 3Cr^{+3} + 7H_2O$	+ 1.33
$Cl_2 + 2e^- = 2Cl^-$	+ 1.35

different for each reaction. Many industrial ORP reactions, however, have a number of different reactions occurring simultaneously.

Since ORP is a characteristic measure of redox equilibrium, it should not require standardization of calibration. The measured potential is absolute in a sense.

HOW TO OPERATE YOUR METER FOR ORP

If day to day relative potential values are to be compared, the pH meter must be standardized to the same starting point.

Ideally, a noble metal ORP electrode will respond rapidly to the electrochemical potential established by the redox equilibrium. The rate of electron transfer across the metal's surface, however, depends on the state of the surface.

Some reports indicate that electrode poisoning can reduce the exchange to one percent of its maximum value. In any case, if poisoning is suspected, the electrode can be restored by following proper cleaning procedure.

WHEN TO USE ORP

Use of an "electrode of the third type" (noble metal in oxidation-reduction system) is essential for the detection of the equivalence point in numerous potentiometric oxidation-reduction titrations. This method of analysis involves the determination of a reducing agent of known concentration or vice versa. Potentiometric redox titrations are among the most accurate methods of chemical analysis. Important uses of this electrode are in the manufacture of bleach, treatment of industrial wastes and in studying biological systems.

SPECIFIC APPLICATIONS

Applications for ORP measurement are not as widespread as for pH, but several reasonably standard applications exist where ORP measurement and control can be very useful. Some of these applications include:

Oxidation of cyanide and
chromatic wastes
Bleaching of pulp
Manufacture of bleach
Water pollution
Reduction of chromate wastes

Œ

OMEGA ENGINEERING, INC. gratefully acknowledges Beckman Instruments, Inc. for permission to use portions of the article "How to Perform Oxidation-Reduction Potential Measurements with Metallic Electrodes".

Theory and Application of Conductivity Measurement

WHAT IS CONDUCTIVITY?

Conductivity is defined as the ability of a substance to conduct electric current. It is the reciprocal of resistivity. All substances possess conductivity to some degree, but the amount varies widely, ranging from extremely low (insulators such as benzene and glass) to very high (silver, copper, and metals in general). Most industrial interest is in measuring the conductivity of liquids, which generally consist of ionic compounds dissolved in water. These solutions have conductivities midway between insulators and metallic conductors. This conductivity can be measured quite easily by electronic means, and this offers a simple test which can tell much about the quality of water, or the make-up of a solution. A broad line of conductivity equipment is available to measure liquids ranging from ultrapure water (low conductivity) to concentrated chemical streams (high conductivity).

UNITS OF CONDUCTIVITY

The units of measurement used to describe conductivity and resistivity are quite fundamental and are frequently misused.

The basic unit of resistance is the ohm. Conductivity is the reciprocal of resistance, and its basic unit is the "siemens," formerly the mho. In discussions of bulk material, it is convenient to talk of its specific conductance, now commonly called conductivity. This is the

conductance as measured between the opposite faces of a 1cm cube of the material. This measurement has units of siemens/cm. Since this unit is much too large for most solutions, the units μS/cm and mS/cm are used instead. The corresponding terms for specific resistance (or resistivity) are ohm-cm, megohm-cm and kilohm-cm.

Users of ultrapure water prefer to use resistivity units of Mohm-cm, because measurement in these units tends to spread the scale out in the range of interest. These same users frequently use kohm-cm when dealing with less pure water such as tap water. Others, however, use the units of μS/cm and mS/cm when dealing with quite pure to very concentrated chemical solutions. In these applications, the use of conductivity has the advantage of an almost direct relationship with impurities especially at low concentration. Hence, a rising conductivity reading shows increasing impurities, or a generally increasing concentration in the case of a chemical stream (with some exceptions in concentrated solutions).

COMMON PROCESS STREAMS

Table 1 presents the conductivity of a number of specific aqueous solutions, while Table 2 gives the ranges encountered in common applications. Conductivity is used extensively in the measurement of water supplies for city,

	Conductivity
Absolute Water (pure H_2O)	0.055 μS/cm
Distilled Water	0.5 μS/cm
Power Plant Boiler Waters	1.0 μS/cm
Pure Mountain Stream	1.0 μS/cm
Good City Water	50 μS/cm
0.01N KCl Soln (Standard)	1409 μS/cm
Maximum for Potable Water	1055 μS/cm
Ocean Water (Mid-North Atlantic)	53 mS/cm
10% NaOH	355 mS/cm
10% H_2SO_4	432 mS/cm
31.0% HNO_3 (Maximum known)	865 mS/cm

Table 1
Conductivity of Various Aqueous Solutions at 25°C

hospital, and industrial use. Although individual ions cannot be differentiated, this is usually not needed and conductivity gives a measure of the impurities present. A useful rule of thumb in this regard is that:

Conductivity in μS/cm$\sim\sim$2 ×
(Dissolved solids in ppm of NaCl)
(1ppm = 1mg/L)

The factor of 2 is a coincidence coming from the various conversion factors involved: the value is about 2.2 for low concentrations and less than 2 for high concentrations.

Resistivity in ohm-cm	100M	10M	1M	0.1M	10K	1K	100	10	1
Conductivity in μS/cm	0.01	0.1	1	10	100	1000	10^4	10^5	10^6
Ultrapure Water	■								
Demineralized Water		■							
Condensate			■						
Natural Waters				■	■				
Cooling Tower Coolants				■	■				
Percent Level of Acids, Bases and Salts						■	■	■	■
5% Salinity							■		
2% NaOH								■	
20% HCl									■
Range of Contacting Cells		■	■	■	■	■	■	■	
Range of Electrodeless Probes				■	■	■	■	■	■

Table 2 *Conductivity/Resistivity Spectrum*

APPLICATIONS

Table 3 lists many of the industries which use conductivity measurements. Table 4 lists the leading conductivity applications.

Table 3
Industries Which Use Conductivity

Chemical	Semiconductor
Power Generation	Agriculture
Hospitals	Food Processing
Textile	Electroplating
Iron and Steel	Paper
Brewing	Petroleum
Beverage	Marine
Mining	

Table 4
Conductivity Applications

Chemical Streams	Cooling Towers
Demineralizer Output	Acid, Salt, and Alkali
Reverse Osmosis	Concentrations
Steam Boilers	Desalinization
Condensate Return	Laboratory Analysis
Waste Streams	Fruit Peeling
Boiler Blowdown	Oceanography-
Interface	Salinity
Determination	Level Detection

ADVANTAGES AND DISADVANTAGES

In general, conductivity offers a fast, reliable, on-line, non-destructive, inexpensive and durable means of measuring the ionic content of a sample stream. Accuracy, repeatability and reliability are excellent. Typically, repeatability is about 1% of the upper range value.

The principal drawback of conductivity is that it is a non-specific measurement; it cannot distinguish between different types of ions, giving instead a reading proportional to the combined effect of all ions present. Some ions contribute far more than others. As a result, multicomponent mixtures may present problems. Common organic compounds such as alcohols, sugars, petroleum products and soil products do not give usable conductivity measurements, although organic acids such as acetic are satisfactory. Some of these materials may also reduce the accuracy by coating the sensor or probe. There is also a relatively high temperature dependence to the measurement, which must be compensated for. In many cases, these difficulties are not serious, or can be circumvented, and a quite accurate reading of a desired component can be obtained.

THEORY AND THE CONCEPT OF CELL CONSTANT

A very simple conductivity sensor could be constructed as a cell as follows:

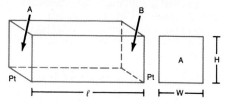

The cell is constructed of an insulating material, with platinum or other metallic pieces at the ends. If the cell is filled with a solution of conductivity L, the conductance as measured between ends A and B is:

$G = L A/\ell$ where:
  G=Conductance in siemens
  L=Conductivity in siemens/cm
  ℓ=Length in cm between electrodes
  A=Area normal to current flow in cm^2

The corresponding equation for resistance is:

$R = p\,\ell/A$ where:
  R=resistance in ohms
  p=Resistivity in ohm-cm
  ℓ=Length in cm between electrodes
  A=Area normal to current flow in cm^2

The term ℓ/A is defined as K_c, the resistivity cell constant, and has dimensions of cm^{-1}. Rather than have a separate reciprocal conductivity constant, the resistivity cell constant is used for all applications, regardless of whether conductivity or resistivity is being measured. As a result, equation 1 becomes:

$$G = L/K_c \text{ or } (K_c) \times (G) = L$$

As the dimensions of the cell are changed, the cell constant varies as the ratio of ℓ to A. A useful theoretical concept is a cell consisting of a cube 1 cm on a side, which has a cell constant of 1.00 and as a result, the conductance reading in microsiemens is numerically equal to the solution conductivity in μS/cm. For solutions of low conductivity, the electrodes can be placed closer together (i.e., the length ℓ is reduced) so that the cell constants of 0.1 and 0.01 cm^{-1} result. This has the effect of raising the conductance as read between A and B and producing a value more easily handled by electronic circuitry. Similarly, the more conductive solutions, the length ℓ is increased so that a cell factor of 10 or occasionally 100 results; this also produces a conductance adaptable to electronic circuits.

Although cells made in this manner are entirely usable, and most early data was taken with them, they rely on insulating walls to define the current path. It is usually more convenient in process work to have other configurations. Cells of 0.01 and 0.1 cm^{-1} constant are usually made with electrodes which are concentric cylinders of inert metal. This configuration produces good shielding of the center electrode and gives a configuration which is more convenient to mount. Cells of 1 and 10 cm^{-1} constant often have a narrow slot, with graphite electrodes (generally three) with the outer ones connected for shielding reasons. These cells have a removable cover, which can be removed for inspection or cleaning of the electrodes.

Any configuration of two or more electrodes has a cell constant. An equivalent prismatic cell could be made with the same cell constant, and it would give identical readings with the same solution. The electrodeless probe also has a definite cell constant determined by the geometry of the conducting loop of solution.

The terms "cell," "probe" and "sensor" are sometimes used interchangeably, but it is useful to maintain the distinction. The electrodes of a "cell" contact the solution directly, and the sample is contained between the electrodes. An electrodeless "probe" is insulated from the solution and relies upon the electric field surrounding it for its operation. Thus, the sample surrounds the probe. Both "cells" and "probe" are "sensors" and this term covers both types.

DATA AVAILABLE

The standards against which conductivity is measured are solutions of potassium chloride (KCl) which are measured to very high accuracy per ASTM Standard D1125-77. Data is as follows:

Approximate Normality	Conductivity μS/cm at 25°C
0.001	146.93
0.01	1408.8
0.1	12,856
1.0	111,342

All conductivity equipment is calibrated directly or indirectly against the solutions.

TEMPERATURE EFFECTS

The conduction process in aqueous solutions is by means of ionic motion, and is different from that of metals. The conductivity invariably increases with increasing temperature, opposite to metals but similar to graphite. It is affected by the nature of the ions, and by the viscosity of the water. In low ionic concentrations (very pure water), the ionization of the water furnishes an appreciable part of the conducting ions.

All these processes are quite temperature dependent, and as a result, the conductivity has a substantial dependence on temperature. This dependency is usually expressed a relative change per degree Celsius at a particular temperature, commonly as percent/°C at 25°C, and this is called the slope of the solution. Ultrapure water has by far the largest slope, 5.2%/°C, while ionic salts run about 2%/°C in the middle ranges. Acids, alkalis and concentrated salt solutions run somewhat lower, typically 1.5%/°C. Nonaqueous materials such as oleum and conducting organics have quite different temperature dependences. From these figures, it is obvious that a small difference in temperature makes a large difference in conductivity, and the effect is very troublesome when a high degree of accuracy is required. In making conductivity readings at high and low temperatures, the data is usually normalized to 25°C, i.e., it is stated as what the reading is with a 25°C solution.

Fortunately, temperature sensors are available which have characteristics similar to those of the solutions to be tested. By the use of supplemental resistors and electronic circuitry, the temperature conductance curves can be shaped to closely match any aqueous solution. The temperature sensor and its associated network are then used as a gain control element in the monitor circuitry, and the conductivity reading is brought to its equivalent value at 25°C.

In general, the most accurate results occur when the excursions around the normal operating temperature are small, or when operation is at or near room temperature. The variation of conductivity due to temperature frequently gives problems when the solution under test has a rapidly varying temperature. The change in conductivity measurement is instantaneous, since this is an electrical measurement. Fortunately, most process streams and vessels have large thermal mass and cannot change temperature rapidly.

SENSOR SELECTION AND MOUNTING CONSIDERATIONS

The choice of a correct sensor, and mounting it so that it has a good sample of solution, are probably the two most important considerations in a conductivity system. The following criteria should be followed:

1) Proper cell constant.
2) Proper range on monitor.
3) Correct materials for corrosion resistance.
4) Electrodeless probe generally preferable when solution

conductivity is in suitable range.
5) Sensor mounting suitable for solution.

Under proper sensor mounting, the following conditions should be observed:

1) The solution between the cell electrodes or around the probe is representative of the solution as a whole.
2) A moderate flow is maintained past the sensor to provide an up to date solution sample.
3) The sensor is mounted so that air or air bubbles do not lodge between the cell electrodes or in the probe area of electrodeless probe. Mounting a sensor at the top of a large pipe is often unsatisfactory, as a layer of air can collect here.
4) The contacting type cell is mounted so that sludge and particulate matter do not collect around the cell electrodes. Particularly unsuitable is a cell mounted vertically in the bottom of a pipe or well, a situation which collects sediment and gives erroneous readings.

MULTICOMPONENT SYSTEMS

A conductivity sensor will give, in almost all cases, a satisfactory conductivity measurement for a single ionic substance dissolved in water. From this, the concentration can be determined (the only exceptions being measurements made at or near a conductivity peak). As other ionic substances are added, however, the conductivity measurement (due to the combined effect of all active ions) becomes more complex. The addition of a small amount of neutral salt usually increase the conductivity reading, while the addition of larger amounts often produces ionic interference and lower ionic dissociation, resulting in lower readings. Salts which hydrolyze (from strong acids and weak bases, or vice-versa) usually decrease the conductivity measurement by tying up the original $(H+)$ or $(OH-)$ ions. Each case must be handled on an individual basis.

In many cases however, the solution is fundamentally acidic or basic, and if it is desired to measure or control on this component, (a very common situation), the presence of relatively small amounts of other salts is usually not too serious. The dominant $(H+)$ or $(OH-)$ ion has a very high conductivity is not greatly affected by the extraneous compound. Ω≡

OMEGA ENGINEERING, INC. gratefully acknowledges the Foxboro Company for permission to use portions of the article "Theory and Application of Electrolytic Conductivity Measurement".

Technical Books

pH and pIon Control In Process and Waste Streams

A comprehensive guide to the measurement and control of various ionic species in manufacturing and industrial processes with emphasis on control of potential pollutants. Contents include measurements, ion measuring systems, the hydrogen ion, other ion selective measurements, oxidation-reduction measurements, the fundamentals of composition control, designing a controllable plant, feedback control systems and feedforward and adaptive control.

ES-0247 $63

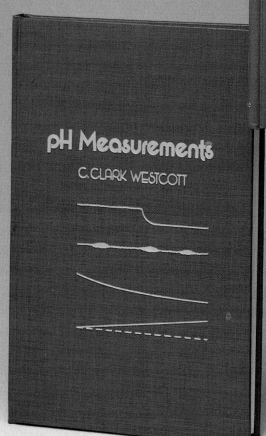

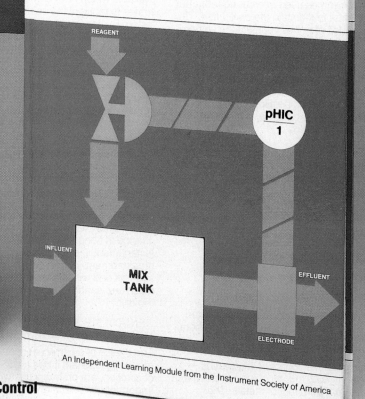

pH Measurements

A complete guide to practical pH measurements and common problem solving techniques. Included is a simplified presentation of basic pH theory, equipment selection and the proper handling of difficult pH applications.

OP-13 $37.50

pH Control

System design and control is thoroughly depicted in this invaluable handbook. Covered is an analysis of pH electrodes, pH transmitters, control valves and mixing equipment, all presented in an easy-to-read textbook format.

OP-15 $39.95

Glossary
Technical Reference Section

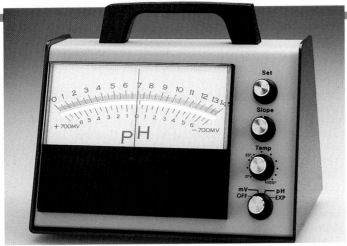

PHB-58 Conductivity and pH   **Meter, Page B-14 $199**

A

Activity (a_i): A thermodynamic term for the apparent or active concentration of a free ion in solution. It is related to concentration by the activity coefficient.

Activity coefficient (f_i): A ratio of the activity of species i(a_i) to its molality (C). It is a correction factor which makes the thermodynamic calculations correct. This factor is dependent on ionic strength, temperature, and other parameters.

> **Individual** ionic activity coefficients, f_+ for cation and f_- for an anion, cannot be derived thermodynamically. They can be calculated only by using the Debye-Hückel law for low concentration solutions in which the interionic forces depend primarily on charge, radius, and distribution of the ions and on the dielectric constant of the medium rather than on the chemical properties of the ions.
>
> **Mean** ionic activity coefficient ($f_\pm$) or the activity of a salt, on the other hand, can be measured by a variety of techniques such as freezing point depression and vapor pressure as well as paired sensing electrodes. It is the geometric mean of the individual ionic activity coefficients:
> $$f_\pm = (f_+{}^n + f_-{}^{n-})^{1/n}$$

Anion: A negatively charged ion ($C1^-$, NO_3^-, S^{2-},etc.)

Asymmetry potential: The potential developed across the glass membrane with identical solutions on both sides. Also a term used when comparing glass electrode potential in pH 7 buffer.

ATC: Automatic temperature compensation.

B

Bias current: (input terminal current) That part of the input current which is independent of the applied voltage from the electrode potentials.

Buffer: Any substance or combination of substances which, when dissolved in water, produces a solution which resists a change in its hydrogen ion concentration on the addition of an acid or alkali.

Buffer capacity (B): A measure of the ability of the solution to resist pH change when a strong acid or base is added.

C

Calibration: The use of two or more standards, one to establish the standardization point and one to establish electrode sensitivity by a slope adjustment.

Cation: A positively charged ion (Na^+, H^+).

Conductance: The measure of the ability of a solution to carry an electrical current. (See Equivalent conductance.)

D

Debye-Huckel equation: Used in relating the activity coefficient (f_i) to ionic strength (see Activity coefficient):

$$-\log f_i = \frac{AZ_i^2 I^{1/2}}{1 + B\mathring{a}I^{1/2}}$$

where

I is the ionic strength,
A and B the temperature-dependent constants (see Table A.5),
Z_i the valence of the ion(i), and
$\mathring{a}$ the ion-size parameter in angstroms.

Dielectric constant: Related to the force of attraction between two opposite charges separated by a distance in a uniform medium.

Dissociation constant (K): A value which quantitatively expresses the extent to which a substance dissociates in solution. The smaller the value of K, the less dissociation of the species in solution. This value varies with temperature, ionic strength, and the nature of the solvent.

E

Electrode potential (E): The difference in potential established between an electrode and a solution when the electrode is immersed in the solution.

Electrolye: Any substance which, when in solution or fused, will conduct an electric current. Acids, bases, and salts are common electrolytes.

Electromotive force (emf): The potential difference between the two electrodes in a cell. The cell emf is the cell voltage measured when no current is flowing through the cell. It can be measured by means of a pH meter with high input impedance.

End point (potentiometric): The apparent equivalence point of a titration at which a relatively large potential change is observed.

Equilibrium constant: The product of the concentrations (or activities) of the substances produced at equilibrium in a chemical reaction divided by the product of concentrations of the reacting substances, each concentration raised to that power which is the coefficient of the substance in the chemical equation.

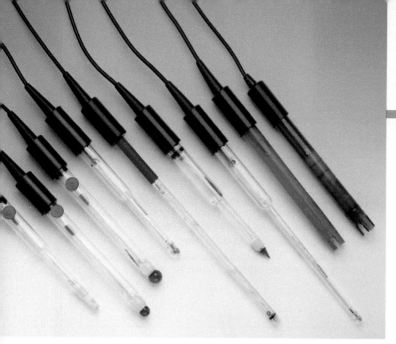

Equitransference: Equal diffusion rates of the positively and negatively charged ions of an electrolyte across a liquid junction without charge separation.

Equivalent conductance (λ): Equivalent conductance of an electrolyte is defined as the conductance of a volume of solution containing one equivalent weight of dissolved substances when placed between two parallel electrodes 1 cm apart, and large enough to contain between them all of the solution. λ is never determined directly, but is calculated from the specific conductance (L_s) If C is the concentration of a solution in gram equivalents per liter, then the concentration per cubic centimeter is C/1000, and the volume containing one equivalent of the solute is, therefore, 1000/C. Since L_s is the conductance of a centimeter cube of the solution, the conductance of 1000/C cc, and hence λ , will be

$$\frac{1000L_s}{C}$$

F

Filling solution: A solution of defined composition to make contact between an internal element and a membrane or sample. The solution sealed inside a pH glass bulb is called an internal filling solution. This solution normally contains a buffered chloride solution to provide a stable potential and a designated zero potential point. The solution which surrounds the reference electrode internal and periodically requires replenishing is called the reference filling solution. It provides contact between the reference electrode internal and sample through a junction.

H

Hydrogen ion activity (a_{H+}): Activity of the hydrogen ion in solution. Related to hydrogen ion concentration (C_{H+}) by the activity coefficient for hydrogen (f_{H+})

Hysteresis (electrode memory): When an electrode system is returned to a solution, equilibrium is usually not immediate. This phenomenon is often observed in electrodes that have been exposed to the other influences such as temperature, light, or polarization.

I

Input resistance (impedance): The input resistance of a pH meter is the resistance between the glass electrode terminal and the reference electrode terminal. The potential of a pH-measuring electrode chain is always subject to a voltage division between the total electrode resistance and the input resistance.

Internal reference electrode (element): The reference electrode placed internally in a glass electrode.

Ionic mobility: Defined similarly to the mobility of nonelectrolytic particles, viz., as the speed that the ion obtains in a given solvent when influenced by unit power.

Ionic strength: The weighted concentration of ions in solution, computed by multiplying the concentration of each ion in solution (C) by the corresponding square of the charge on the ion (Z) summing this product for all ions in solution and dividing by 2:

$$\text{ionic strength} = \tfrac{1}{2} \Sigma Z^2 C.$$

Isopotential point: A potential which is not affected by temperature changes. It is the pH value at which dE/dt for a given electrode pair is zero. Normally, for a glass electrode and SCE reference, this potential is obtained approximately when immersed in pH 7 buffer.

L

Liquid junction potential: The potential difference existing between a liquid-liquid boundary. The sign and size of this potential depends on the composition of the liquids and the type of junction used.

M

Mean ionic activity coefficient: See Activity coefficient.

Medium effect (f^m): For solvents other than water the medium effect is the activity coefficient related to the standard state in water at zero concentration. It reflects differences in the electrostatic and chemical interactions of the ions with the molecules of various solvents. Solvation is the most significant interaction.

Membrane: The pH-sensitive glass bulb is the membrane across which the potential difference due to the formation of double layers with ion-exchange properties on the two swollen glass surfaces is developed. The membrane makes contact with and separates the internal element and filling solution from the sample solution.

Millivolt: Unit of electromotive force. It is the difference in potential required to make a current of 1 milliampere flow through a resistance of 1 ohm.

Molality: A measure of concentration expressed in mols per kilogram of solvent.

Molarity: A measure of concentration expressed in mols per liter of solution.

Monovalent ion: An ion with a single positive or negative charge (H +, C1 −).

Nernst equation: A mathematical description of electrode behavior:

$$E = E_x + \frac{2.3RT}{nF} \log a_i$$

E is the total potential, in millivolts, developed between the sensing and reference electrodes; E_x varies with the choice of electrodes, temperature, and pressure: $2.3RT/nF$ is the Nernst factor (R and F are constants, n is the charge on the ion, including sign, T is the temperature in degrees Kelvin), and a_i is the activity of the ion to which the electrode is responding.

Nernst factor (S, slope): The term $2.3RT/nF$ is the Nernst equation, which is equal (at T = 25°C) to 59.16 mV when $n = 1$ and 29.58 mV when $n = 2$, and which includes the sign of the charge on the ion in the term n. The Nerst factor varies with temperature.

Normal hydrogen electrode: A reversible hydrogen electrode (Pt) in contact with hydrogen gas at 1 atmosphere partial pressure and immersed in a solution containing hydrogen ions at unit activity.

Open circuit: The lack of electrical contact in any part of the measuring circuit. An open circuit is usually characterized by rapid large jumps in displayed potential, followed by an off-scale reading.

Operational pH: The determination of sample pH by relating to pH measurements in a primary standard solution. This relationship assumes that electrode errors such as sensitivity and changes in asymmetry potential can be disregarded or compensated for, provided the liquid junction potential remains constant between standard and sample.

pH(S) (standard pH scale): The conventional standard pH scale established on the basis that an individual ionic activity coefficient can be calculated from the Debye-Hückel law for primary buffers.

Polarization: The inability of an electrode to reproduce a reading after a small electrical current has been passed through the membrane. Glass pH electrodes are especially prone to polarization errors caused by small currents flowing from the pH meter input circuit and from static electrical charges built up as the electrodes are removed from the sample solution, or when the electrodes are wiped.

Primary standards: Aqueous pH buffer solutions established by the National Bureau of Standards within the 2.5 to 11.5 pH range of ionic strength less than 0.1 and which provide stable liquid junction potential and uniformity of electrode sensitivity.

Redox potential: The potential developed by a metallic electrode when placed in a solution containing a species in two different oxidation states.

Salt bridge: The salt bridge of a reference electrode is that part of the electrode which contains the filling solution to establish the electrolytic connection between reference internal cell and the test solution.

> **Auxiliary salt bridge:** A glass tube open at one end to receive intermediate electrolyte filling solution, and the reference electrode tip and a junction at the other end to make contact with the sample.

Salt effect (f^x): The effect on the activity coefficient due to salts in the solution.

SCE: Saturated calomel electrode.

Secondary standard: pH buffer solutions which do not meet the requirements of primary standard solutions but provide coverage of the pH range not covered by primary standards. Used when the pH value of the primary standard is not close to the sample pH value.

Slope (electrode sensitivity, span): See Nernst factor.

Solvation: Ions in solution are normally combined with at least one molecule of solvent. This phenomenon is termed solvation.

Standard electrode potential (E^0): The standard potential E^0 of an electrode is the reversible emf between the normal hydrogen electrode and the electrode with all components at unit activity.

Standardization: A process of equalizing electrode potentials in one standardizing solution (buffer) so that potentials developed in unknown solutions can be converted to pH values.

Suspension effect: The source of error due to varied reference liquid junction potential depending upon whether the electrodes are immersed in the supernatant fluid or deeper in the sediment. Normally encountered with solutions containing resins or charged colloids.

Z

Zero point
> **pH meters:** The electrical zero point where zero millivolts would be displayed. Used in conjunction with the slope control to provide a narrower range calibration.

> **Electrode:** See Isopotential point.

Reprinted with permission of the Academic Press, Inc. Orlando, FL. Glossary, pH Measurement by Clark Westcott

(Copyright © 1978 by Academic Press, Inc.)

Z

TECHNICAL REFERENCE

pH Measurement Tips

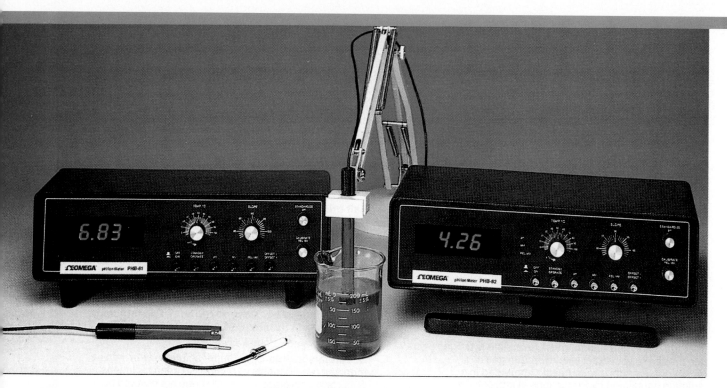

The measurement of pH is very important in many laboratories and industries. Below are a few guidelines to aid in making accurate and precise pH readings.

Meter Calibration

Frequency—For accurate results a pH meter should be calibrated at least once per 8-hour shift.

Buffers—Standard buffers should always be used for meter calibrations. Buffers can be purchased already prepared or in capsule form.

Standard buffers usually are available in three pH values pH 4.00, pH 7.00, and pH 10.00.

Buffers should be stored away from heat and in tightly sealed containers. Always use freshly poured buffers for meter calibration.

All buffers should be used at room temperature, 25°C.

Types of Calibration

One-Point Calibration—Meter calibration using only one buffer. The value of buffer used should be that closest to value anticipated for sample.

Two-Point Calibration—Meter calibration using two buffers, one of which should always be 7.00. The second buffer used would depend on user application.

Method—Here is a general method for most pH meters. Some pH meters require slightly different techniques. Please read the instructions for their particular procedures.

1. The temperature setting on the meter must correspond to the temperature of the buffers used, or an automatic temperature compensator must be employed.

2. Turn pH meter to "pH" or "ATC" if automatic temperature compensation is used.

3. Place clean electrode into fresh, room temperature pH 7.00 buffer.

4. Adjust the pH reading to exactly 7.00 using the ZERO OFFSET, STANDARDIZE or SET knob.

5. Rinse the electrode with distilled or deionized water.
   (This would be the procedure for a one-point calibration. Continue through step 8 for a two-point calibration.)

6. Place electrode into the second buffer, either pH 4.00 or pH 10.00.

7. Adjust the pH reading to display the correct value using the SLOPE, CALIBRATE or GAIN controls.

8. Adjust the pH reading to read the correct value using the SLOPE knob.

The pH meter is now calibrated and ready to use.

Electrode Care—Over 80% of pH measurement difficulties are due to electrode problems. Proper storage, use, and maintenance increases accuracy.

Storage—Electrodes should be stored in an acidic solution with a low salt content. Commercial soaking solutions are available or you can make your own by mixing a 1M KCl solution adjusted to pH 4.0.

Use and Maintenance—Electrodes should always be used in a vertical position.

Electrodes should be rinsed between samples with distilled or deionized water. NEVER wipe an electrode to remove excess water, just blot the end of the electrode with a lint-free paper. Wiping electrode can cause spurious reading due to static charges.

The level of filling solution in refillable electrodes should be kept at least ⅔ full. The filling hole should be open during use.

pH electrodes are fragile. A proper electrode holder should be used to provide support and aid in raising and lowering the probe into solutions.

Standard Buffers for Calibration of pH Meters

Temperature °C	pH values					
	0.1 M Hydrochloric Acid	Saturated Potassium Hydrogen Tartrate	0.05 M Potassium Hydrogen Phthalate	0.05 M Phosphate	0.01 M Borax	Saturated Calcium Hydroxide
0	1.10		4.003	6.984	9.464	13.423
5	1.10		3.999	6.951	9.395	13.207
10	1.10		3.998	6.923	9.332	13.003
15	1.10		3.999	6.900	9.276	12.810
20	1.10		4.002	6.881	9.225	12.627
25	1.10	3.557	4.008	6.865	9.180	12.454
30	1.10	3.552	4.015	6.853	9.139	12.289
35	1.10	3.549	4.024	6.844	9.102	12.133
38	1.10	3.548	4.030	6.840	9.081	12.043
40	1.10	3.547	4.035	6.838	9.068	11.984
45	1.10	3.547	4.047	6.834	9.038	11.841
50	1.10	3.549	4.060	6.833	9.011	11.705
55	1.11	3.554	4.075	6.834	8.985	11.574
60	1.11	3.560	4.091	6.836	8.962	11.449
70	1.11	3.580	4.126	6.845	8.921	
80	1.11	3.609	4.164	6.859	8.885	
90	1.12	3.650	4.205	6.877	8.850	
95	1.12	3.674	4.227	6.886	8.833	

Preparation of Solutions

0.1 M Hydrochloric Acid. Prepare 0.1 M hydrochloric acid by diluting reagent-grade hydrochloric acid. Determine the molarity by titration with standard alkali and adjust to 0.1000 ±0.005M.

Saturated Potassium Hydrogen Tartrate. Shake an excess of reagent-grade potassium hydrogen tartrate with water at 25 ±5°C for about 3 minutes.

0.05 M Potassium Hydrogen Phthalate. Dissolve 10.21 ±0.05 g of reagent-grade potassium hydrogen phthalate in sufficient water to make 1000 mL of solution.

0.05 M Phosphate. Dissolve 3.40 ±0.01 g of reagent-grade potassium dihydrogen phosphate and 3.55 ±0.01 g of reagent-grade anhydrous disodium hydrogen phosphate in sufficient water to make 1000 mL of solution.

0.01 M Borax. Dissolve 3.81 ±0.01 g of reagent-grade sodium tetraborate decahydrate in sufficient water to make 1000 mL of solution.

Saturated Calcium Hydroxide. Shake large excess of finely granulated calcium hydroxide with water in polyethylene bottle at 25°C and filter prior to use.

pH Values of Standard Solutions

Normality	pH values			
	HCl	CH_3COOH	NaOH	NH_3
1	0.10	2.37	14.05	11.77
0.1	1.07	2.87	13.07	11.27
0.01	2.02	3.37	12.12	10.77
0.001	3.01	3.87	11.13	10.27
0.0001	4.01			

OMEGA ENGINEERING, INC. gratefully acknowledges Merck & Company, Inc. for permission to reproduce "Standard Buffers for Calibration of pH Meters".

Z

TECHNICAL REFERENCE

NEMA Enclosures

CODE DEFINITIONS

Class 1 locations require the type explosion-proof electrical equipment where, in case of an explosion, the hazardous flames would be contained. In Class II or III locations, dust, fibers, and flyings are the combustible materials and it is only necessary to keep these materials out of the electrical equipment (where an arc may take place) and to maintain safe external temperatures.

A brief explaination of the three classifications covering Hazardous Locations follows:

Class 1 Locations – are those in which flammable gases or vapors are, or may be, present in the air in quantities sufficient to produce explosive or ignitable mixtures.

Class 1, Division 1 – are those where such hazardous concentrations of flammable gases or vapors exist continuously, intermittently, or periodically under normal operating conditions.

Class 1, Division 2 – are those where such hazardous concentrations of flammable gases or vapors are handled in closed containers or closed systems.

Class II Locations – are those where the presence of combustible dust present a fire or explosion hazard.

Class II, Division 1 – are those where dust is suspended in the air continuously, intermittently or periodically under normal operating conditions, in quantities sufficient to produce explosive or ignitable mixtures.

Class II, Division 2 – are those where such dust is not suspended in the air, but where deposits of it accumulating on the electrical equipment will interfere with the safe dissipation of heat, causing a fire hazard.

Class III Locations – are those where easily ignitable fibers or flyings are present but not likely to be suspended in the air in quantities sufficient to produce ignitable mixtures.

Class III, Division 1 – are those where ignitable fibers or materials producing combustible flyings, are handled, manufactured or used.

Class III, Division 2 – are those where easily ignited fibers are stored or handled (except in process of manufacture).

Further refinement created for the purpose of testing and approving electrical equipment divides Class 1 into four separate designations, A, B, C, D, and Class II into three separate designations, E, F, and G. Underwriters' Laboratories test and approve electrical equipment for the following specific groups:

Class I, Group A, Atmospheres containing acetylene;

Class I, Group B, Atmospheres containing hydrogen, or gases or vapors of equivalent hazard such as manufactured gas;

Class I, Group C, Atmospheres containing ethyl-ether vapors, ethylene, or cyclo-propane;

Class I, Group D, Atmospheres containing gasoline, hexane, naphtha, benzene, butane, propane, alcohol, acetone, benzol, lacquer solvent vapors, or natural gas;

Class II, Group E, Atmospheres containing metal dust, including aluminum, magnesium, and their commercial alloys, and other metals of similarly hazardous characteristics.

Class II, Group F, Atmospheres containing carbon black, coal or coke dust;

Class II, Group G, Atmospheres containing flour, starch, or grain dusts.

NEMA CLASSIFICATIONS:

In addition to the definitions provided in the National Electrical Code, NEMA also has set certain classifications for electrical equipment for use in various areas. They are listed on the following pages.

CLASSIFICATION OF HAZARDOUS ATMOSPHERES
NATIONAL ELECTRICAL CODE
ARTICLE 500 HAZARDOUS LOCATIONS

Class I Flammable Gases

Division	Group	Typical Atmosphere
1 Normally hazardous	A	acetylene

	B	butadiene
		ethylene oxide
		hydrogen
		manufactured gases
		  containing more than
		  30% hydrogen (by volume)
		propylene oxide

	C	acetaldehyde cyclopropane diethylether ethylene unsymmetrical dimethyl hydrazine (UDMH1, 1-dimethyl hydrazine)

	D	acetone
		acrylonitrile
		ammonia
		benzene
		butane
		1-butanol (butyl alcohol)
		2-butanol (secondary butyl
		  alcohol)
		n-butyl acetate
		isobutyl acetate
		ethane
		ethanol (ethyl alohol)
		ethyl acetate
		ethylene dichloride
		gasoline
		heptanes
		hexanes
		isoprene
		methane (natural gas)
		methanol (methyl alcohol)
		3-methyl-1 butanol
		  (Isoamyl alcohol)
		methyl ethyl ketone
		methyl Isobutyl ketone
		2-methyl-1-propanol
		  (Isobutyl alcohol)
		2-methyl-2-propanol
		  tertiary butyl alcohol)
		petroleum naptha
		octanes
		pentanes
		1-pentanol (amylalcohol)
		  propane
		1-propanol (propyl
		alcohol)
		2-propanol (Isopropyl
		  alcohol)
		propylene
		styrene
		toulene
		vinyl acetate
		vinyl chloride
		xylenes

Z

Class I Flammable Gases

Division	Group	Typical Atmosphere
2	A	Same as Division 1
Not	B	Same as Division 1
Normally	C	Same as Division 1
hazardous	D	Same as Division 1 (not normally hazardous means that the gases aren't normally present.)

Class II Combustible Dusts

Division	Group	Typical Atmosphere
1 Normally hazardous	E	Metal dust, including aluminum, magnesium and their commercial alloys, hazardous characteristics.
	F	Carbon black, coal, coke dust with more than 8% volatile material.
	G	Flour, starch, grain dusts.
2 Not normally hazardous	E,F,G	Same as Division 1

Class III
Easily
Ignitable
fibers and
flyings

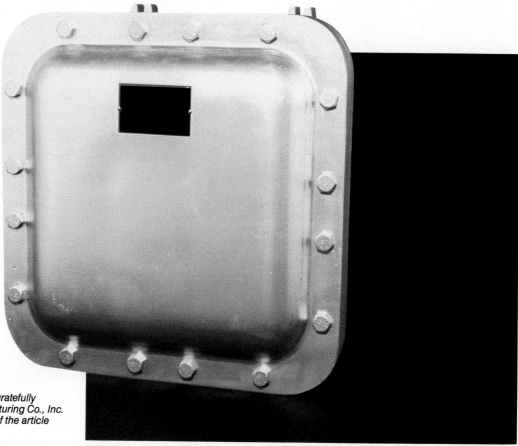

OMEGA ENGINEERING, INC. gratefully acknowledges Curlee Manufacturing Co., Inc. for permission to use portions of the article "Code Definition".

Product Index

pH Product Index
by Part Number

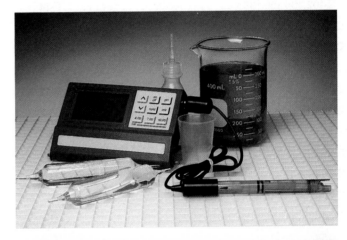

pH Product Index
by Part Number

OMEGASAYS®
TALKING MULTIMETER/THERMOMETER

**Shown Smaller
Than Actual Size**

Model HHM1
$349
**Complete with
English Chip**

- ✔ **It Talks!**
- ✔ **Voltage, Current, Resistance Measurement**
- ✔ **Dual Type-K Thermocouple Inputs With Differential Measurement**
- ✔ **Autoranging Voltage and Resistance Readings**
- ✔ **True RMS ac Voltage and Current**
- ✔ **50-10k Hz ac Bandwidth**
- ✔ **0.25% Basic dc Accuracy**

Introducing OMEGASAYS, the digital multimeter/type-k thermometer with voice annunciation. Inside this compact, handheld meter, you can measure voltage, current, resistance and temperature, and NEVER HAVE TO LOOK AT A DISPLAY! OMEGASAYS has a built-in speaker, and at the touch of a button, will tell you what the reading is.

The front panel display will indicate the measurement function, speech function (continuous, on demand, or off), measurement units, thermocouple probe (T1, T2, T1-T2), display hold, and low battery. All DMM connections are also made from the unit front.

The rear panel of OMEGASAYS has connections for two thermocouple probes (type SMP compatible), along with ac adaptor and earphone connections. The rear panel also has a 3 position volume selector switch.

OMEGASAYS comes complete with fuses, two beaded wire type-K thermocouple probes, TAS transition adaptor, custom test leads, English voice chip, earphone, soft carrying case, 9V lithium battery, 110 Vac adaptor and user's manual.

Plug-in voice chips for OMEGASAYS are currently available for English, German and Japanese. Other languages, such as French, Spanish, Russian, Mandarin Chinese and Italian will be available shortly. Chips can be easily removed and exchanged, for different users.

To Order *(Specify Model Number)*

Model No.	Price	Description
HHM1	$349	Talking DMM/Thermometer with English Voice Chip
HHM1-GR	44	Voice Chip - German
HHM1-JP	44	Voice Chip - Japanese
SDX-HHM1	35	Special thermocouple handle with pushbutton voice actuator

Note: Consult sales on availability of voice chip modules. For French, Spanish, Russian, Chinese and Italian.

High Performance Temperature/Humidity Recorder for Controlled Environments

CT485 Series From

$497

- ✓ **Versatile Remote Mounting Sensor**
- ✓ **Convenient Front Panel Programming**
- ✓ **8″ Chart for 1, 7, or 32-Day Recording**
- ✓ **Fully Electronic Microprocessor Control**
- ✓ **May Also be Wall Mounted**
- ✓ **Double Sided Chart**
- ✓ **Complete with Paper, Pens, Batteries and Charger**

Includes 120 Charts
20 charts of each style

Shown with sensor, also includes 6′ extension cord for remote sensing applications.

Shown Smaller Than Actual Size.

The CT485RS Includes:

QTY	DESCRIPTION
1	Package of 120 charts (20 of each style)
1	Remote mounting sensor and 6′ extension cord
1	AC adaptor/power cord
4	"D" cell batteries
1	Wall mounting template with mounting hardware
1	Temperature pen (red)
1	Humidity pen (blue)
1	Operator's Manual

To Order *(Specify Model Number)*

Model No.	Price	Description
CT485RS-110V	$497.00	charcoal gray color recorder-110 Vac
CT485RS-110V-W	525.00	almond color recorder-110 Vac
CT485-PR	4.50	red pen (temperature)
CT485-PB	4.50	blue pen (humidity)
CT-485-PS	8.00	pen set, red and blue
CT485-CDF	12.00	100 charts, 1 day, °F (printed both sides)
CT485-CDC	12.00	100 charts, 1 day, °C (printed both sides)
CT485-CWF	12.00	100 charts, 7 day, °F (printed both sides)
CT485-CWC	12.00	100 charts, 7 day, °C (printed both sides)
CT485-CMF	12.00	100 charts, 32 day, °F (printed both sides)
CT485-CMC	12.00	100 charts, 32 day, °C (printed both sides)
CT485-CSP	15.00	120 charts, 20 of each style (printed both sides)

For 220V option, replace "110 V" in part no. with "220 V" and add $20 to price.
Example: CT485RS-220V, calls for 220V version of the recorder in charcoal gray. **Price: $517**